Which Formulas Do I Need to Know?

Algebra

Multiplication of binomials, EWE (each with each): $(a+b)(c+d) = ac + ad + bc + bd$

Square of sum/difference: $(a \pm b)^2 = a^2 \pm 2ab + b^2$

Cube of sum/difference: $(a \pm b)^3 = a^3 \pm 3a^2b + 3ab^2 \pm b^3$

Difference of squares: $a^2 - b^2 = (a+b)(a-b)$ (sum of squares $a^2 + b^2$ cannot be factored)

Sum/difference of cubes: $a^3 \pm b^3 = (a \pm b)(a^2 \mp ab + b^2)$

Absolute value: $|-a| = |a|$, $|ab| = |a|\,|b|$, $|a/b| = |a|/|b|$ $(b \neq 0)$, $|a^n| = |a|^n$

Distance between points a and b on a number line: $|b - a| = |a - b|$.

Radicals: $a^{m/n} = \sqrt[n]{a^m}$, $\sqrt[n]{a}\,\sqrt[n]{b} = \sqrt[n]{ab}$, $\sqrt[n]{a}/\sqrt[n]{b} = \sqrt[n]{a/b}$ $(b \neq 0)$, $\sqrt[m]{\sqrt[n]{a}} = \sqrt[mn]{a}$

Quadratic equation $ax^2 + bx + c = 0$: solutions are $x = \dfrac{-b \pm \sqrt{b^2 - 4ac}}{2a}$

Factoring: if x_1 and x_2 are solutions of $ax^2 + bx + c = 0$, then $ax^2 + bx + c = a(x - x_1)(x - x_2)$

Geometry

Triangle with sides a, b, c: sum of angles $= 180^{\circ}$; perimeter $= a + b + c$; area $= \frac{1}{2}ah$ (h is height)

Right triangle with sides a, b and hypotenuse c: $c^2 = a^2 + b^2$ (Pythagorean Theorem); area $= \frac{1}{2}ab$

Rectangle with sides a, b: perimeter $= 2(a + b)$; area $= ab$

Square with side a: perimeter $= 4a$; area $= a^2$; diagonal $= a\sqrt{2}$

Circle of radius r: diameter $= 2r$; circumference $= 2\pi r$; area $= \pi r^2$

Sector of a circle of radius r and angle α (in radians): arc length $= r\alpha$; area $= r^2\alpha/2$

Ellipse with semi-axes a and b: area $= \pi ab$

Trapezoid with sides a, b, c, d and height h (sides a and c are parallel; h is distance between a and c): perimeter $= a + b + c + d$; area $= \frac{1}{2}(a + c)h$

Parallelepiped of length a, width b, and height c: volume $= abc$; surface area $= 2(ab + ac + bc)$

Cube of side a: volume $= a^3$; surface area $= 6a^2$

Sphere of radius r: volume $= \frac{4}{3}\pi r^3$; surface area $= 4\pi r^2$

Ellipsoid with semi-axes a, b and c: volume $= \frac{4}{3}\pi abc$

Cylinder of radius r and height h: volume $= \pi r^2 h$; lateral surface area $= 2\pi rh$

Cone of radius r and height h: volume $= \frac{1}{3}\pi r^2 h$

Pyramid of height h whose base is a rectangle with sides a, b: volume $= \frac{1}{3}abh$

Functions

Composition of functions: $(g \circ f)(x) = g(f(x))$

Functions $f(x)$ and $g(x)$ are inverse of each other if $f(g(x)) = x$ and $g(f(x)) = x$

Analytic Geometry

Distance between $P_1(x_1, y_1)$ and $P_2(x_2, y_2)$: $d(P_1, P_2) = \sqrt{(x_2 - x_1)^2 + (y_2 - y_1)^2}$

Point-slope equation of a line: $y - y_0 = m(x - x_0)$ (line goes through $P(x_0, y_0)$, m is its slope)

Slope-intercept (explicit) equation of a line: $y = mx + b$ (m is slope, b is y-intercept)

Lines of slope m_1 and m_2: parallel if $m_2 = m_1$; perpendicular if $m_2 = -1/m_1$

Midpoint of the line segment joining $P_1(x_1, y_1)$ and $P_2(x_2, y_2)$ has coordinates $\left(\dfrac{x_1 + x_2}{2}, \dfrac{y_1 + y_2}{2} \right)$

Circle of radius r centred at (p, q): $(x - p)^2 + (y - q)^2 = r^2$

Ellipse with semi-axes a and b: $\dfrac{x^2}{a^2} + \dfrac{y^2}{b^2} = 1$

Hyperbola in regions above and below its asymptotes $y = \pm \frac{b}{a}x$: $-\dfrac{x^2}{a^2} + \dfrac{y^2}{b^2} = 1$

Hyperbola in regions to the left and right of its asymptotes $y = \pm \frac{b}{a}x$: $\dfrac{x^2}{a^2} - \dfrac{y^2}{b^2} = 1$

Parabola that opens up or down: $y = ax^2 + bx + c$

Parabola that opens to the left or to the right: $x = ay^2$

Exponentials and Logarithms

Laws of exponents: $a^0 = 1$, $a^1 = 1$, $a^{-x} = \dfrac{1}{a^x}$, $a^x \cdot a^y = a^{x+y}$, $\dfrac{a^x}{a^y} = a^{x-y}$, $(a^x)^y = a^{xy}$,

$\quad (ab)^x = a^x b^x$, $\dfrac{a^x}{b^x} = \left(\dfrac{a}{b} \right)^x$?

Laws of logarithms: $\log_a 1 = 0$, $\log_a a = 1$, $a^{\log_a x} = x$ $(x > 0)$, $\log_a a^x = x$ $(x \in \mathbb{R})$;

$\quad \log_a(xy) = \log_a x + \log_a y$, $\log_a \dfrac{x}{y} = \log_a x - \log_a y$, $\log_a(x^n) = n \log_a x$

Natural exponential function/logarithm: $\ln 1 = 0$, $\ln e = 1$, $e^{\ln x} = x$ $(x > 0)$, $\ln e^x = x$ $(x \in \mathbb{R})$;

$\quad \ln(xy) = \ln x + \ln y$, $\ln \dfrac{x}{y} = \ln x - \ln y$, $\ln(x^n) = n \ln x$

Conversion: $\log_a x = \dfrac{\log_b x}{\log_b a}$, $\log_a x = \dfrac{\ln x}{\ln a}$, $\ln x = \dfrac{\log_a x}{\log_a e}$ Do we need to know that?

Trigonometry

Angle measure: 1 degree $= \pi/180$ radians; 1 radian $= 180/\pi$ degrees

Range of sine and cosine: $-1 \le \sin x \le 1$, $-1 \le \cos x \le 1$

Basic identities: $\sin^2 x + \cos^2 x = 1$, $\tan^2 x + 1 = \sec^2 x$, $\tan x = \sin x / \cos x$, $\cot x = \cos x / \sin x$

Periodicity: $\sin(x + 2\pi) = \sin x$, $\cos(x + 2\pi) = \cos x$, $\tan(x + \pi) = \tan x$

Period of $\sin(ax)$ and $\cos(ax)$ is $2\pi/a$; period of $\tan(ax)$ is π/a

Complementary angles: $\sin\left(\frac{\pi}{2} - x\right) = \cos x$, $\cos\left(\frac{\pi}{2} - x\right) = \sin x$

Symmetry: $\sin(-x) = -\sin x$, $\cos(-x) = \cos x$

Addition formulas: $\sin(x \pm y) = \sin x \cos y \pm \cos x \sin y$, $\cos(x \pm y) = \cos x \cos y \mp \sin x \sin y$

Double angle formulas: $\sin 2x = 2 \sin x \cos x$, $\cos 2x = \cos^2 x - \sin^2 x = 2\cos^2 x - 1 = 1 - 2\sin^2 x$

SECOND EDITION

Calculus...
FEAR NO MORE

A Review and Reference for College and University Courses

MIROSLAV LOVRIC
MCMASTER UNIVERSITY

NELSON EDUCATION

NELSON
EDUCATION

Calculus...Fear No More: A Review and
Reference for College and University
Courses, Second Edition

by Miroslav Lovric

**Vice President, Editorial
Higher Education:**
Anne Williams

Publisher:
Jackie Wood

Marketing Manager:
Leanne Newell

Technical Reviewer:
Andrijana Burazin

Developmental Editor:
Sven Pinczewski

Design Director:
Ken Phipps

Managing Designer:
Franca Amore

Cover Design:
Courtney Hellam

Cover Image:
Ascent Xmedia/Getty Images

**Library and Archives Canada
Cataloguing in Publication Data**

Lovric, Miroslav, author

   Calculus...fear no more : a review
and reference for college and
university courses / Miroslav Lovric.
— Second edition.

Includes index.
ISBN 978-0-17-650991-0 (paperback)

   1. Mathematics—Textbooks. I.
Title.

QA39.3.L69 2015   510
C2015-903323-3

ISBN-13: 978-0-17-650991-0
ISBN-10: 0-17-650991-7

What's *Calculus: Fear No More* About?

A leap from secondary education to university environment will be, without doubt, one of the most challenging and stressful events in your life. It is a true rite of passage, with all of its anxieties, pains, hopes, frustrations, joys and rewards. You have probably created a mental image of the new environment you will be encountering soon — but it is blurry, lots of fine detail is missing. The better prepared you are, the easier it will be to adjust to new situations, demands and expectations that university life will place on you.

No matter which high school you came from, you have certain strengths and weaknesses. There are things that you learned well in high school, things you know and are comfortable with. But, there are things that you forgot, or you don't know or have little experience with. In high school, you acquired certain skills, but you need to brush up on others. Or, you have been away from school for some time, and are now coming back ... Review your math! This book will help you identify those areas of math that you are good at, and those areas that you need to learn, review and work on. All you need is some dedication, pencil and paper, and about an hour of uninterrupted time per day (say, during the last three weeks before school starts).

We have strong evidence that shows that *the key to success in calculus at university or college is knowing the background material (algebra, geometry, functions) really well* — read the section "Why Background Knowledge Matters" on page *viii*. If you don't understand fractions, or forgot how to apply laws of exponents or graph the quadratic function, you will have problems with any math that is built on those concepts and techniques. And rather than trying to understand new calculus material your instructor is explaining, you are wasting your time, getting stuck with things you are supposed to know.

What will my first-year instructors assume that I know about mathematics? The big part of this book is dedicated to answering this question. Look at the table of contents to see what's done here.

The first part of this book is about the things you have probably thought a lot about. How is life in university different from high school? What should I expect from my first-year classes? How is university math different from math in high school? Read, and reflect on the issues raised ... discuss it with your parents, friends, teachers, or older colleagues. Nobody can give you detailed and precise answers to all questions that you have, but at least you will get a good feeling about certain aspects of your first-year university life.

The second part of this book is math. Look at the table of contents to see what is covered. One thing is certain: the more math you do, the easier it gets — experience helps! Do as many problems as you can; don't give up because the stuff looks difficult or you feel bored with it. A little investment of your time now will make studying mathematics a whole lot easier.

This is a Second Edition ...

The material covered is the same as in the first edition. What is new? Narratives have been improved (more details provided at places which appear to be challenging), there are more fully solved examples (especially in sections 1, 2, 4, and 5), and several hundred new exercises have been added for extra practice. Analytic geometry (section 5) has been expanded, and now includes graphing as it appears in various applications.

Good luck!

Miroslav Lovric
Department of Mathematics and Statistics
McMaster University

Get ready!!!!!

It's now May or June, the summer before you start your university life. For a second, let's change things a bit. Assume that you are good at basketball, play on a team, and in September you have an important competition. Or you are a pianist and have a major concert in September. What are you going to do over the summer? Nothing? Will you wait until September and then practice a bit, or not even warm up before your first basketball game? Just show up at your concert and hope things will go well?

So, then, what about that calculus course that you are taking soon?

Working on math is not the coolest thing to do in summer — but think a bit about the future. High school to university is a big change — the better prepared you are, the easier it will be for you to adjust successfully to your new life as a university student.

Student life is a busy life. It will be quite difficult for you (we did not say impossible!) to find time to do two things: to learn new material presented in lectures and, at the same time, to review background material that you are assumed to know. Not to mention that, without adequate preparation, you will have difficulties following math lectures.

Review your math now, while you have lots of free time on your hands!

If, for some reason, you developed negative attitudes and feelings towards mathematics in high school, then leave them there! You will have a chance to start fresh at a university. First-year math courses start at a level that is appropriate for most high school graduates.

Take this book with you to university and use it as reference — there are lots of important formulas, concepts and ideas in it that you will need in your calculus course.

What Is in This Book?

Narratives that this book starts with contain important and relevant information about studying mathematics in university. You can read it all right away, or skim over to see what's there, and come back to it later.

What Is in This Book? v
How Do I Use This Book? vii
Why Background Knowledge Matters.. viii
How Does Math in University Differ from High School Math? xi
How To Be Successful in Math xii
What Else Is Important? xiii
Your Lecture and Tutorial Notes xiv
Learning from Internet xiv
Transition to University xv

Now the math! Material in the following five sections is usually not reviewed in university courses (except for some small part, on occasion). However, what is here will be used in calculus all the time, and you have to know it and be good at it. Each section starts with a quiz that you might want to use to determine whether or not you need to study what's there.

1. Numbers and Operations 1
   Real Numbers and Its Famous Subsets, Division Involving Zero, Algebraic Operations with Fractions (Rational Numbers), Real Numbers are Ordered, Number Line and Intervals, Absolute Value, Integers as Exponents, Radicals and Rational Exponents

2. Basic Algebra 21
   Polynomials, Completing the Square, Factoring, Fractions, Division of Polynomials (Long Division), Rationalizing the Denominator

3. Basic Facts and Formulas from Geometry 41
   Plane Geometry, Miscellaneous Facts, Geometry in Three-Dimensional Space

4. Equations and Inequalities 51
   Linear Equations, Quadratic Equations, Inequalities, Equations and Inequalities Involving Absolute Value, Using Graphs to Solve Inequalities, Systems of Equations

5. Elements of Analytic Geometry 73
   Cartesian Coordinate System, Distance Between Points, Equations of a Line, Circle, Ellipse, Parabola, Hyperbola, Curves in Applications

Material in the following three sections forms the core background of calculus and is, to an extent, reviewed in first-year university courses. Even if you think that you know it and are good at it, have a look. You might find things you did not know or were not sure about. Since knowing trigonometric, exponential, and logarithmic functions is really important, at the end of sections 7 and 8 you will find extra practice problems.

6. Functions 93
   Definition, Domain, Range and Graph, List of Important Functions, New Functions from Old (Composition of Functions), Inverse Functions, New Functions from Old (Geometric Transformations)

7. Trigonometric Functions 115
    Angles, Degrees and Radians, Values of Trigonometric Ratios for Special Angles,
    Trigonometric Functions, Trigonometric Equations, Inverse Trigonometric Functions

8. Exponential and Logarithmic Functions 141
    Exponential Functions, Logarithms, Logarithmic Functions

The following section covers something that's usually not done in high school; however, many university instructors assume that their students know it, and will use it!

9. Mathematical Language; Mathematical Thinking and Logic 159
    Math Language, Definition, Theorem, Other Mathematical Statements, Context,
    Implication and Equivalence: *If-Then* and *If-And-Only-If*, Universal and Existential
    Quantifiers: *For All* and *There Exists*

At the end of the book, you will find

Answers to Selected Exercises* 173
Index 185

* Complete, detailed solutions to all exercises in this book are available (free download) at ms.mcmaster.ca/lovric/calculusfnm.html

How Do I Use This Book?

Read the narrative parts to become familiar with the number of issues and situations that you will face as a university student. The most important message is—*get prepared!*

How to work on math? Read the text slowly, and, as you go along, make notes, diagrams, whatever might help you understand the material. Keep asking yourself: why is this true; why does it work? How did they get this? How does this line follow from the previous line?

You will see the following icons in the text:

 Important formula or a rule, alternative interpretation, or facts that really need to be understood and remembered. As well, warning about notation or most common errors.

 Most often asked question about a particular step in a calculation, or about the material discussed. Request for clarification or more detail.

 Do these exercises to test yourself on understanding the material, knowing and applying formulas and algorithms, and in general to gain valuable routine. Answers to these questions are given at the back of this book.

 If you feel that you need more practice, work on some (or all!) of these questions. Answers to exercises marked with * appear at the end of this book.

Fully worked solutions to all exercises in this book can be downloaded (for free) in pdf format from ms.mcmaster.ca/lovric/calculusfnm.html

If you do not understand something, pause and think about it. Write a question that you have, or your comment, in the margin or in your notes. Move on, and come back to it later. You might find an answer as you continue reading, or find something else that will help you figure it out yourself.

Do not give up just because it feels difficult or you cannot get it right away! Math is not easy, and it does take time for everyone to understand concepts and practice calculations and algorithms.

Work through all solved examples. The best way to do that is to read the question and try to do the example yourself, without looking at the solution. If you get stuck, do not look at the solution right away. Try to identify what the problem is. Is it something technical, such as simplifying or solving an equation? Or is it related to some concept that you forgot about, or aren't sure how to apply? Review your attempt — are there alternative approaches? After you have thought about it for some time, look at the solution and make sure you understand every word of it. When done, move your notes aside and try to do the example again, from the start, without any outside help.

Work on exercises as you encounter them in the text. They will help you gain valuable routine and will tell you whether or not you understand the stuff. The key to getting good at math is practice. The more, the better!

Why Background Knowledge Matters

> Math is cumulative: new material builds upon the previously covered (i.e., learned, understood) material. It is not possible to truly understand and apply an advanced concept (such as derivatives) without understanding all basic concepts and techniques that are used to define it (fractions, limits, graphs, etc.).

Very often, the reasons why students lose marks on tests in calculus (and other math courses!) are due to a problem with something elementary, such as fractions, simplifying, solving equations, or recalling basic properties of exponents or trigonometric functions. Let us look at a few samples of actual test solutions.

In the case below, the student chose the appropriate integration method (which is taught in calculus and which is supposed to be the hard part of the question!), but then did not correctly simplify the fraction in the integral (see the last two lines). This error cost the student 50% of the credit for the question. [Correct way — long division: see Section 2 in this book.]

(b)[4] Find $\int x \arctan x \, dx$.

$$\int x \arctan x \, dx$$

let $u = \arctan x$ $\quad dv = x$

$du = \dfrac{1}{x^2+1} dx$ $\quad v = \dfrac{1}{2}x^2$

$$= uv - \int v \, du$$

$$= \arctan x \left(\tfrac{1}{2}x^2\right) - \int \tfrac{1}{2}x^2 \left(\dfrac{1}{x^2+1}\right) dx$$

$$\dfrac{x^2 \arctan x}{2} - \tfrac{1}{2}\int \dfrac{x^2}{x^2+1} \, dx$$

$$= \dfrac{x^2 \arctan x}{2} - \tfrac{1}{2}\int 1 + x^2 \, dx$$

In the next example, things started well — the calculation of $f'(x)$ is correct (second line). As well, the student knew that the expression had to be simplified. But that's where it all went wrong. Two attempts led nowhere. Lots of effort was put into simplifying — not to mention valuable time that was lost! As in the previous case, note that the credit lost was not due to a new concept learned in calculus (such as the product rule, correctly applied here, going from the first to the second line!), but due to errors related to high school material. [Simplifying and factoring: see sections 1 and 2 in this book.]

3.(a)[4] Find all critical points (critical numbers) of the function $f(x) = x^{4/5}(x-4)^2$.

$$f(x) = x^{4/5}(x-4)^2$$

$$f'(x) = \frac{4}{5}x^{-1/5}(x-4)^2 + [2(x-4)(1)(x^{4/5})]$$

$$= \frac{4}{5}x^{-1/5}(x-4)^2 + (2x-8)x^{4/5}$$

$$\frac{(x-4)^2 + \frac{2}{5}(x-4)(x^{4/5})}{5x^{1/5}}$$

$$4x^{-1/5}[\frac{4}{5}(x-4) + (2x-8)(x)]$$

$$\frac{x^2 - 32x + 64(\frac{2}{5}(x-4))}{5x^{1/5}}$$

It is not just that the student lost 4 points (which was 10% of the test!). The frustration from unsuccessful attempts contributes to increased feelings of panic and stress — pressure mounts — not a desirable state to be in when working on test questions. One more thing: the most-often-heard comment from students about a test is that there was not enough time. Certainly, if it takes you more than five to six minutes to do the question above correctly, you will not have enough time to complete your test.

In the case below, the student tried to analyze the expression for $f'(x)$ by looking at the graphs of *sin x* and *cos x* (good idea!). However, the graphs of the two functions are incorrect (as well, which is which?), and the answer ($2n\pi$, if that's the answer) does not make sense. The student lost all credit for the question. [For trig, equations and graphs, see Section 7.]

3.[3] Find all critical points (critical numbers) of the function $f(x) = \sin x + \cos x$.

$$f'(x) = \cos x - \sin x$$

$$2n\pi$$

The question in the next example requires that we graph the given function. For some reason, the student decided that it was a line, and proceeded to graph by plotting points. The points are correctly calculated, but the graph is not a line! It is a scaled and shifted version of the hyperbola $f(t)=1/t$ (the curve in the diagram was drawn by the person who marked the test). [Lines and equations: Section 5; graphs of functions, scaling and shifting: Section 6.]

5. At time $t = 0$, a patient is given an initial dose of morphine (pain reliever). The amount of morphine left in the patient's body is given by the formula $M(t) = \dfrac{33}{3+t}$, where $M(t)$ is the level of morphine and t is time in hours.

(a)[3] Make a rough sketch of the graph of $M(t)$. Label the initial amount of morphine in your graph.

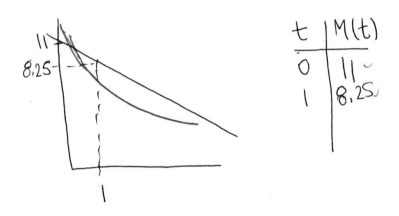

One more example: the student clearly knew what to do, but failed to simplify first. Trying to calculate the derivative of the complicated expression caused further mistakes (chain and quotient rules were used incorrectly). All credit for the question was lost. [Expressions involving logarithms: Section 8.]

(c)[4] Find an equation of the line tangent to the graph of the function $f(x) = \ln \dfrac{x^2 e^x}{1+x^2}$ at the point where $x = 1$.

$$f'(x) = \frac{1}{\ln \frac{x^2 e^x}{1+x^2}} \cdot \frac{(x^2 e^x + 2x e^x)(1+x^2) + x^2 e^x \cdot 2x}{(1+x^2)^2}$$

$$= \ln\left(\frac{x^2 e^x}{1+x^2}\right)^{-1} \frac{x^2 e^x + 2x e^x + x^4 e^x + 2x^3 e^x + 2x^3 e^x}{(1+x^2)^2}$$

$$f'(1) = \ln\left(\frac{(1)^3 e^{(1)}}{2}\right)^{-1} \cdot \frac{e^1 + 2e + e + 2e + 2e}{4}$$

x

How Does Math in University Differ from High School Math?

You will have to do lots of work on your own!

Lectures move at a faster pace than high school classes. Usually, one lecture covers one section from a textbook. Although lectures provide necessary theoretical material, they rarely present a sufficient number of worked examples and problems. You will have to do those on your own.

Certain topics (trigonometry, exponential and logarithm functions, etc.) will be taught and/or reviewed in your calculus course. However, the time spent reviewing in lectures will not suffice to cover all details, nor will it provide a sufficient number of routine exercises — again, you are expected to do it on your own.

In university, there is more emphasis on understanding than in high school. For instance, your math tests and exams will include questions that will ask you to quote a definition, or to explain and/or use a theorem, or answer a "theoretical question." Here is a sample of questions that appeared on past exams and tests in a calculus course:

- Is it true that $f'(x) = g'(x)$ implies $f(x) = g(x)$? Answering "yes" or "no" will not suffice. You must explain your answer.
- State the definition of a horizontal asymptote.
- Using the definition, compute the derivative of $f(x) = (x - 2)^{-1}$.
- Given the graph of $1/x$, explain in words how to construct the graph of $1 + 1/(x + 6)$.
- Can a polynomial of degree 3 have two inflection points? You must explain your answer to get full credit.
- Define what "function $f(x)$ is continuous at a" means.
- It is true that every increasing function has an inverse function? Explain why or why not.

You will be allowed — and encouraged — to use your (graphing) calculator and/or computer software (such as Maple, WolframAlpha) to study mathematics, to do homework assignments and computer labs. On tests and exams, either no calculator will be allowed, or you will be asked to use the calculator that your university chose as standard (this way, everyone uses the same calculator). Calculators and software are an aid, but not a replacement for your brain, and you should treat them as such. If your calculator says something, it is not necessarily a correct answer.

Mathematics is not just formulas, rules and calculations. In university courses, you will study definitions, theorems, and other pieces of theory. Proofs are integral parts of mathematics, and you will meet a few in your first-year courses. You will learn how to approach learning theory, how to think about proofs, how to use theorems, and so on.

Layperson-like attitude towards mathematics (and other disciplines!) — accepting facts, formulas, statements, etc., at face value — is no longer acceptable in university. Thinking (critical thinking!) must be (and will be) an integral part of your student life. In that sense, you must accept the fact that proofs and definitions are as much a part of mathematics as computations of derivatives and operations with matrices.

How To Be Successful at Math

Like everything you care for, learning mathematics requires your seriousness, dedication, a significant amount of time and hard work.

To learn mathematics means to understand, to memorize and to practice a lot.

To understand something means to be able to correctly and effectively communicate it to somebody else, in writing and orally; to be able to answer questions about it, and to be able to relate it to known mathematics material. Understanding is a result of a mental process. It is not a mere transfer from the one who understands (your instructor) to the one who is supposed to understand (you).

How do you make yourself understand math?

- Ask questions as you study. Being able to answer questions such as 'Why is this true?' 'Why does it work?' 'How does this line follow from the previous line?' is a big step towards making yourself understand.
- Discuss what you're studying with your colleagues, teaching assistant or instructor. Can you explain something you learned to someone else? Can you answer their questions about it?
- Approach material from various perspectives (draw a graph, make a diagram).
- Attempt to solve many exercises on your own; as well, study solved problems to see how to write down solutions and answers to questions.
- Make connections with previously taught material and apply what you learned to new situations.
- It is impossible to understand new mathematics unless one has mastered (to a certain extent) the required background material. Don't skip something just because it is not in your homework assignment.

Keep in mind that building understanding does not happen right away — it takes time, and lots of hard work.

It is necessary to memorize certain mathematics facts, formulas and algorithms. Memorizing is accomplished by exposure: by doing drill exercises, by using formulas and algorithms to solve exercises, by using mathematics facts in solving problems. Remember: the more you understand, the less is left to you to memorize.

The only way to master basic technical and computational skills is to solve a large number of exercises. Drill is essential!

If needed, consult your high school textbooks, or go to a local library and find a reference (say, with more practice exercises). Ask somebody who knows the stuff to discuss it with you. If you prefer, hire a private math tutor for a few sessions.

What Else Is Important?

Make a habit of coming to all lectures, tutorials and/or labs.

In class, be active. Think, ask questions, try to understand as much as possible. Keep in mind that you are not expected to understand everything your instructor says, but leave a lecture with a good idea of what the whole thing was about. Even if you did not sleep much the night before, feel a bit sick or have headache, go to the lecture! Just by being there and listening, you will learn something. As well, you will have your own class notes (always beats borrowing and photocopying notes from someone else).

Don't miss tutorials! You might think that you know the stuff, but it's almost certain that, in any given tutorial, you will come across something that you did not know or were not sure about. As well, it's much-needed extra practice.

Don't fall behind! Catching up is never fun. Cramming is not studying.

Lectures and tutorials alone will not suffice. You need to spend time on your own doing math: studying, working on assignments, preparing for tests and exams, etc. As a rule of thumb, spend three hours of your own time doing math for each hour of lecture.

It is not just knowing how to do a question on a test or exam — you must be able to do it relatively quickly. If it takes you 10 minutes to compute a common denominator or simplify an expression with logarithms, you will — guaranteed — not have enough time to finish all questions. Drill is essential for success (not just in math!). It's boring, but it works! Solving hundreds of problems will help you establish routine and build the confidence you need (together with a few other things) to write good tests and exams.

Plan your study time carefully. Don't underestimate the amount of time you need to prepare for a test or to work on an assignment. Avoid doing things last-minute.

Make sure that you are aware of (and use!) learning resources available to you. Here are some of them:
- Your instructor or teaching assistant might be giving a review session.
- Visit your instructor or teaching assistant during their office hours; come prepared, ask specific questions.
- The course web page might suggest additional reading, or might post additional questions.
- Many math departments offer some kind of walk-in math help (usually called Math Help Centre, Tutorial Centre, Study Centre, etc.).
- Ask your colleagues for help, or just to discuss questions you have; if it's your mode of studying, form a study group.
- If necessary, hire a private tutor.

Your Lecture and Tutorial Notes

Your lecture (and tutorial) notes will be your most valuable resource. You will refer to them when you do homework, computer lab, or prepare for a test or an exam. So:

- During a lecture, take notes as carefully as possible.
- Later, read your notes; make sure that you have correct statements of all definitions, theorems, and other important facts; make sure that all formulas and algorithms are correct and illustrated by examples.
- Fill in the gaps in your notes; fix mistakes; supplement with additional examples, if needed.
- Add your comments; interpret definitions in your own words; restate theorems in your own words and pick exercises that illustrate their use.
- Write down your questions and attempts at answering them; discuss your questions with your colleague, instructor or teaching assistant; write down the answers.
- It is a waste of time to try again and yet again to understand a concept; so, once you understand it, write it down correctly, in a way that you will be able to understand later; this way, studying for an exam consists of recalling and not relearning; recalling takes less time, and is easier than relearning.
- Keep your notes for future reference: you might need to recall a formula, an algorithm or a definition in another math course.

Learning from Online Resources

There is lots of valuable math stuff on Internet. However—as with other things we do online—be sure that the site you are using is reliable, and that it gives you correct information.

- Math on Internet is posted by thousands of people, so it takes some time to get used to the page layout and the language, as well as the notation used. Sometimes non-standard notation makes fairly simple concepts look quite complicated.
- Wikipedia is a great resource for math but it might not provide sufficient detail and examples for math at the level of this book.
- Math on Internet is, in general, correct (who would want to hack a math site?) However, some solutions posted at various Q&A (question and answer) sites are not correct. In some cases the answer is correct, but there are errors in the calculation or in the reasoning.
- There are good math videos online. For instance, typing "long division video" into your browser will identify many videos, of great help if you're not sure about long division.

Transition to University

What is new and different in university? Almost everything: new people (your peers/colleagues, teaching and lab assistants, instructors, administrators, etc.), a new environment, new social contexts, new norms, and—very important—new demands and expectations.

Think about the issues raised below. How do you plan to deal with it? Read tips and suggestions, and try to devise your own strategies.

First-year classes are usually very large — you will find yourself in a huge auditorium, surrounded by 300, 400, or perhaps even more students. Large classes create intimidating situations. For instance: you listen to a lecture, and hear something that you do not understand. Will you have the courage to raise your hand and ask the instructor to repeat something, or to clarify the point you missed? It's hard to break the ice, but you have to try. Keep in mind that you are not alone — other students feel the same way you do. They will be grateful that you asked the question — you can be sure that lots of them had exactly the same question in mind.

Learning is your responsibility. Come to classes regularly, be active, take notes, ask questions. Find a quiet place to study. Use all resources available to you. Discuss material with your peers, teaching and lab assistants, and/or professors.

The amount of personal attention you get from your instructors, compared to high school, is drastically lower. If you have a question, or a problem, you will have to make an effort to talk to your lecturer, or to contact the most appropriate person.

Courses have different requirements and restrictions with regards to calculators and computer software. You will find the information about it in the course syllabus (course outline) that will be given to you (usually) in the first lecture of a course and/or posted on the course web page.

Good time management is essential. Do not leave everything for the last moment. Can you complete three assignments in one evening? Or write a major essay and prepare for a test over a weekend? Plan your study time carefully, and stick to your plan (that's harder than it sounds).

The amount of material covered in a unit of time increases at least threefold in university courses, compared to high school. This means that things happen very quickly. If you miss classes and do not study regularly, you will get behind in your courses. Trying to catch up is not easy. For each hour of lecture, plan to spend (at least) two to three hours studying, reviewing, working on assignments, making sure your notes are complete and accurate, etc.

"In university grades drop by 30%." Not necessarily. Study regularly (do you know how to study math? chemistry? physics? Why not discuss it with your lecturer?). You might have to adjust/modify your study habits. One thing is certain: the amount of work that earned you good marks in high school will not suffice to keep those marks in university.

It is possible to study hard and still fail a test. If you fail a test, react immediately. Identify reasons for your poor performance. Visit your instructor during office hours, bring your test and discuss it. Be ready to re-examine and modify your study strategies. **Do not get discouraged by initial bad marks that you might get.**

Be prepared for a fail (for instance, getting a low mark on a test), because quite likely it will happen. When it happens, what do you plan to do? Think about it, identify the reasons why you did not do well, and make appropriate changes.

Inquire about learning resources available to you. Do you know where the science (engineering, humanities) library is? Is there a math help/tutorial centre? Are there online resources available? When are computer labs open? Before coming to university, browse through its Internet site. Bookmark the sites that link to learning resources.

If you experience problems of any kind, academic, personal or otherwise, react and deal with it immediately. Ask your friends, family, peers, instructors for advice. As well, talk to an adviser in your faculty office, and visit a student support centre.

Eat well, exercise regularly, do not neglect social activities — have a life!

Think about all this …

Your university/college life is supposed to be challenging, but fun!

By preparing yourself now, you will have more free time
when you come to school, to learn new things, enjoy things you like,
play sports, have a rich social life, and generally
enjoy your time as a student.

1. Numbers and Operations

What is in this section?

Real numbers and the number line; operations with fractions; intervals and inequalities; absolute value; radicals and rational exponents; laws of exponents, laws of radicals.

Do I need to read this?

Answer the quiz questions below. If you get all of them right, or make a few smaller mistakes, then you can skip this section. Otherwise, identify what you don't know or are not sure about and read relevant parts of this section (or read all of it!).

Quiz

1. Describe the following sets of real numbers in interval notation:

(a) $\{x \in \mathbb{R} \mid 4 \le x \le 7\}$ (b) all real numbers smaller than 3

(c) $\{x \in \mathbb{R} \mid x \le -31\}$ (d) all real numbers

2. What intervals are represented in the figure below?

3. Find the distance on the number line between -11 and 14.

4. Compute $\dfrac{4 - |3 - 2|}{5 - |-4 - 3|}$.

Over ...

5. Compute the following:

(a) $(-3)^4$ (b) 4^{-3} (c) 0^{-3} (d) $(1/2)^{-3}$

6. Simplify $\left(\dfrac{x^6}{x^4 x^{-1}}\right)^5$.

7. Evaluate, if possible, the following expressions:

(a) $\sqrt[3]{125}$ (b) $\sqrt[5]{0}$ (c) $\sqrt[3]{-64}$ (d) $\sqrt{-32}$ (e) $\sqrt{9/4}$

8. Simplify $\sqrt{12}/\sqrt{27}$.

9. Simplify $16^{-3/2} 9^{3/2}$.

[Answers to this quiz are at the bottom of page 19.]

Real Numbers and Its Famous Subsets

In calculus and many areas of mathematics, we deal with the set of *real numbers* and its subsets. One important subset is the set of *integers*

$$\ldots, -3, -2, -1, 0, 1, 2, 3, 4, \ldots$$

The numbers $0, 1, 2, 3, 4, \ldots$ are called *non-negative integers*; the set of *natural numbers* consists of the numbers $1, 2, 3, 4, \ldots$ The quotient $\frac{p}{q}$ of two integers p and q (where $q \neq 0$) is called a *rational number*. For example, $\frac{1}{3}, \frac{-4}{11}, 0.47 = \frac{47}{100}, -32 = \frac{-32}{1}, 13 = \frac{13}{1}$ are rational numbers. (Looking at the last two examples, we see that integers belong to the set of rational numbers.) We wrote -32 above as $\frac{-32}{1}$. Instead, we could have represented it as $-32 = -\frac{32}{1} = \frac{32}{-1}$.

The numbers that cannot be represented as quotients of rational numbers are called *irrational numbers*. Numbers such as $\sqrt{2}$, π, or $\sqrt{5}$ are irrational. The set of *real numbers* consists of rational and irrational numbers. It is usually denoted by $\mathbb{R}$.

We can use decimal notation to express real numbers. Rational numbers have either finite, or repeating infinite decimal representation.

For example, $\frac{1}{2} = 0.5 = 0.50000\ldots = 0.5\overline{0}$, $\frac{1}{3} = 0.33333\ldots = 0.\overline{3}$, $\frac{13}{44} = 0.295454545\ldots = 0.29\overline{545}$, etc. Non-repeating infinite decimal expressions represent irrational numbers: $\pi = 3.1415926535\ldots$, $\sqrt{2} = 1.414213562\ldots$, etc.

Division Involving Zero

How do we compute fractions which involve zero, such as $\frac{0}{7}$, $\frac{7}{0}$, and $\frac{0}{0}$?

Knowing the definition helps. Recall that the *division* (or the *quotient*) $\frac{a}{b}$ of a real number a by a real number b is the real number c such that $a = b \cdot c$. Briefly,

$$\frac{a}{b} = c \quad \text{means that} \quad a = b \cdot c.$$

For example, $\frac{14}{7} = 2$, since $14 = 7 \cdot 2$ (in this case, $a = 14$, $b = 7$ and $c = 2$). As well, $\frac{-36}{3} = -12$, since $-36 = 3 \cdot (-12)$.

What is $\frac{0}{7}$? Writing $\frac{0}{7} = c$ and using the definition, we obtain $0 = 7 \cdot c$, so c must be zero (when the product of real numbers is zero, at least one of them is zero). Thus, $\frac{0}{7} = 0$. This calculation can be repeated with 7 replaced by any non-zero real number b, and we conclude that

$$\boxed{\frac{0}{b} = 0 \quad \text{for any} \quad b \neq 0}$$

In words, zero divided by a non-zero number is zero.

Using the same approach, we now find out what $\frac{a}{0}$ is, where a is a non-zero real number. Writing $\frac{a}{0} = c$, we obtain $a = 0 \cdot c$. No matter what c is, the right side is zero, and we obtain $a = 0$, which does not make sense (since we assumed that $a \neq 0$). In other words, there is no real number c such that $\frac{a}{0} = c$. We conclude that

$$\text{if } a \neq 0, \text{ then the quotient } \frac{a}{0} \text{ is not a real number}$$

In particular, $\frac{7}{0}$ is not a real number.

Finally, to figure out what $\frac{0}{0}$ is, we look for a real number c such that $\frac{0}{0} = c$. By definition, $\frac{0}{0} = c$ means $0 = 0 \cdot c$. The right side is zero no matter what real value we assign to c. So $\frac{0}{0} = c$ could be *any* real number. (If you're not convinced: $\frac{0}{0} = 3.7$ is true, since $0 = 0 \cdot 3.7$ is true (both sides are zero); likewise, $\frac{0}{0} = 11$ is true, since $0 = 0 \cdot 11$ is true, and $\frac{0}{0} = -6$ is true, since $0 = 0 \cdot (-6)$ is true; and so on.) Since a real number has a unique value (7 is always 7, and never equal to 8 or -1) we conclude that $\frac{0}{0}$ is not a real number.

Putting the last two cases together we conclude that

$$\boxed{\text{For any real number } a, \text{ the quotient } \frac{a}{0} \text{ is not a real number.}}$$

To repeat—division by zero generates an expression which is not a real number. This is the precise meaning of the commonly used phrases "division by 0 is not allowed" and "division by 0 is not defined." Another commonly used phrase "division by 0 gives infinity" makes sense *only* within the context of limits (which is discussed in a calculus course).

Algebraic Operations with Fractions (Rational Numbers)

To *cancel a fraction* means to divide both the numerator and the denominator by the same *non-zero* real number.

For instance, by dividing the numerator and denominator by 9, we obtain $\dfrac{45}{99} = \dfrac{5 \cdot 9}{11 \cdot 9} = \dfrac{5}{11}$. Likewise, $\dfrac{7x^2y}{21y} = \dfrac{x^2}{3}$ after dividing by $7y$ (and assuming that $y \neq 0$).

(extra)   **Exercise 1.**   Cancel each fraction.

(a) $\dfrac{360}{72}$ (b) $\dfrac{3 \cdot 33 \cdot 24}{4 \cdot 5 \cdot 6}$ (c)* $\dfrac{121 \cdot 13}{169 \cdot 11}$ (d) $\dfrac{14ab}{7bc}$ (e) $\dfrac{90z}{33x^2z}$ (f)* $\dfrac{36x(x-y)}{24(x-y)}$

A fraction has the same value no matter whether a minus sign is placed in front of it, in the numerator or in the denominator. Remember:

$$\boxed{-\frac{a}{b} = \frac{-a}{b} = \frac{a}{-b}}$$

Thus, $-\dfrac{x - y^2}{z} = \dfrac{-(x - y^2)}{z} = \dfrac{-x + y^2}{z}$ and $-\dfrac{x - y^2}{z} = \dfrac{x - y^2}{-z}$.

As well, $\dfrac{4}{y - x} = \dfrac{4}{-(-y + x)} = -\dfrac{4}{x - y}$.

(extra)   **Exercise 2.*** Which of the following fractions are equal to $\dfrac{a - b}{c - d}$?

(a) $-\dfrac{-a + b}{c - d}$ (b) $\dfrac{a - b}{d - c}$ (c) $\dfrac{b - a}{d - c}$ (d) $\dfrac{b - a}{c - d}$

(e) $-\dfrac{b - a}{c - d}$ (f) $-\dfrac{b - a}{d - c}$ (g) $-\dfrac{a - b}{d - c}$ (h) $-\dfrac{a - b}{c - d}$

(extra) **Exercise 3.** Which of the following fractions are equal to $\dfrac{(x-y)(z-t)}{a-b}$?

(a) $-\dfrac{(x-y)(z-t)}{a-b}$ (b) $-\dfrac{(x-y)(z-t)}{b-a}$ (c) $-\dfrac{(y-x)(z-t)}{b-a}$ (d) $\dfrac{(y-x)(z-t)}{b-a}$

(e) $-\dfrac{(x-y)(t-z)}{a-b}$ (f) $\dfrac{(y-x)(t-z)}{a-b}$ (g) $-\dfrac{(y-x)(t-z)}{a-b}$ (h) $\dfrac{(y-x)(t-z)}{b-a}$

To add and subtract fractions we compute a common denominator.

For instance (the common denominator, i.e., the least common multiple of 15, 5, and 10 is 30):

$$\frac{2a}{15} - \frac{b}{5} + \frac{a+b}{10} = \frac{2a(2)}{15(2)} - \frac{b(6)}{5(6)} + \frac{(a+b)(3)}{10(3)} = \frac{4a - 6b + 3a + 3b}{30} = \frac{7a - 3b}{30}$$

and (the common denominator of $x+y$, x^2 and $x(x+y)$ is $x^2(x+y)$)

$$\frac{3}{x+y} - \frac{y}{x^2} + \frac{2y}{x(x+y)} = \frac{3(x^2)}{(x+y)(x^2)} - \frac{y(x+y)}{x^2(x+y)} + \frac{2y(x)}{x(x+y)(x)}$$

$$= \frac{3x^2 - xy - y^2 + 2xy}{x^2(x+y)} = \frac{3x^2 + xy - y^2}{x^2(x+y)}$$

(extra) **Exercise 4.** Compute each expression and simplify as much as possible.

(a) $\dfrac{5x}{3y} - \dfrac{7}{3y} + \dfrac{11x}{3y}$

(b) $\dfrac{2a+b}{7} - \dfrac{a}{7} + \dfrac{b}{7} - \dfrac{b-a}{7}$

(c) $\dfrac{(a+b)^2}{ab} - \dfrac{(a-b)^2}{ab}$

(d) $\dfrac{c}{c+d} - \dfrac{d}{c+d} + \dfrac{3c-d}{c+d}$

(e)* $4x + \dfrac{x+y}{3} - \dfrac{5y}{3}$

(f) $\dfrac{3x-y}{4} + \dfrac{x+y}{2} - \dfrac{5y}{8}$

(g)* $\dfrac{a}{2b} + \dfrac{2b}{3a} - 4$

(h)* $\dfrac{x-y}{2} - \dfrac{x+y}{5x} - \dfrac{1}{3y} + \dfrac{4}{15x}$

(i) $a + 4b - \dfrac{a+1}{b} - \dfrac{2}{ab^2} + \dfrac{3}{a^2b}$

The numerator (denominator) of the product of two fractions is the product of their numerators (denominators). To divide two fractions we multiply the fraction in the numerator by the reciprocal of the fraction in the denominator. Thus

$$\boxed{\frac{a}{b} \cdot \frac{c}{d} = \frac{ac}{bd} \quad \text{and} \quad \frac{\frac{a}{b}}{\frac{c}{d}} = \frac{a}{b} \cdot \frac{d}{c} = \frac{ad}{bc}}$$

For example, $\dfrac{7x}{y} \cdot \dfrac{3x}{14} = \dfrac{21x^2}{14y} = \dfrac{3x^2}{2y}$, after cancelling by 7. As well,

$$\frac{x-y}{a-b} \cdot \frac{(a+b)^2}{2x-2y} = \frac{(x-y)(a+b)^2}{(a-b)(2x-2y)} = \frac{(x-y)(a+b)^2}{(a-b)2(x-y)} = \frac{(a+b)^2}{2(a-b)}$$

In the last step we cancelled by $x-y$.

Keep in mind that we write $a = \frac{a}{1}$ to convert a number into a fraction. This is useful when we need to multiply a number by a fraction, e.g., $a \cdot \dfrac{b}{c} = \dfrac{a}{1} \cdot \dfrac{b}{c} = \dfrac{ab}{c}$.

Here is another example:

$$\frac{\frac{22}{17}}{11} = \frac{\frac{22}{17}}{\frac{11}{1}} = \frac{22}{17} \cdot \frac{1}{11} = \frac{22}{17 \cdot 11} = \frac{2}{17}$$

(In the last step we cancelled the fraction by 11.)

(extra) **Exercise 5.** Compute each expression and simplify as much as possible.

(a) $\dfrac{a}{bc} \cdot \dfrac{b}{ac} + \dfrac{3}{c^2}$

(b) $\dfrac{x+y+z}{xy} \cdot \dfrac{xy}{x+y}$

(c)* $3mn \cdot \dfrac{3}{n} \cdot \dfrac{m}{27}$

(d) $xyz \left(\dfrac{x}{yz} + \dfrac{y}{xz} \right)$

(e) $3x(x+y) \cdot \dfrac{3}{(x+y)(x-2y)}$

(f) $xy \cdot \dfrac{3x-2}{x} + x^2 y \cdot \dfrac{4-y}{y}$

(g)* $\dfrac{a+2b}{3a-b} \cdot \dfrac{42}{a+2b} \cdot \dfrac{7(3a-b)}{4}$

(extra) **Exercise 6.** Compute each expression and simplify as much as possible.

(a) $\dfrac{\frac{11}{17}}{\frac{44}{51}}$

(b) $\dfrac{4}{\frac{128}{21}}$

(c)* $\dfrac{\frac{60}{13}}{5}$

(d)* $\dfrac{3}{6} + \dfrac{2}{\frac{3}{4}} - \dfrac{\frac{1}{2}}{\frac{3}{4}}$

(e) $\dfrac{\frac{3ab}{c^2}}{3c}$

(f) $\dfrac{\frac{3ab}{c^2}}{\frac{1}{3c}}$

(g) $\dfrac{x+\frac{y}{z}}{x-\frac{y}{z}}$

(h) $\dfrac{\frac{a}{17}-b}{\frac{c}{51}-d}$

(i)* $\dfrac{\frac{a}{b}+\frac{b}{a}}{a^2+b^2}$

(j) $\dfrac{\frac{1}{x}-\frac{1}{2}}{2-x}$

Real Numbers are Ordered

$a < b$ means that "a is less than b," $a > b$ means that "a is greater than b," $a \le b$ means that "a is less than b or a is equal to b," and $a \ge b$ means that "a is greater than b or a is equal to b." For example, $\sqrt{2} < 1.42$, $\frac{3}{5} \ge \frac{2}{5}$, $4 \le 4$, $4 \le 5$, $-2 < -1.9$, $\pi > 3.14$, etc.

Number Line and Intervals

Real numbers can be represented visually as points on a *number line*

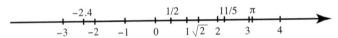

We choose an arbitrary point on the line to be the *origin* (denoted by 0, it represents the number zero), and indicate the direction in which the numbers increase by an arrow. For example, $a < b$ means that a lies to the left of b on the number line.

An *open interval* (a, b) consists of all real numbers between a and b, not including a and b. In symbols, (a, b) contains all real numbers x such that $a < x < b$. If we need to include endpoints, we use square brackets. For example, $[a, b)$ represents all numbers x such that $a \le x < b$.

Interval $[a, b]$, both of whose endpoints are included, is called a *closed interval*.

To denote the set of all numbers that are greater than a, we use (a, ∞). If we need all numbers that are greater than or equal to a, we use $[a, \infty)$. The numbers smaller than b form the interval $(-\infty, b)$.

Remember that ∞ and $-\infty$ are not real numbers (therefore, when infinity is involved, we always use round parentheses/brackets). We could also use set notation. For example,

$$[a, b) = \{x \in \mathbb{R} \mid a \le x < b\}, \quad (-\infty, b] = \{x \in \mathbb{R} \mid x \le b\} \quad \text{or} \quad (a, \infty) = \{x \in \mathbb{R} \mid x > a\}.$$

Recall that the curly braces { } denote a set (read "set of all"), $\in$ means "belong(s) to" and $\mid$ is read "such that." Thus, $\{x \in \mathbb{R} \mid a \le x < b\}$ means "set of all real numbers x such that x is greater than or equal to a and x is smaller than b."

Example 1. Describe the following sets of real numbers in interval notation:

(a) $\{x \in \mathbb{R} \mid 4 \leq x \leq 7\}$ (b) all real numbers smaller than 3

(c) $\{x \in \mathbb{R} \mid x \leq -31\}$ (d) all real numbers

Solution. (a) $[4, 7]$ (b) $(-\infty, 3)$ (c) $(-\infty, -31]$ (d) $(-\infty, \infty)$

In the figure below we drew the intervals $(-\infty, -3)$, $[-1, 0)$, $[1, 2]$ and $[\pi, \infty)$. Filled dots represent a point that is included in the interval, whereas empty dots indicate that a point is not included.

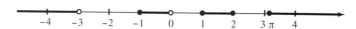

try it!   **Exercise 7.** On the same number line, sketch the intervals $(-3, -1.4)$, $[-1/2, 1/4]$ and $[2, \infty)$.

try it!   **Exercise 8.** What intervals are represented on the number line below?

The *midpoint* between two numbers A and B on the number line is given by $\frac{A+B}{2}$.

For instance, the midpoint between -3 and 5 is $\frac{-3+5}{2} = 1$. The midpoint between 4 and 4.1 is $\frac{4+4.1}{2} = \frac{8.1}{2} = 4.05$.

extra   **Exercise 9.** Write the following sets in interval notation (in some cases you will need two intervals):

(a) All real numbers greater than or equal to $-4/9$

(b) All real numbers between -7 and -4.4 including -7 and not including -4.4

(c)* All real numbers smaller than -8 or greater than -2

(d) All real numbers greater than zero and different from 5.5

(e) All real numbers between 3 and 4 including both 3 and 4, and different from 3.7.

(f)* All negative real numbers, excluding -4.

extra   **Exercise 10.** Fill in the blanks in the table below.

interval notation	inequality	number line	verbal description
$(-1/2, 7/3)$			
		$\begin{array}{ccc} \circ & \quad & \circ \\ -2 & 0 & \pi \end{array}$	
			all real numbers greater than 0.7
	$-2.3 \leq x < -0.9$		
$[0, 127.4]$			

extra **Exercise 11.** Identify each formula as correct or incorrect.

(a) $\frac{-4}{11} = \frac{4}{-11}$ (b) $\frac{0}{-4} = 0$ (c)* $4.7 \geq 4.7$ (d)* $4.7 > 4.7$ (e)* $\frac{-4}{0} = 0$ (f) $-2.2 \leq -3.1$

Absolute Value

The *absolute value* of a real number a is defined as

$$|a| = \begin{cases} a & \text{if } a \geq 0 \\ -a & \text{if } a < 0 \end{cases}$$

Using the definition, we compute $|6| = 6$, $|0| = 0$ and $|-13| = -(-13) = 13$. Thus, the absolute value of any number is either zero or positive.

A good way to visualize $|a|$ is to think of the distance between 0 (origin) and the number a on the number line. If $a = 0$, then the distance is zero. If a is positive, the distance from 0 to a is a (for instance, $|6|$ represents the distance from the origin to number 6, which is 6).

To find $|-13|$, we measure the distance from the origin to -13, which is 13 units (and not -13 units). Algebraically, we need to convert the negative number -13 to the positive number 13. So if a is negative, to find the distance between 0 and a we need to convert a to a positive number—we do it by placing the minus sign in front of a, and write $-a$ in the second line of the definition of $|a|$.

 Just because there is a minus sign in front of a variable, such as $-a$, the resulting number does not have to be negative; e.g., if $a = -4$ then $-a = -(-4) = 4$, which is positive. Likewise, a variable a, without the minus sign in front, does not have to be positive. For example, think of $a = -7$.

(So, it is not correct to read $-a$ as "negative a"; instead, it should be read as "minus a.")

In light of these comments, it is not correct to say that "absolute value removes the minus sign"; instead, we should say that "absolute value transforms a given expression into a positive expression (or zero)."

Better yet, we rephrase the definition as follows:

- If an expression is positive, then the absolute value does not do anything, it remains the same.
- If an expression is negative, then the absolute value inserts the minus sign in front, making it positive.
- The absolute value of zero is zero.

The symbol a in the definition of the absolute value can represent any expression.

For instance, if we replace a by $x - 2$, we get

$$|x - 2| = \begin{cases} x - 2 & \text{if } x - 2 \geq 0 \\ -(x - 2) & \text{if } x - 2 < 0 \end{cases} = \begin{cases} x - 2 & \text{if } x \geq 2 \\ -x + 2 & \text{if } x < 2 \end{cases}$$

extra **Exercise 12.** Imitating the above, write (and simplify) the definition of:

(a) $|x + 2.9|$ (b) $|4x - 7|$ (c) $|3 - x|$ (d)* $|10 - 0.2x|$

Expressions involving the absolute value of a function (such as the ones above) appear often in calculus; we will meet them many times in this book.

Example 2. Compute:

(a) $|-4.3|$ (b) $-|4.3|$ (c) $-|-4.3|$

Solution.

(a) We use the definition (keep in mind that $a = -4.3 < 0$) to get $|-4.3| = -(-4.3) = 4.3$.

(b) Since the absolute value does not change positive quantities, $|4.3| = 4.3$, and so $-|4.3| = -4.3$.

(c) In (a), we calculated that $|-4.3| = 4.3$. Thus, $-|-4.3| = -4.3$.

Example 3. Compute: (a) $\dfrac{|3-3.5|}{3+3.5}$ (b) $\dfrac{4-|3-2|}{5-|-4-3|}$

Solution.

(a) $\dfrac{|3-3.5|}{3+3.5} = \dfrac{|-0.5|}{6.5} = \dfrac{0.5}{6.5} = \dfrac{5}{65} = \dfrac{1}{13}$

(b) $\dfrac{4-|3-2|}{5-|-4-3|} = \dfrac{4-|1|}{5-|-7|} = \dfrac{4-1}{5-7} = -\dfrac{3}{2}$

In terms of the order of operations, absolute value is treated as brackets (parentheses). For example, $3 + |-1| = 3 + 1 = 4$, and $3 - |-4| = 3 - 4 = -1$.

We have already mentioned the relation between absolute value and distance. In general:

> The *distance* between numbers a and b on a number line is given by $|a - b|$ or $|b - a|$.

The two expressions $|b-a|$ and $|a-b|$ are equal (we'll show that soon). Sounds reasonable: it should not make any difference whether we measure the distance from a to b or from b to a.

The distance between a number a and 0 (the origin) is $|a - 0| = |a|$, as mentioned earlier.

The distance between -3.5 and 4.2 is $|-3.5 - 4.2| = |-7.7| = 7.7$. The order does not matter, and we could have used $|4.2 - (-3.5)| = |7.7| = 7.7$ instead to measure the distance.

The distance between -7 and -2 is $|-7 - (-2)| = |-7+2| = |-5| = 5$. Alternatively, $|-2 - (-7)| = |-2 + 7| = |5| = 5$.

Example 4. Find the distance on the number line between:

(a) -11 and 14 (b) the origin and -13.2 (c) 15 and -15

Solution.

(a) $|-11 - (14)| = |-25| = 25$. Or, switching the two numbers, $|14 - (-11)| = |25| = 25$.

(b) $|0 - (-13.2)| = |13.2| = 13.2$

(c) $|15 - (-15)| = |30| = 30$

Example 5. (a) Explain why $|x^2 + 1| = x^2 + 1$ for any real number x.

(b) Explain why $|-x^2| = x^2$ for any real number x.

(c) Does the formula $|x + y| = |x| + |y|$ hold for all real numbers?

(d) Show that the formula $|x - y| = |x| - |y|$ does not hold for all real numbers.

(e) If $|x| = |y|$, then $x = y$. True or false?

Solution.

(a) The square of any number x is zero or positive, i.e., $x^2 \geq 0$. Adding 1 to both sides, we get $x^2 + 1 \geq 1$, and so $x^2 + 1$ must be positive. From the definition of absolute value, we then conclude that $|x^2 + 1| = x^2 + 1$.

(b) If $x \neq 0$ then $x^2 > 0$ and $-x^2 < 0$. By the definition (since we are computing the absolute value of a negative number, we have to insert the minus sign!), $|-x^2| = -(-x^2) = x^2$, and we are done. When $x = 0$, both sides of $|-x^2| = x^2$ are zero, so the identity holds in this case as well.

(c) Picking $x = 6$ and $y = 10$, we compute: $|x+y| = |6+10| = |16| = 16$. Since $|x|+|y| = |6|+|10| = 6 + 10 = 16$, the formula is true *in this case*. Let's try a negative number—pick $x = 2$ and $y = -5$. Then $|x+y| = |2+(-5)| = |-3| = 3$, but $|2|+|-5| = 2+5 = 7$. We conclude that $|x+y| = |x|+|y|$ does not hold in general, for all real numbers.

(d) All we need to do is to find one pair of values for x and y for which $|x - y|$ is not equal to $|x| - |y|$. If $x = 10$ and $y = 3$ then $|x - y| = |10 - 3| = 7$ and $|x| - |y| = |10| - |3| = 7$. Will not do, so we try another pair. If $x = -10$ and $y = 3$ then $|x - y| = |-10 - 3| = |-13| = 13$ but $|x| - |y| = |-10| - |3| = 10 - 3 = 7$.

(e) False. Two numbers with equal absolute values do not have to be equal. For instance, $5 \neq -5$, but $|5| = |-5|$. In other words, we cannot cancel the absolute value sign in the equation $|x| = |y|$.

The following properties of the absolute value will be useful in various calculations.

> Let a and b be real numbers ($b \neq 0$ for the fraction); then
>
> $$|-a| = |a| \qquad |ab| = |a|\,|b| \qquad \left|\frac{a}{b}\right| = \frac{|a|}{|b|} \qquad |a^n| = |a|^n$$

As consequence of the first formula in the box above, we compute

$$|a - b| = |-(b - a)| = |b - a|$$

(In the first step, we factored out the minus sign and then used the absolute value formula.) So, as we claimed before, it does not matter whether we compute the distance from a to b or from b to a.

The remaining three formulas state that, as long as the operations involved are defined, the order of doing multiplication (or division or computing powers) and absolute value is irrelevant. Thus

$$\left|\frac{2x^2 - 7}{-3}\right| = \frac{|2x^2 - 7|}{|-3|} = \frac{|2x^2 - 7|}{3}.$$

As well, $|(x - 2)^3| = |x - 2|^3$, or $|(x - 2)x^3| = |x - 2|\,|x^3| = |x - 2|\,|x|^3$.

extra **Exercise 13.** (a) Compute $|\pi|$, $-|-1/2|$ and $|-0.33|$.

(b) Find the distance between -3 and -4 on a number line.

(c) Compute $\dfrac{|4 - 4.5|}{4.5 - 5}$.   (d) Compute $\dfrac{2 + |3 - (-4)|}{|-3 - 4|}$.

extra **Exercise 14.** (a) Write and simplify the definition of $|1 - 4x|$.

(b) Write and simplify the definition of $|6x - 5|$.

(c) Find all real numbers whose distance from 5 is 12.

(d)* Find all real numbers whose distance from -2 is 11.

(e)* Explain why the formula $|5x| = 5|x|$ is correct (i.e., holds for all real numbers).

(f) Is the formula $|-3x| = -3|x|$ correct (i.e., does it hold for all real numbers)?

Integers as Exponents

If a is a real number and $n = 1, 2, 3, \ldots$ a positive integer, then

$$a^n = \underbrace{a \cdot a \cdot \ldots \cdot a}_{n \text{ factors}}$$

By definition, $a^0 = 1$ (for $a \neq 0$). We usually drop the exponent 1, and write a instead of a^1. If $a \neq 0$ and $n = 1, 2, 3, \ldots$, we define

$$a^{-n} = \frac{1}{a^n}$$

Later, we will discuss fractional exponents (such as $a^{1/2}$ or $a^{-3/2}$) and real exponents (such as $a^{\sqrt{2}}$).

Example 6. By definition, $2^0 = 1$ and $2^1 = 2$. As well,

$$2^6 = 2 \cdot 2 \cdot 2 \cdot 2 \cdot 2 \cdot 2 = 64, \text{ and so } 2^{-6} = \frac{1}{2^6} = \frac{1}{64}$$

Since $2^{10} = 1024$ (check that!), we get that $2^{-10} = 1/1024$. We compute $(0.1)^3 = 0.1 \cdot 0.1 \cdot 0.1 = 0.001$ and

$$0.2^{-2} = \frac{1}{0.2^2} = \frac{1}{0.04} = \frac{100}{4} = 25$$

In the next-to-last step above we multiplied both numerator and denominator of the fraction by 100, so that we were able to cancel it.

Remember that a non-zero number raised to the power of zero is 1; e.g., $76.3^0 = 1$, and $(-3.1)^0 = 1$.

try it! **Exercise 15.** Compute the following:

(a) $(-3)^4$ (b) 4^{-3} (c) 0^{-3} (d) $(1/2)^{-3}$

extra **Exercise 16.** Find the value of each expression, and simplify when possible.

(a) $(-0.1)^4$ (b) -0.1^4 (c) $(-0.1)^{-4}$ (d)* $(1/10)^{-4}$ (e) $(1/1000)^{-2}$

(f)* $(-5)^{-2}$ (g)* -5^{-2} (h) -5^{-3} (i) $(-5)^{-3}$ (j)* $(-0.5)^{-3}$

We often use the following formulas.

$$\boxed{\begin{array}{c} \text{Laws of Exponents} \\[4pt] a^m \cdot a^n = a^{m+n} \qquad (ab)^n = a^n b^n \qquad (a^m)^n = a^{mn} \\[10pt] \dfrac{a^m}{a^n} = a^{m-n} \qquad \dfrac{a^n}{b^n} = \left(\dfrac{a}{b}\right)^n \end{array}}$$

The formulas above that involve fractions hold only when the denominator is not zero.

Example 7. Simplify:

(a) $\dfrac{x^2 x^{-3}}{x^{-4}}$ (b) $\left(\dfrac{x^6}{x^4 x^{-1}}\right)^5$ (c) $\dfrac{(a+2b)^{-2}}{(a+2b)^2}$ (d) $\dfrac{1}{(x-y)^3}\left((x-y)^2\right)^{-4}$

Solution.

(a) Assuming that $x \neq 0$, $\dfrac{x^2 x^{-3}}{x^{-4}} = \dfrac{x^{2+(-3)}}{x^{-4}} = \dfrac{x^{-1}}{x^{-4}} = x^{-1-(-4)} = x^3$

(b) We simplify the expression inside brackets first (and again assume that $x \neq 0$):

$$\left(\frac{x^6}{x^4 x^{-1}}\right)^5 = \left(\frac{x^6}{x^3}\right)^5 = \left(x^3\right)^5 = x^{3 \cdot 5} = x^{15}$$

(c) Assuming that $a + 2b \neq 0$, we get

$$\frac{(a+2b)^{-2}}{(a+2b)^2} = (a+2b)^{-2-2} = (a+2b)^{-4} = \frac{1}{(a+2b)^4}$$

(d) $\dfrac{1}{(x-y)^3}\left((x-y)^2\right)^{-4} = (x-y)^{-3}(x-y)^{-8} = (x-y)^{-11} = \dfrac{1}{(x-y)^{11}}$, if $x - y \neq 0$

(extra)   **Exercise 17.**   Using laws of exponents simplify each expression.

(a) $a^4 a^{-3} a^2 a^{-1}$ (b) $\dfrac{a^4}{a^{-22}}$ (c) $\dfrac{x^{12} x^{-2}}{x}$ (d) $\dfrac{2}{y^{-12}} \cdot \dfrac{y^3}{16}$ (e)* $\dfrac{(x^{15})^3}{(x^{-1})^{-22}}$

(f) $\left(\dfrac{x^{-1}}{x^4}\right)^2$ (g) $\left(\dfrac{x^4}{x^{-1}}\right)^{-2}$ (h)* $\left(\dfrac{c^{-1}}{c^4}\right)^{-5}$ (i) $\left(\dfrac{a^2 b}{ab^{-3}}\right)^{-3}$ (j) $\left(\dfrac{a^{-8}}{b^{-1}}\right)^2 \left(\dfrac{b^{-8}}{a^{-1}}\right)^{-2}$

(k) $\left(\dfrac{3x-y}{(3x-y)^4}\right)^{-7}$ (l)* $\left(\dfrac{a}{b^2}\right)^{-4}\left(\dfrac{a^2}{b}\right)^4$ (m) $\left(\dfrac{(a+b-c)^4}{(a+b-c)^{-3}}\right)^{-2}$ (n)* $\left(\dfrac{xy^3}{x+y}\right)\left(\dfrac{(x+y)^3}{x^2 y^2}\right)^{-2}$

Radicals and Rational Exponents

We first recall what a *radical* is. Here, $n = 2, 3, 4, \ldots$

$$\boxed{\text{The expression } a^n = b \text{ can also be written as } a = \sqrt[n]{b}.}$$

If $n = 2$, then $\sqrt[2]{b}$ is denoted by $\sqrt{b}$.

For example, since $4^3 = 64$, we conclude that $\sqrt[3]{64} = 4$; similarly, $\sqrt[5]{-32} = -2$, since $(-2)^5 = -32$.

Note that $\sqrt[n]{0} = 0$ for all $n = 2, 3, 4, \ldots$, since $0^n = 0$.

In the case of even values of n, there are two possibilities. When $x^2 = 16$, then $x = 4$ or $x = -4$, since $4^2 = 16$ and $(-4)^2 = 16$. To avoid ambiguity, we adopt the following convention:

> We define $\sqrt[n]{b}$ for even n and $b \geq 0$ to be the *positive* n-th root of b.

Thus, $\sqrt{16} = 4$, $\sqrt[4]{16} = 2$; as well, $4 + \sqrt{81} = 4 + 9 = 13$, etc.

If n is even and $b < 0$, then $\sqrt[n]{b}$ is not defined (that means that it is not a real number). For example, $a = \sqrt{-25}$ would imply that $a^2 = -25$; but a square of a real number cannot be negative.

Example 8. Evaluate, if possible, the following expressions:

(a) $\sqrt[3]{125}$ (b) $\sqrt[5]{0}$ (c) $\sqrt[3]{-64}$ (d) $\sqrt{-32}$ (e) $\sqrt{9/4}$ (f) $\sqrt[4]{-64}$ (g) $\sqrt[3]{1/27}$

Solution.

(a) $\sqrt[3]{125} = 5$, since $5^3 = 125$

(b) $\sqrt[5]{0} = 0$, since $0^5 = 0$

(c) From $(-4)^3 = -64$ we conclude that $\sqrt[3]{-64} = -4$.

(d) The expression $\sqrt{-32}$ is not defined, since no real number squared gives -32.

(e) Since $(3/2)^2 = 9/4$, we conclude that $\sqrt{9/4} = 3/2$.

(f) Not defined, since there is no number x such that $x^4 = -64$, i.e., such that x^4 is negative.

(g) From $(1/3)^3 = 1/3^3 = 1/27$, we conclude that $\sqrt[3]{1/27} = 1/3$.

What is $\sqrt{a^2}$, if a is a real number?

By the convention we mentioned above, we know that $\sqrt{a^2}$ cannot be negative. Thus, saying that $\sqrt{a^2} = a$ is not correct: take, for instance, $a = -2$; the left side is $\sqrt{a^2} = \sqrt{(-2)^2} = \sqrt{4} = 2$, whereas the right side is $a = -2$.

To fix the formula, we need to make the right side positive, and so we write $\sqrt{a^2} = |a|$. In general,

$$\sqrt[n]{a^n} = |a|, \qquad \text{if } n \text{ is even}$$

On the other hand,

$$\sqrt[n]{a^n} = a, \qquad \text{if } n \text{ is odd}$$

To illustrate: $\sqrt[3]{(-5)^3} = -5$ and $\sqrt[4]{(-5)^4} = |-5| = 5$.

Next, we recall how to compute a rational power of a real number.

> For a rational number m/n, we define $a^{m/n} = \sqrt[n]{a^m}$.

Thus, $9^{1/2} = \sqrt{9} = 3$, $(-8)^{1/3} = \sqrt[3]{-8} = -2$, and $4^{3/2} = \sqrt{4^3} = \sqrt{64} = 8$.

We need to remember the following (assume that $b \neq 0$ in the second formula).

Laws of Radicals

$$\sqrt[n]{a}\,\sqrt[n]{b} = \sqrt[n]{ab} \qquad \frac{\sqrt[n]{a}}{\sqrt[n]{b}} = \sqrt[n]{\frac{a}{b}} \qquad \sqrt[m]{\sqrt[n]{a}} = \sqrt[mn]{a}$$

As well, in case n or m (or both) are even, we must assume that $a > 0$ and $b > 0$.

It can be proven that the laws of exponents that we stated earlier for *integer* exponents hold for *rational* exponents as well. Using this fact, we see that the laws of radicals follow from the laws of exponents: for instance,

$$\sqrt[n]{a}\,\sqrt[n]{b} = a^{1/n}b^{1/n} = (ab)^{1/n} = \sqrt[n]{ab}$$

or

$$\sqrt[m]{\sqrt[n]{a}} = \sqrt[m]{a^{1/n}} = \left(a^{1/n}\right)^{1/m} = a^{(1/n)\cdot(1/m)} = a^{1/mn} = \sqrt[mn]{a}$$

Laws of radicals tell us that we can manipulate expressions that involve products, quotients, or multiple roots. However, sums and differences, such as $\sqrt{a+b}$ or $\sqrt{a-b}$, *cannot be simplified.* Never write $\sqrt{a+b} = \sqrt{a} + \sqrt{b}$, it is wrong! You can easily convince yourself that this is so: take $a = 16$ and $b = 9$; then $\sqrt{a+b} = \sqrt{25} = 5$, whereas $\sqrt{a} + \sqrt{b} = \sqrt{16} + \sqrt{9} = 7$.

A minus sign in the exponent does not mean that the number is negative!

For instance, $7^{-1} = 1/7$, $2^{-3} = 1/2^3 = 1/8$, and $0.1^{-1} = 1/0.1 = 10$.

In some cases, expressions involving negative exponents are not defined, such as 0^{-1}.

Which way is better: x^{-1} or $1/x$, $x^{3/2}$ or $\sqrt{x^3}$?

It depends: for instance, to calculate $4^{3/2}$ we prefer to use root notation $4^{3/2} = \sqrt{4^3} = \sqrt{64} = 8$; however, to simplify $x^2\sqrt{x^3}$, we convert to power notation: $x^2\sqrt{x^3} = x^2 x^{3/2} = x^{7/2}$.

There are no set rules that would tell us which form, power or root, is best. It is a matter of experience. The more problems we solve, the easier these calculations will become.

(extra) **Exercise 18.** Evaluate each expression, or say that it is not defined.

(a) $\sqrt[4]{-16}$ (b) $\sqrt[5]{32}$ (c)* $\sqrt[5]{-32}$ (d) $\sqrt[4]{16/81}$ (e) $\sqrt{10000}$

(f) $\sqrt{1/100}$ (g)* $\sqrt[5]{0}$ (h)* $\sqrt[4]{(-2)^4}$ (i) $\sqrt[4]{2^4}$ (j) $\sqrt[3]{(-2)^3}$

(k) $\sqrt{-1/10000}$ (l) $\sqrt{\sqrt{16}}$ (m)* $\sqrt{-\sqrt{16}}$ (n) $\sqrt{100/121}$ (o) $\sqrt{16}\sqrt{1/64}$

(extra) **Exercise 19.** Simplify each expression so that the number under the radical sign is the smallest possible integer.

(a) $\sqrt{32}$ (b)* $\sqrt{45}$ (c)* $\sqrt{1000}$ (d) $\sqrt{72}$ (e) $\sqrt[3]{16}$ (f) $\sqrt[3]{32}$

(g)* $\sqrt[3]{81}$ (h) $\sqrt[3]{10000}$ (i)* $\sqrt[4]{32}$ (j) $\sqrt[4]{100000}$

Example 9. Simplify, using rules for radicals, to obtain a single term:

(a) $6\sqrt{20} - \sqrt{45}$ (b) $3\sqrt{32} + 5\sqrt{8} - 3\sqrt{2}$ (c) $\sqrt{27} + 2\sqrt{3} - 4\sqrt{75}$

Solution. (a) The idea is to write the number inside the square root as a product, and calculate the square root of one factor. For instance,

$$\sqrt{20} = \sqrt{4 \cdot 5} = \sqrt{4}\sqrt{5} = 2\sqrt{5}$$

Likewise, $\sqrt{45} = \sqrt{9 \cdot 5} = \sqrt{9}\sqrt{5} = 3\sqrt{5}$, and so

$$6\sqrt{20} - \sqrt{45} = 6(2\sqrt{5}) - 3\sqrt{5} = 12\sqrt{5} - 3\sqrt{5} = 9\sqrt{5}$$

(b) Using the same idea, we get

$$3\sqrt{32} + 5\sqrt{8} - 3\sqrt{2} = 3\sqrt{16 \cdot 2} + 5\sqrt{4 \cdot 2} - 3\sqrt{2}$$
$$= 3\sqrt{16}\sqrt{2} + 5\sqrt{4}\sqrt{2} - 3\sqrt{2} = 12\sqrt{2} + 10\sqrt{2} - 3\sqrt{2} = 19\sqrt{2}$$

(c) As above, $\sqrt{27} + 2\sqrt{3} - 4\sqrt{75} = \sqrt{9 \cdot 3} + 2\sqrt{3} - 4\sqrt{25 \cdot 3} = 3\sqrt{3} + 2\sqrt{3} - 20\sqrt{3} = -15\sqrt{3}$.

Example 10. Simplify or evaluate the following expressions:

(a) $x\sqrt{x}\sqrt[3]{x^2}$ (b) $4 \cdot 4^{3/2}$ (c) $\sqrt{12}/\sqrt{27}$ (d) $(3 + \sqrt{7})\sqrt{7}$

Solution.

(a) $x\sqrt{x}\sqrt[3]{x^2} = x^1 x^{1/2} x^{2/3} = x^{1 + 1/2 + 2/3} = x^{13/6} = \sqrt[6]{x^{13}}$.

(b) Recall that $4 = 4^1$; thus, $4 \cdot 4^{3/2} = 4^1 4^{3/2} = 4^{1 + 3/2} = 4^{5/2}$. To calculate $4^{5/2}$ we write 4 as 2^2, and so $4^{5/2} = (2^2)^{5/2} = 2^{2 \cdot (5/2)} = 2^5 = 32$.

(c) We simplify the terms under the square roots and then cancel:

$$\frac{\sqrt{12}}{\sqrt{27}} = \frac{\sqrt{4 \cdot 3}}{\sqrt{9 \cdot 3}} = \frac{2\sqrt{3}}{3\sqrt{3}} = \frac{2}{3}$$

(d) We compute $(3 + \sqrt{7})\sqrt{7} = 3\sqrt{7} + \sqrt{7}\sqrt{7} = 3\sqrt{7} + 7$. Note that $\sqrt{7}\sqrt{7} = (\sqrt{7})^2 = 7$.

(extra) **Exercise 20.** Using laws of radicals, simplify each expression.

(a) $2^{1/9}2^{-3/4}$ (b)* $\sqrt[5]{\sqrt{2^{10}}}$ (c) $\left(12^{1/4}\right)^{3/5}$ (d) $\left(33^{-1/4}\right)^{4/5}$ (e)* $3\sqrt{\frac{14}{9}}$

(f) $x^{1/4}\sqrt[3]{x}$ (g) $\left(2x - \sqrt{y}\right)\sqrt{y}$ (h) $\left(2x - \sqrt{y}\right)\sqrt[3]{x}$ (i) $y^{-1/4}y\sqrt[4]{y}$ (j) $\sqrt[3]{ab^6c^{-12}}$

(k) $\left(\sqrt{a} + \sqrt{b}\right)\left(\sqrt{a} - \sqrt{b}\right)$ (l)* $\left(2\sqrt{a} - \sqrt{b}\right)\left(\sqrt{a} + 5\sqrt{b}\right)$ (m) $\sqrt{xy}\left(\sqrt{x} - 3\sqrt{y}\right)$

(n)* $\left(\sqrt[3]{a} + \sqrt[3]{b}\right)\left(\sqrt[3]{a^2} - \sqrt[3]{ab} + \sqrt[3]{b^2}\right)$

(extra) **Exercise 21.** Identify each formula as correct or incorrect.

(a) $\sqrt{2y} = \sqrt{2}\sqrt{y}$ (b)* $\sqrt{2 - y} = \sqrt{2} - \sqrt{y}$ (c) $\sqrt{\frac{16}{x}} = \frac{4}{\sqrt{x}}$

(d) $\left(x^3\right)^{1/2} = x^{7/2}$ (e)* $\left(x^2\right)^{1/3} = x^{2/3}$ (f)* $x^3 + x^2 = x^5$

(g) $\frac{a^{3/2}}{a^{1/2}} = a^3$ (h) $\left(a^{-1}b\right)^2 = a^{-2}b^2$ (i)* $(a + b)^{-1} = a^{-1} + b^{-1}$

Example 11. Evaluate each expression.

(a) $(9/16)^{1/2}$ (b) $(9/16)^{3/2}$ (c) $(9/16)^{-3/2}$

Solution.

(a) Starting with the law of exponents $\left(\dfrac{a}{b}\right)^n = \dfrac{a^n}{b^n}$ (with $n = 1/2$) we get

$$\left(\frac{9}{16}\right)^{1/2} = \frac{9^{1/2}}{16^{1/2}} = \frac{\sqrt{9}}{\sqrt{16}} = \frac{3}{4}$$

(b) Likewise, $\left(\dfrac{9}{16}\right)^{3/2} = \dfrac{9^{3/2}}{16^{3/2}}$. As in the previous example, we write $9 = 3^2$ and $16 = 4^2$ and so

$$\frac{9^{3/2}}{16^{3/2}} = \frac{(3^2)^{3/2}}{(4^2)^{3/2}} = \frac{3^{2\cdot(3/2)}}{4^{2\cdot(3/2)}} = \frac{3^3}{4^3} = \frac{27}{64}$$

(c) Using the formula $a^{-n} = 1/a^n$, and then (b), we get $\left(\dfrac{9}{16}\right)^{-3/2} = \dfrac{1}{\left(\frac{9}{16}\right)^{3/2}} = \dfrac{1}{\frac{27}{64}} = \dfrac{64}{27}$.

Note that, in the last step above, we used $\dfrac{1}{\frac{c}{d}} = \dfrac{d}{c}$, which follows from the definition ("the top times the reciprocal of the bottom").

(try it!) **Exercise 22.** Simplify or evaluate each of the following:

(a) $\sqrt[3]{-125/64}$ (b) $\sqrt{100}/\sqrt{200}$ (c) $(4/9)^{-3/2}$ (d) $16^{-3/2}9^{3/2}$

Example 12. Write each expression as a square.

(a) 7   (b) 0.64   (c) 10^{-4} (d) a^3 (e) $\sqrt{x}$ (f) $a^{5/3}$

Solution.

(a) $7 = (\sqrt{7})^2$

(b) $0.64 = (0.8)^2$

(c) Recall that the formula $(a^m)^n = a^{mn}$ states that raising a power to another power amounts to multiplying exponents. Thus, the exponent -4 has to be written as $(-2)\cdot 2$, and so $10^{-4} = (10^{-2})^2$

(d) Reasoning as in (c), we get $(a^{3/2})^2 = a^3$

(e) As well, $\sqrt{x} = x^{1/2} = x^{(1/4)\cdot 2} = (x^{1/4})^2$

(f) $a^{5/3} = a^{(5/6)\cdot 2} = (a^{5/6})^2$.

(extra) **Exercise 23.** Simplify or evaluate each expression.

(a) $\sqrt[3]{20}\sqrt[3]{50} + 7$ (b) $-4^{5/2} + 4^{3/2} - 4^{1/2}$ (c) $(25/16)^{-3/2}$

(d)* $8^{2/3} + 0.01^{-1/2}$ (e) $0.09^{1/2} + 0.04^{-3/2}$ (f)* $\dfrac{\sqrt{200}}{\sqrt{2}}\sqrt{3} + \sqrt{75}$

(g)* $-7\sqrt{5} + \sqrt{125} - \sqrt{45}$ (h) $\left(\sqrt{8} + 7\sqrt{2}\right)\sqrt{2}$

extra **Exercise 24.** Write each expression as a square.

(a) 127 (b) $a^2 + b^2$ (c)* x^5 (d)* xyz^3 (e)* $\sqrt[3]{x}$ (f) $\sqrt[4]{x}$

extra **Exercise 25.** Write each expression as a cube.

(a) 127 (b) $x - y$ (c)* x^2 (d) $a^4 b^6 c^8$ (e)* $\sqrt{x}$ (f)* $1/x$

So far we have talked about integer and rational exponents and their properties.

> The laws of exponents we stated earlier hold for real numbers in exponents as well.

Example 13. Simplify:

(a) $\left(x^{0.4} y^{-3.56}\right)^2$ (b) $x^{-3.1} y^{1.4} \left(x y^{-1.6}\right)^5$ (c) $\left(\dfrac{a}{b}\right)^4 \left(\dfrac{2}{a}\right)^{-1.5} \left(\dfrac{ab}{2}\right)^{2.5}$

Solution.

(a) $\left(x^{0.4} y^{-3.56}\right)^2 = \left(x^{0.4}\right)^2 \left(y^{-3.56}\right)^2 = x^{0.4 \cdot 2} y^{-3.56 \cdot 2} = x^{0.8} y^{-7.12}$

(b) Simplifying the term in brackets first, we get

$$x^{-3.1} y^{1.4} \left(x^1 y^{-1.6}\right)^5 = x^{-3.1} y^{1.4} x^{(1)(5)} y^{(-1.6)(5)} = x^{-3.1} y^{1.4} x^5 y^{-8} = x^{-3.1+5} y^{1.4-8} = x^{1.9} y^{-6.6}$$

(c) $\left(\dfrac{a}{b}\right)^4 \left(\dfrac{2}{a}\right)^{-1.5} \left(\dfrac{ab}{2}\right)^{2.5} = \dfrac{a^4}{b^4} \dfrac{2^{-1.5}}{a^{-1.5}} \dfrac{a^{2.5} b^{2.5}}{2^{2.5}} = \dfrac{a^{6.5} 2^{-1.5} b^{2.5}}{b^4 a^{-1.5} 2^{2.5}} = a^8 b^{-1.5} 2^{-4} = \dfrac{a^8}{2^4 b^{1.5}}$

try it! **Exercise 26.** Simplify each expression.

(a) $\left(\dfrac{x^{0.4} x^{4.5}}{x^{-1.3}}\right)^{0.9}$ (b) $\left(\dfrac{x^3 y^{-2}}{x^{-1} y^4}\right)^{-1/2} \left(x^{-1/2} y^{3/4}\right)^{-1}$ (c) $\dfrac{(x-a)^{-2}}{(x-a)^{-3}} (x-a)^0$

extra **Exercise 27.** Simplify each expression.

(a) $\left(x y^{0.3}\right)^2$ (b) $\left(x y^{-0.3} z^{-0.11}\right)^{0.6}$ (c)* $\left(\dfrac{y^{0.4}}{y^{-0.7}}\right)^{-3.2}$

(d)* $\left(a^{\sqrt{2}} b^2\right)^{3\sqrt{2}}$ (e) $\left(\dfrac{c}{2d}\right)^{0.6} \left(\dfrac{4d^{2.4}}{c}\right)^{-0.6}$ (f)* $x^3 (x+y)^{-1.3} \left(\dfrac{x}{x+y}\right)^{7.2}$

Frequently Asked Questions

(1) How many decimal places do I need to show in my calculations?

That's not easy to answer, and the best thing to do is to ask your instructor. As well, it depends on the nature of the calculation: if it is related to accuracy of some calculus algorithm (such as Newton's Method for solving equations or numeric methods to calculate definite integrals), then we use larger numbers, say 5–8 decimal places. However, in general, 2–3 decimals will suffice.

(2) Do I leave my answer as a fraction, or do I convert it to a decimal number? Do I leave $\sqrt{2}$ as is, or evaluate it?

In general, answers such as $\frac{1}{2}$, $\sqrt{2} + \sqrt{3}$, $\frac{1}{\sqrt[3]{5}}$, or $\sqrt{3/7}$ can be left in that form (we have done it many times in this book). If possible, we reduce a fraction: $\frac{1}{2}$ is preferred to $\frac{5}{10}$.

If, for some reason, we do have to convert into decimal numbers, we need to be aware of a small issue: it's the use of $\approx$ (approximately equals sign) in contrast to $=$ (equals sign).

While $1/2 = 0.5$ and $3/8 = 0.375$ are exact equalities, writing $\frac{13}{44} = 0.295$ is not really correct, since $\frac{13}{44} = 0.295454545\ldots = 0.295\overline{45}$. So, we need to write $\frac{13}{44} \approx 0.295$, or $\frac{13}{44} \approx 0.30$ if we wish to round off to three or two decimals.

Likewise, using the equals sign in $\sqrt{2} = 1.41$ or $\sqrt{2} = 1.4142$ is not correct. The irrational number $\sqrt{2}$ has infinitely many non-repeating decimals, so we should use $\sqrt{2} \approx 1.41$ or $\sqrt{2} \approx 1.4142$ instead. Likewise, writing $\pi \approx 3.14$ or $\pi \approx 3.14159$ is correct.

In reality, quite often, we ignore this distinction and use the equals sign in all situations.

Common Errors. Avoid These !!!

Some of the most common errors that students make in calculus (and elsewhere) relate to basic properties of algebraic operations. We now list those, and show that they cannot be true.

These are NOT CORRECT although many students try them !!!

$$\frac{1}{a+b} = \frac{1}{a} + \frac{1}{b}, \quad \frac{1}{a-b} = \frac{1}{a} - \frac{1}{b}$$

$$\sqrt{a \pm b} = \sqrt{a} \pm \sqrt{b}, \quad \sqrt[3]{a \pm b} = \sqrt[3]{a} \pm \sqrt[3]{b}, \quad \sqrt[4]{a \pm b} = \sqrt[4]{a} \pm \sqrt[4]{b}, \quad \text{etc.}$$

$$(a \pm b)^2 = a^2 \pm b^2, \quad (a \pm b)^3 = a^3 \pm b^3, \quad (a \pm b)^4 = a^4 \pm b^4, \quad \text{etc.}$$

$$a^{m+n} = a^m + a^n, \quad a^{m-n} = a^m - a^n, \quad (a^m)^n = a^{m+n}$$

$$|a + b| = |a| + |b|, \quad |a - b| = |a| - |b|$$

We can easily convince ourselves that none of the statements above hold for *arbitrary* real numbers a and b, for which the operations involved are defined. Some statements might hold for some special choices of a and b, but they do not hold true in general.

For instance, to show that $\dfrac{1}{a+b} = \dfrac{1}{a} + \dfrac{1}{b}$ is incorrect, pick $a = 1$ and $b = 2$ (actually any choice of non-zero a and b for which $a + b \neq 0$ will do!). Then $\dfrac{1}{a+b} = \dfrac{1}{3}$, whereas $\dfrac{1}{a} + \dfrac{1}{b} = \dfrac{1}{1} + \dfrac{1}{2} = \dfrac{3}{2}$.

To show that $\sqrt{a+b} = \sqrt{a} + \sqrt{b}$ is incorrect, pick $a = b = 1$; then $\sqrt{a+b} = \sqrt{2} = 1.4142$, whereas $\sqrt{a} + \sqrt{b} = \sqrt{1} + \sqrt{1} = 1 + 1 = 2$.

The same choice for a and b shows that $(a + b)^2 = a^2 + b^2$ does not hold: the left side is $(a + b)^2 = (1 + 1)^2 = 2^2 = 4$, whereas the right side is $a^2 + b^2 = 1^2 + 1^2 = 1 + 1 = 2$.

To show that $a^{m+n} = a^m + a^n$ does not hold, pick $a = 2$, $m = 3$ and $n = 4$: then $a^{m+n} = 2^{3+4} = 2^7 = 128$, whereas $a^m + a^n = 2^3 + 2^4 = 8 + 16 = 24$.

Recall that the correct formula states that $a^{m+n} = a^m a^n$.

If you are not sure whether or not some statement you wish to use is correct, test it! It is very likely that, if it is not correct, you will be able to identify it right away by picking values for the variables, as we did above.

extra **Exercise 28.** Identify each formula as correct or incorrect.

(a) $\dfrac{1}{x^2 y} = \dfrac{1}{x^2} \cdot \dfrac{1}{y}$ 　　(b) $\dfrac{1}{x^2} + \dfrac{1}{y} = \dfrac{1}{x^2 + y}$ 　　(c)* $\sqrt{xy} + \sqrt{y} = \sqrt{xy^2}$ 　(d) $\dfrac{x^2}{\frac{1}{x^2}} = 1$

(e) $\sqrt{xy}\sqrt{y} = \sqrt{xy^2}$ 　　(f) $\dfrac{1}{x} - \dfrac{1}{y} = \dfrac{x-y}{xy}$ 　　(g)* $\dfrac{5}{7} - \dfrac{3}{4} = \dfrac{2}{3}$ 　　(h) $(x+y-2)^2 = x^2 + y^2 - 4$

(i)* $|3a - 4| = |3a| - 4$ 　(j) $x^k + x^k = x^{2k}$ 　　(k)* $x^k \cdot x^{2k} = x^{3k}$ 　　(l) $\left(x^k\right)^k = x^{2k}$

2. Basic Algebra

What is in this section?

Polynomials, rational functions, roots, multiplication, factoring, long division.

Do I need to read this?

Answer the quiz questions below. If you get all of them right, or make a few smaller mistakes, then you can skip this section. Otherwise, identify what you don't know or are not sure about and read relevant parts of this section (or read all of it!).

Quiz

1. Compute the following products:

(a) $(x-4)(2x^2+x)$ (b) $(x-4)^2$ (c) $(x^3+x^2)^2$ (d) $(x^2-12)(x^2+12)$ (e) $(x+1)^3$

2. Complete the square in $x^2 + 7x + 4$.

3. Factor the following expressions:

(a) $6x^6 - 24x^2 + 12x$ (b) $4y^5 - 3y^3 - 4y^2 + 3$ (c) $x^2 + 7x + 10$

4. Factor the quadratic polynomial $4x^2 + 9x + 2$.

Over ...

5. Factor $5x^2 - 55$ using the difference of squares formula.

6. Factor the following expressions:

(a) $x^5 - x$ 　　　　　　　(b) $8x^2 - 50$ 　　　　　　　(c) $x^2/16 - y^2/49$

7. Simplify by calculating the common denominator: $\dfrac{2x+1}{x^2 - 5x + 6} - \dfrac{1}{x-2} + \dfrac{x}{x-3}$.

8. Divide the polynomial $x^3 - 3x + 5$ by $x - 4$.

9. Factor the polynomial $x^3 + 2x^2 - 11x - 12$.

10. Rationalize the denominator in $\dfrac{1}{\sqrt{5} + \sqrt{6}}$.

[Answers to this quiz are at the bottom of page 39.]

Polynomials

A *term* (or a *monomial*) is either a real number or a product of a real number and a positive integer power of one (or more) variables. Examples of terms are: 0.4, $3x^3$, $-4.5y^5$, $2x^3y^4$, etc.

A *polynomial* is a sum or a difference of terms (monomials). The expressions $0.5 + 2x - 4x^3 + x^5$ and $4x^2y - 3xy^3z - 12xyz$ are examples of polynomials. The former is a polynomial in one variable, and the latter is a polynomial in three variables.

A polynomial consisting of two terms is called a *binomial*. If a polynomial contains three terms, it is called a *trinomial*. Polynomials are added/subtracted by adding/subtracting the like terms. For example, the sum of the binomial $5x^2y^3 - x^3y^3$ and the trinomial $x - 2x^2y^3 + x^3y^3$ is equal to

$$(5x^2y^3 - x^3y^3) + (x - 2x^2y^3 + x^3y^3) = x + 3x^2y^3$$

Their difference is

$$(5x^2y^3 - x^3y^3) - (x - 2x^2y^3 + x^3y^3) = 7x^2y^3 - 2x^3y^3 - x$$

We will not discuss most general cases of polynomials. In introductory calculus courses we study polynomials in one variable only, so we focus primarily on such polynomials.

Real numbers that multiply variables are called *coefficients*. In the polynomial $0.5 + 2x - 4x^3 + x^5$, the coefficient of x^3 is -4, the coefficient of x^5 is 1, and the coefficient of x is 2. The number 0.5 is called a *free coefficient* (or a coefficient without x). Since the polynomial $0.5 + 2x - 4x^3 + x^5$ does not contain any terms that involve x^2 or x^4, we say that the coefficients of x^2 and x^4 are zero.

The highest power of the variable appearing in a polynomial in one variable is called the *degree* of the polynomial (thus, the degree is the highest power of x whose coefficient is not zero). For instance, $2x + 6$ is a polynomial of degree 1 (also called *linear*), $x^2 - 5x - 3$ is a polynomial of degree 2 (also called *quadratic*), and $0.5 + 2x - 4x^3 + x^5$ is a polynomial of degree 5.

Two polynomials are called *equal* if all their respective coefficients are equal. Thus, if

$$ax^2 + bx + c = 3.2x^2 - 4x - 1/2$$

then $a = 3.2$, $b = -4$ and $c = -1/2$. Likewise, if $mx^3 + nx^2 + px + q = -6 - 3x^3$, then $m = -3$, $n = 0$, $p = 0$ and $q = -6$.

extra · **Exercise 1.** State the values of m and b if

(a) $mx + b = 4x - 2.3$ (b) $mx + b = -2 - 6x$ (c) $mx + b = 3x - \dfrac{2}{7}$ (d) $mx + b = \dfrac{4x}{5} - 12$

(e)* $mx + b = -3$ (f)* $mx + b = x$ (g)* $mx + b = 0$ (h) $mx + b = \dfrac{2x - 1}{6}$

(i) $mx + b = \dfrac{x}{5} - \dfrac{3}{11}$ (j) $mx + b = 4(2 - x)$ (k) $mx + b = -2 \cdot \dfrac{2x - 1}{5}$

extra · **Exercise 2.** State the values of a, b and c if

(a) $ax^2 + bx + c = 4 - x^2 + 9x$ (b) $ax^2 + bx + c = 1 - \dfrac{x}{7} + \dfrac{x^2}{3}$ (c) $ax^2 + bx + c = \dfrac{3 - 2x + x^2}{4}$

(d)* $ax^2 + bx + c = -x^2$ (e)* $ax^2 + bx + c = 1 - x$ (f)* $ax^2 + bx + c = 0$

(extra) **Exercise 3.** State the values of m, n and p if

(a) $mx^2 + nx + p = -32$ 　　(b) $mx^2 + nx + p = \dfrac{3x}{16}$ 　　(c)* $mx^2 + nx + p = \dfrac{x - 3x^2}{2}$

(d) $mx^2 + nx + p = -3(2x - 14)$

To multiply two polynomials, we multiply each term of the first polynomial with each term of the second polynomial (EWE, short for each-with-each). In case of two binomials, EWE gives

$$\boxed{(a + b)(c + d) = ac + ad + bc + bd}$$

For example,

$$(2x^2 - x + 3)(6 - x) = 2x^2(6) - x(6) + 3(6) + 2x^2(-x) - x(-x) + 3(-x)$$
$$= 12x^2 - 6x + 18 - 2x^3 + x^2 - 3x = -2x^3 + 13x^2 - 9x + 18$$

In particular, we find
$$(a + b)^2 = (a + b)(a + b) = a^2 + ab + ba + b^2 = a^2 + 2ab + b^2$$

and

$$(a + b)(a - b) = a^2 - ab + ba - b^2 = a^2 - b^2$$

We need to remember these special products:

$$\boxed{\begin{array}{ll} \text{square of the sum:} & (a + b)^2 = a^2 + 2ab + b^2 \\ \text{square of the difference:} & (a - b)^2 = a^2 - 2ab + b^2 \\ \text{difference of squares:} & (a + b)(a - b) = a^2 - b^2 \end{array}}$$

Example 1. Compute the following products:

(a) $(x - 4)(2x^2 + x)$ 　　(b) $(x - 4)^2$ 　　(c) $(x^3 + x^2)^2$ 　　(d) $(x^2 - 12)(x^2 + 12)$ 　　(e) $(x + 1)^3$

Solution.

(a) Using EWE, we get

$$(x - 4)(2x^2 + x) = (x)(2x^2) + (x)(x) + (-4)(2x^2) + (-4)(x)$$
$$= 2x^3 + x^2 - 8x^2 - 4x = 2x^3 - 7x^2 - 4x$$

(b) We use the square of the difference formula:

$$(x - 4)^2 = (x)^2 - 2(x)(4) + (4)^2 = x^2 - 8x + 16$$

(c) Using the square of the sum formula, we get

$$(x^3 + x^2)^2 = (x^3)^2 + 2(x^3)(x^2) + (x^2)^2 = x^6 + 2x^5 + x^4$$

(d) Using the difference of squares formula, we get

$$(x^2 - 12)(x^2 + 12) = (x^2)^2 - (12)^2 = x^4 - 144$$

(e) We compute $\quad (x+1)^3 = (x+1)^2(x+1) = (x^2+2x+1)(x+1)$
$$= x^3 + 2x^2 + x + x^2 + 2x + 1 = x^3 + 3x^2 + 3x + 1$$

Alternatively, we could have used the ready-made formula for $(a+b)^3$:

$$\text{cube of the sum/difference:} \quad (a \pm b)^3 = a^3 \pm 3a^2b + 3ab^2 \pm b^3$$

extra **Exercise 4.** Compute each product and simplify when possible.

(a)* $(x^2 - x + 1)(3x - 4)$
(b)* $(x^2 - 0.2)^2$
(c)* $x(x^3 - 1)(x^3 + 1)$

(d)* $(2x - 1)^3$
(e) $\left(3x - \dfrac{5}{2}\right)^2$
(f) $\left(\dfrac{5 + 2x}{4}\right)^2$

(g) $(0.1x - 0.03)^2$
(h) $(x^4 - x^2 + 1)(2 - x)$
(i) $(2x - 7y)(2x + 7y)$

(j) $(x^2 - 11)(x^2 + 11)$
(k) $-2(7 + x^4)(7 - x^4)$
(l) $(-1 - x^2)(-1 + x^2)$

(m) $\left(\dfrac{x}{3} - 12\right)\left(\dfrac{x}{3} + 12\right)$
(n) $4x(x+2)^3$
(o) $\left(\dfrac{x}{2} - 4\right)^3$

extra **Exercise 5.** State the values of a, b and c if

(a) $ax^2 + bx + c = -3x(x - 4)$
(b) $ax^2 + bx + c = (2x - 1)(3 - 7x)$

(c) $ax^2 + bx + c = (x - 5)\left(\dfrac{3}{4} - x\right)$
(d)* $ax^2 + bx + c = (0.4 - 0.1x)(2.5x + 1.5)$

(e)* $ax^2 + bx + c = \left(\dfrac{3}{4} - x\right)\left(\dfrac{2x}{3} - \dfrac{1}{6}\right)$
(f) $ax^2 + bx + c = (2.8x - 1.2)(0.2 - 2.2x)$

extra **Exercise 6.** Using the EWE rule, or otherwise, find each product. Simplify when possible.

(a) $\left(x^{-2} + 1\right)^2$
(b) $(x^{-1} + 1)(3x + 2x^{-3})$
(c)* $\left(\dfrac{2}{x} - 1\right)\left(4 - \dfrac{3}{5x}\right)$

(d) $\left(x^{-1} + 3\right)\left(x^{-1} - 3\right)$
(e) $\left(\sqrt{2x} - 3\right)\left(\sqrt{2x} + 3\right)$
(f) $\left(\sqrt{x} + 4\right)^2$

(g)* $\left(3\sqrt{x} - 5\right)^2$
(h) $\left(\sqrt{x+1} - \sqrt{3x}\right)^2$
(i) $\left(\dfrac{1}{x} - 2\right)^3$

(j) $\left(\sqrt{x} + 3\right)^3$
(k)* $\left(\sqrt{x^2 + 1} - \sqrt{7}\right)\left(\sqrt{x^2 + 1} + \sqrt{7}\right)$

Using the square of the sum formula, we compute $(x + 3)^2 = x^2 + 6x + 9$. In the next exercise we ask the following question: knowing that $x^2 + 6x + 9$ is the square of a binomial, find that binomial; i.e., given $x^2 + 6x + 9$, our answer is $(x + 3)^2$.

extra **Exercise 7.** Write each expression as the square of a binomial.

(a) $x^2 + 12x + 36$
(b) $x^2 - 14x + 49$
(c)* $a^2 + 4ab + 4b^2$
(d) $16x^2 + 8x + 1$

(e) $9x^2 - 12x + 4$
(f) $16a^2 - 40ab + 25b^2$
(g) $x^2 + 0.2x + 0.01$
(h)* $x^2 + x + \frac{1}{4}$

(i) $\dfrac{x^2}{9} - 6x + 81$
(j)* $\dfrac{4x^2}{9} - \dfrac{x}{3} + \dfrac{1}{16}$

Completing the Square

In certain situations (solving equations, integration techniques in calculus), we need to make the expression $x^2 + bx$ into a square. The technique that accomplishes that (called *completing the square*), is based on the fact that, if we add $(b/2)^2$ to $x^2 + bx$, we obtain a square, i.e.,

$$x^2 + bx + \left(\frac{b}{2}\right)^2 = \left(x + \frac{b}{2}\right)^2$$

We check this by squaring the binomial on the right:

$$\left(x + \frac{b}{2}\right)^2 = x^2 + 2x\frac{b}{2} + \left(\frac{b}{2}\right)^2 = x^2 + bx + \left(\frac{b}{2}\right)^2$$

Consider an example: assume that we need to write $x^2 + 8x$ as a square (so, $b = 8$). Of course, we cannot just add something to $x^2 + 8x$, because we would change its value. So, we both add and subtract $(b/2)^2 = (8/2)^2 = 16$, to get

$$x^2 + 8x = x^2 + 8x + (16 - 16) = (x^2 + 8x + 16) - 16$$

Now the first three terms are equal to $\left(x + \frac{b}{2}\right)^2 = (x + 4)^2$, and thus

$$x^2 + 8x = (x^2 + 8x + 16) - 16 = (x + 4)^2 - 16$$

Remember that 4 in $x + 4$ is one half of the coefficient of x.

Example 2. Complete the square.

(a) $x^2 - 10x$ (b) $x^2 - 10x + 7$ (c) $2x^2 - 16x$ (d) $x^2 - 3x - 1$

Solution. Keep in mind the idea: take the coefficient of x, divide by 2, square, and then add to and subtract from the given expression.

(a) In this case, $b = -10$, so we add and subtract $(b/2)^2 = (-10/2)^2 = 25$:

$$x^2 - 10x = x^2 - 10x + (25 - 25) = (x^2 - 10x + 25) - 25 = (x - 5)^2 - 25$$

(b) We proceed as in (a):

$$x^2 - 10x + 7 = (x^2 - 10x + 25) - 25 + 7 = (x - 5)^2 - 25 + 7 = (x - 5)^2 - 18$$

(c) The coefficient of x^2 is not 1, so we factor 2 out before completing the square:

$$2x^2 - 16x = 2(x^2 - 8x) = 2\left((x^2 - 8x + 16) - 16\right) = 2\left((x - 4)^2 - 16\right) = 2(x - 4)^2 - 32$$

(d) Here, $b = -3$, so we add and subtract $(b/2)^2 = (-3/2)^2 = 9/4$:

$$x^2 - 3x - 1 = \left(\left(x^2 - 3x + \frac{9}{4}\right) - \frac{9}{4}\right) - 1 = \left(x - \frac{3}{2}\right)^2 - \frac{9}{4} - 1 = \left(x - \frac{3}{2}\right)^2 - \frac{13}{4}$$

Exercise 8. Complete the square.

(a)* $x^2 + 16x$ (b) $x^2 + 16x + 9$ (c) $x^2 + 7x$ (d)* $x^2 + 7x + 4$

(e)* $3x^2 - 12x$ (f) $3x^2 - 12x + 5$ (g) $4x^2 - 9x$ (h)* $3x^2 - 9x + 2$

(i) $\dfrac{x^2}{4} + 6x - 1$ (j) $x^2 + \dfrac{x}{7} - 1$ (k) $\dfrac{x^2}{3} - \dfrac{x}{6} + \dfrac{1}{9}$ (l) $0.1x^2 + 0.2x - 0.5$

Factoring

There are many situations (such as solving equations) when it is useful (or essential) to rewrite a given polynomial as product.

Most elementary methods consist of *factoring out a common expression*; for example,

$$16x^4 - 4x^3 - 4x = 4x(4x^3 - x^2 - 1)$$

As well, we can try factoring by grouping, such as in

$$x^3 - 4x^2 + 2x - 8 = (x^3 - 4x^2) + (2x - 8) = x^2(x - 4) + 2(x - 4) = (x^2 + 2)(x - 4)$$

Quite often, we need to factor quadratic polynomials.

> If quadratic polynomial $x^2 + mx + n$ can be factored as $(x + a)(x + b)$,
> then the sum $a + b$ must be equal to m, and the product ab must be n.

We obtain this fact by comparing the initial expression $x^2 + mx + n$ with the expression obtained by factoring: $(x + a)(x + b) = x^2 + ax + bx + ab = x^2 + (a + b)x + ab$.

 Actual factoring using this strategy works in the case when a and b are *small integers*. In order to factor $x^2 + 16 - 561$ (where a and b are not small integers: $x^2 + 16 - 561 = (x + 33)(x - 17)$) or $x^2 - 2x - 9$ (where a and b are not integers: $x^2 - 2x - 9 = (x - 1 - \sqrt{10})(x - 1 + \sqrt{10})$) we need to use the quadratic formula (which will be shown in Section 4).

Example 3. Factor each expression.

(a) $6x^6 - 24x^2 + 12x$ (b) $4y^5 - 3y^3 - 4y^2 + 3$ (c) $x^2 + 7x + 10$

(d) $x^4 + 7x^3 + 10x^2$ (e) $x^2 - 5x + 6$

Solution.

(a) Factoring out $6x$, we get $6x^6 - 24x^2 + 12x = 6x(x^5 - 4x + 2)$.

(b) Grouping the first two and the last two terms, we get

$$4y^5 - 3y^3 - 4y^2 + 3 = (4y^5 - 3y^3) - (4y^2 - 3) = y^3(4y^2 - 3) - (4y^2 - 3) = (y^3 - 1)(4y^2 - 3)$$

We could have grouped the first and the third and the second and the fourth terms:

$$4y^5 - 3y^3 - 4y^2 + 3 = (4y^5 - 4y^2) - (3y^3 - 3) = 4y^2(y^3 - 1) - 3(y^3 - 1) = (4y^2 - 3)(y^3 - 1)$$

(c) The two numbers whose sum is 7 and whose product is 10 are 2 and 5. Thus,

$$x^2 + 7x + 10 = (x + 2)(x + 5)$$

By calculating the product $(x + 2)(x + 5)$ using EWE, we can check that our factoring is correct.

(d) Factoring out x^2 and then using (c), we get

$$x^4 + 7x^3 + 10x^2 = x^2(x^2 + 7x + 10) = x^2(x + 2)(x + 5)$$

(e) We are looking for two numbers whose product is 6 and whose sum is -5. Of all (integer) combinations that give 6 (1 and 6, -1 and -6, -2 and -3, 2 and 3) it is -2 and -3 that add up to -5. Thus, $x^2 - 5x + 6 = (x - 2)(x - 3)$.

extra **Exercise 9.** Factor each expression.

(a) $3x^4 - 6x^2 + 42x$

(b) $x^3 + 4x^2 - 3x - 12$

(c)* $x^3 + xy - x^2y^2 - y^3$

(d) $2a^2 - 6ab + 2ab^2 - 6b^3$

(e) $x^2 + 11x + 28$

(f)* $x^2 + 3x - 28$

(g) $3x^2 + 3x - 60$

(h)* $5x^3 - 5x$

(i) $x^5 + 5x^4 + 4x^3$

Clearly, the technique we used in parts (c) and (e) of Example 3 requires that we deal with simple quadratic polynomials (i.e., having small coefficients and integer roots). We can also try to factor slightly more complicated polynomials, namely those whose coefficient of x^2 is not 1; for instance, let's factor $3x^2 + 11x - 4$. By starting with

$$3x^2 + 11x - 4 = (3x + a)(x + b)$$

we made sure that the coefficient of x^2 is 3. Next, we try numbers a and b whose product is -4, making sure that the x terms add up to 11. For instance, try $a = -4$ and $b = 1$; then

$$(3x - 4)(x + 1) = 3x^2 + 3x - 4x - 4 = 3x^2 - x - 4$$

this does not work. Try $a = -2$ and $b = 2$; then

$$(3x - 2)(x + 2) = 3x^2 + 6x - 2x - 4 = 3x^2 + 4x - 4$$

this does not work again. We keep trying (this takes some practice!); let $a = -1$ and $b = 4$; then

$$(3x - 1)(x + 4) = 3x^2 + 12x - x - 4 = 3x^2 + 11x - 4$$

this works! Thus, $3x^2 + 11x - 4 = (3x - 1)(x + 4)$.

Example 4. Factor each quadratic polynomial.

(a) $5x^2 + 13x - 6$

(b) $3x^2 - 2x - 8$

(c) $4x^2 + 9x + 2$

Solution.

(a) Start with $5x^2 - 13x - 6 = (5x + a)(x + b)$ and try combinations of a and b whose product is -6: Try $a = 1$, $b = -6$: $(5x + 1)(x - 6) = 5x^2 - 30x + x - 6 = 5x^2 - 29x - 6$, which does not work. Choosing $a = -1$ and $b = 6$, we get $(5x - 1)(x + 6) = 5x^2 + 30x - x - 6 = 5x^2 + 29x - 6$, which does not work either.

We keep going: try $a = 2$, $b = -3$: $(5x + 2)(x - 3) = 5x^2 - 15x + 2x - 6 = 5x^2 - 13x - 6$, which does not work. Try $a = -2$, $b = 3$: $(5x - 2)(x + 3) = 5x^2 + 15x - 2x - 6 = 5x^2 + 13x - 6$, and it works! So,

$$5x^2 + 13x - 6 = (5x - 2)(x + 3)$$

(b) We could proceed as in (a), or use the following approach (not significantly different, though). From

$$3x^2 - 2x - 8 = (3x + a)(x + b) = 3x^2 + (3b + a)x - ab$$

we see that we are looking for two numbers, a and b, whose product is -8 and where $3b + a = -2$. So, we try $a = 1$, $b = -8$: we compute $3b + a = -23 \neq -2$. Next, we switch the signs: $a = -1$ and $b = 8$ give $3b + a = 23 \neq -2$. And so on ... when $a = 4$, $b = -2$, we get $3b + a = -2$. Thus, $3x^2 - 2x - 8 = (3x + 4)(x - 2)$.

(c) This time, there are two possibilities:

$$4x^2 + 9x + 2 = (2x + a)(2x + b) \quad \text{and} \quad 4x^2 + 9x + 2 = (4x + a)(x + b)$$

We start with $4x^2 + 9x + 2 = (2x + a)(2x + b)$ and try integers a and b whose product is 2. For instance, $a = 1$, $b = 2$ will give $(2x + 1)(2x + 2) = 4x^2 + 6x + 2 \neq 4x^2 + 9x + 2$. (Note that both brackets contain $2x$, so we do not have to check the case $a = 2$, $b = 1$ since it is the same as above.) Next, we check that $a = -1$, $b = -2$ will not give the desired factorization, so we move on to the case

$$4x^2 + 9x + 2 = (4x + a)(x + b)$$

and proceed as in (a) or (b). By trial and error, we find out that $4x^2 + 9x + 2 = (4x + 1)(x + 2)$

Once we learn how to factor with the help of the quadratic formula, we will not need the methods that we used in the previous example. But, nevertheless, it is good to know them!

(extra) **Exercise 10.** Factor each quadratic polynomial.

(a) $2x^2 - x - 1$ (b) $2x^2 + x - 1$ (c)* $5x^2 - 12x + 4$ (d) $3x^2 - 22x + 7$

(e)* $6x^2 + 7x + 2$ (f)* $6x^2 - x - 2$ (g) $4x^2 - 4x - 3$ (h) $8x^2 - 6x + 1$

Next, we review several formulas that are commonly used for factoring:

> difference of squares: $a^2 - b^2 = (a + b)(a - b)$
>
> difference of cubes: $a^3 - b^3 = (a - b)(a^2 + ab + b^2)$
>
> sum of cubes: $a^3 + b^3 = (a + b)(a^2 - ab + b^2)$

The expressions $a^2 + ab + b^2$ and $a^2 - ab + b^2$ cannot be factored any further.

All of the above formulas can be checked by direct calculation. For instance,

$$(a - b)(a^2 + ab + b^2) = a^3 + a^2 b + ab^2 - a^2 b - ab^2 - b^3 = a^3 - b^3$$

Remember that the sum of the squares, $a^2 + b^2$, cannot be factored.

Thus, $x^2 - 1 = (x - 1)(x + 1)$, but $x^2 + 1$ cannot be written as a product of linear factors. Likewise, $3x^2 + 16$ and $7x^2 + 5$ cannot be broken down into linear factors.

Example 5. Factor each polynomial using the difference of squares formula:
(a) $x^2 - 18$ (b) $3x^2 - 18$ (c) $0.1x^2 - 3.5$ (d) $x^4 - 4$

Solution.

(a) $x^2 - 18 = x^2 - (\sqrt{18})^2 = (x - \sqrt{18})(x + \sqrt{18})$

Note that $\sqrt{18}$ can be simplified as $\sqrt{18} = \sqrt{9 \cdot 2} = \sqrt{9}\sqrt{2} = 3\sqrt{2}$. So, if needed, we write

$$x^2 - 18 = (x - 3\sqrt{2})(x + 3\sqrt{2})$$

(b) $3x^2 - 18 = (\sqrt{3}x)^2 - (\sqrt{18})^2 = (\sqrt{3}x - \sqrt{18})(\sqrt{3}x + \sqrt{18})$

An alternative way is to factor 3 out first:

$$3x^2 - 18 = 3(x^2 - 6) = 3(x - \sqrt{6})(x + \sqrt{6})$$

(c) $0.1x^2 - 3.5 = 0.1(x^2 - 35) = 0.1(x - \sqrt{35})(x + \sqrt{35})$

Without factoring:

$$0.1x^2 - 3.5 = (\sqrt{0.1}x)^2 - (\sqrt{3.5})^2 = (\sqrt{0.1}x - \sqrt{3.5})(\sqrt{0.1}x + \sqrt{3.5})$$

(d) $x^4 - 4 = (x^2)^2 - 2^2 = (x^2 - 2)(x^2 + 2)$

Now $x^2 + 2$ cannot be factored any further, but $x^2 - 2$ can:

$$x^2 - 2 = x^2 - (\sqrt{2})^2 = (x - \sqrt{2})(x + \sqrt{2})$$

Thus, $x^4 - 4 = (x - \sqrt{2})(x + \sqrt{2})(x^2 + 2)$.

 Exercise 11. Factor each expression using the difference of squares formula.

(a)* $x^2 - 0.04$ (b) $x^2 - \frac{4}{81}$ (c) $2x^2 - \frac{3}{5}$ (d)* $5x^2 - 125$

(e)* $5x^2 - 55$ (f) $a^2 - b^2c^4$ (g)* $x^4 - 2$ (h) $x - 16$

(i) $2x - 5$ (j) $(x + 1)^2 - (y - 1)^2$

Example 6. Factor each expression using either the sum or the difference of cubes formula.

(a) $x^3 - 8$ (b) $x^3 + 125$ (c) $2x^3 - 12$

Solution.

(a) Write $x^3 - 8 = x^3 - 2^3$; referring to the box above, we use $a = x$ and $b = 2$. Thus

$$x^3 - 8 = x^3 - 2^3 = (x - 2)(x^2 + x(2) + (2)^2) = (x - 2)(x^2 + 2x + 4)$$

(b) $x^3 + 125 = x^3 + 5^3 = (x + 5)(x^2 - x(5) + (5)^2) = (x + 5)(x^2 - 5x + 25)$

(c) Factor 2 out: $2x^3 - 12 = 2(x^3 - 6)$ and then write $6 = (\sqrt[3]{6})^3$; thus,

$$2x^3 - 12 = 2(x^3 - (\sqrt[3]{6})^3) = 2(x - \sqrt[3]{6})(x^2 + x\sqrt[3]{6} + (\sqrt[3]{6})^2) = 2(x - \sqrt[3]{6})(x^2 + \sqrt[3]{6}\,x + \sqrt[3]{36})$$

 Exercise 12. Factor each expression using either the sum or the difference of cubes formula (and other formulas, if needed).

(a) $x^3 + 27$ (b) $x^3 + 64$ (c)* $x^6 - 1$

(d)* $x + 1$ (e) $x^3 + y^3z^6$ (f) $a^4b^4 - ab^7$

In the box on page 29 we showed how to factor $a^2 - b^2$, $a^3 - b^3$ and $a^3 + b^3$. These formulas generalize: it is possible to factor $a^n - b^n$, for $n = 2, 3, 4, \ldots$ and $a^n + b^n$, if $n = 3, 5, 7, \ldots$ (i.e., n is positive and odd). Expressions $a^n + b^n$, if $n = 2, 4, 6, \ldots$ (i.e., n is positive and even) cannot be factored; keep in mind that we allow real numbers only (and not complex numbers).

$$\boxed{\begin{aligned}
&\text{Factoring } a^n - b^n \text{ and } a^n + b^n\\[4pt]
&a^2 - b^2 = (a - b)(a + b)\\[4pt]
&a^3 - b^3 = (a - b)(a^2 + ab + b^2)\\[4pt]
&a^4 - b^4 = (a - b)(a^3 + a^2b + ab^2 + b^3)\\[4pt]
&a^5 - b^5 = (a - b)(a^4 + a^3b + a^2b^2 + ab^3 + b^4), \text{ etc.}\\[4pt]
&a^3 + b^3 = (a + b)(a^2 - ab + b^2)\\[4pt]
&a^5 + b^5 = (a + b)(a^4 - a^3b + a^2b^2 - ab^3 + b^4), \text{ etc.}
\end{aligned}}$$

(try it!)   **Exercise 13.**   Factor each expression.

(a)* $2x^2y + y^2 - 4x^2 - 2y$ (b) $x^4 - x^2$ (c)* $27y^2 - 75x^2$

(d) $x^5 - x$ (e) $8x^2 - 50$ (f)* $x^2/16 - y^2/49$

(g) $4x^2 - 12$ (h)* $4x^2 - 11x + 6$ (i)* $3x^2 - 8x - 3$

(j) $x^2 + 3x - 10$ (k) $2x^2 + 7x - 4$ (l) $2x^2 + 2x - 24$

(m) $x^3 - 2x^2 - 15x$ (n) $x^4 - 16$ (o)* $a^2b - ac + ab^2c - bc^2$

(extra)   **Exercise 14.**   Factor each expression.

(a)* $4x^3y^{1/2} - 2xy^{3/2}$ (b)* $a^{x+4} - a^x + a^{x+1}$ (c) $xyz - 3x^2z^3 + xyz^2$

(d) $a(x + 2y) - c(x + 2y)$ (e) $3x(a - b) - a + b$ (f) $ac + bc - ad - bd$

(g) $x^2y + y - 4x^2 - 4$ (h)* $3a(y - x) - ab(x - y)$ (i) $ab - 2xb - 2xa + 4x^2$

(j) $a^2 - 9c^2$ (k) $1 - 49y^2$ (l) $x^4 - x^2$

(m) $a^3b^3 - 27$ (n)* $1 - (x + y)^2$ (o) $x^4y^2 - y^4$

(p) $x^2 - 4 - (x + 2)^2$ (q) $1 + x + x^2 + x^3$ (r) $a^5b^2 - a^2b^5$

(s) $(a - b)^2 - c^2$ (t) $(2x - y)^2 - (x + 4y)^2$ (u)* $a^2 - b^2 - a^3 + b^3$

Fractions

In this part, we review operations with fractions, in contexts that we encounter in calculus courses.

Example 7. Simplify by cancelling each fraction.

(a) $\dfrac{x^2 - 2x}{x^2 - 4}$ (b) $\dfrac{2x^2 - 3x - 2}{x^2 + 2x - 8}$ (c) $\dfrac{\frac{12}{x}}{\frac{6}{5x^3}}$ (d) $\dfrac{\frac{x+4}{x-3}}{\frac{x^2-16}{x^2-2x-3}}$

Solution.

(a) Using the difference of squares to factor the denominator, we get

$$\frac{x^2 - 2x}{x^2 - 4} = \frac{x(x - 2)}{(x - 2)(x + 2)} = \frac{x}{(x + 2)}$$

(b) Factor both the numerator and the denominator and cancel:

$$\frac{2x^2 - 3x - 2}{x^2 + 2x - 8} = \frac{(2x+1)(x-2)}{(x+4)(x-2)} = \frac{2x+1}{x+4}$$

(c) We first simplify the double fraction, and then cancel:

$$\frac{\frac{12}{x}}{\frac{6}{5x^3}} = \frac{12}{x} \cdot \frac{5x^3}{6} = \frac{12}{6} \cdot \frac{5x^3}{x} = \frac{2}{1} \cdot \frac{5x^2}{1} = 10x^2$$

(d) We get rid of the double fraction first, then factor and cancel:

$$\frac{\frac{x+4}{x-3}}{\frac{x^2-16}{x^2-2x-3}} = \frac{x+4}{x-3} \cdot \frac{x^2 - 2x - 3}{x^2 - 16} = \frac{x+4}{x-3} \cdot \frac{(x+1)(x-3)}{(x-4)(x+4)} = \frac{x+1}{x-4}$$

To factor $x^2 - 16$, we used the difference of squares formula, and to factor $x^2 - 2x - 3$ as a product of linear factors, we had to find the two numbers whose sum is -2 and product is -3.

For a systematic review of cancelling fractions, and as extra practice, work on the following questions.

(extra) **Exercise 15.** Cancel each fraction, if possible.

(a) $\dfrac{(2x - y)(x + y)}{4(x + y)}$ (b) $\dfrac{7x}{21x(x^2 + y)}$ (c)* $\dfrac{(2a + b)^2}{(2a + b)^3}$ (d) $\dfrac{4x + y + 6}{3}$

(e) $\dfrac{x^2 - 9}{(x - 3)^2}$ (f) $\dfrac{4 - x^2}{x - 2}$ (g) $\dfrac{(x + y)^2}{6x + 6y}$ (h) $\dfrac{(x - y)^2(x + 3y)^3}{(x + 3y)^4}$

(i) $\dfrac{x^2 - 4}{x^2 + 5x + 6}$ (j) $\dfrac{(x^2 - 4)^2}{x^2 - 5x + 6}$ (k) $\dfrac{x^2 - a^2}{x^3 - a^3}$ (l)* $\dfrac{x^2 + a^2}{x^3 + a^3}$

(m)* $\dfrac{x - y}{3y - 3x}$ (n) $\dfrac{(c - d)^2}{d^2 - c^2}$ (o) $-\dfrac{x^2 - 100}{10 - x}$ (p) $\dfrac{x^2 - x}{x - 1}$

(q) $\dfrac{x^3 - x}{(1 - x)^2}$ (r) $\dfrac{(a - b)(c^2 - d^2)}{d^2 - c^2}$ (s)* $\dfrac{64 - a^3}{a^2 - 16}$ (t) $\dfrac{(x - y)(z - t)^3}{(y - x)(t - z)^2}$

(extra) **Exercise 16.** Cancel each fraction, if possible.

(a) $\dfrac{15xy - 55x^2}{20x}$ (b) $\dfrac{x^3y - 9xy}{x^3y + 3x^3}$ (c)* $\dfrac{ax + bx - ay - by}{ax + bx + ay + by}$ (d) $\dfrac{a^3b + ab^2}{a^3b - a^2b^2}$

(e) $\dfrac{15xy - 55x^2}{20x - 15x^3}$ (f)* $\dfrac{x^4 + y^2x^2}{x^2y + xy^2}$ (g) $\dfrac{3xy - x^2y}{9y - yx^2}$ (h) $\dfrac{2ax + 2bx - ay - by}{4xa^2 - 2ya^2}$

(extra) **Exercise 17.** Cancel each fraction.

(a) $\dfrac{a^3 - a^5 + a}{a^2}$ (b) $\dfrac{a^3 + a^6}{a + a^4}$ (c) $\dfrac{a^2 + a^3}{b + ab}$ (d) $\dfrac{a^2b^3 + ab^4}{a^2b^2 + a^3b}$

(e)* $\dfrac{a^x + a^{x+2}}{a^{x+1}}$ (f) $\dfrac{a^x + a^{x+2}}{a^{x-1}}$ (g)* $\dfrac{a^x + a^{x+1}}{a^y + a^{y+1}}$ (h) $\dfrac{a^x}{a^x - a^{x+1}}$

Example 8. Cancel the fraction $\dfrac{|x+5|}{x+5}$.

Solution. We cannot cancel the fraction in its present form — we need to get rid of the absolute value first. So, we start with the definition

$$|x+5| = \begin{cases} x+5 & \text{if } x+5 \geq 0 \\ -(x+5) & \text{if } x+5 < 0 \end{cases} = \begin{cases} x+5 & \text{if } x \geq -5 \\ -(x+5) & \text{if } x < -5 \end{cases}$$

Therefore, we have two cases:

$$\text{if } x > -5, \text{ then } \frac{|x+5|}{x+5} = \frac{x+5}{x+5} = 1$$

$$\text{if } x < -5, \text{ then } \frac{|x+5|}{x+5} = \frac{-(x+5)}{x+5} = -1$$

If $x = -5$, the fraction is not defined.

Alternatively, we write the answer as

$$\frac{|x+5|}{x+5} = \begin{cases} 1 & \text{if } x > -5 \\ -1 & \text{if } x < -5 \end{cases}$$

(extra) **Exercise 18.** As in Example 8, cancel each fraction.

(a) $\dfrac{|x|}{x}$
(b) $\dfrac{|x-2|}{x-2}$
(c)* $\dfrac{|3x-5|}{5-3x}$
(d) $\dfrac{|1-2x|}{2x-1}$

Example 9. Reduce each expression to a single fraction by computing the common denominator.

(a) $\dfrac{1}{2} - \dfrac{2}{3} + \dfrac{3}{4}$
(b) $\dfrac{3}{x} - \dfrac{6}{x^2} + \dfrac{4}{x^3}$
(c) $\dfrac{3}{x-2} - \dfrac{7}{x+1}$
(d) $\dfrac{4x-1}{x^2-1} - \dfrac{x+1}{x-1}$

Solution.

(a) The lowest common denominator is 12; thus,

$$\frac{1}{2} - \frac{2}{3} + \frac{3}{4} = \frac{6}{12} - \frac{8}{12} + \frac{9}{12} = \frac{7}{12}$$

(b) Since the lowest common denominator is x^3, we write

$$\frac{3}{x} - \frac{6}{x^2} + \frac{4}{x^3} = \frac{3x^2}{x^3} - \frac{6x}{x^3} + \frac{4}{x^3} = \frac{3x^2 - 6x + 4}{x^3}$$

(c) The lowest common denominator of $x-2$ and $x+1$ is their product; thus,

$$\frac{3}{x-2} - \frac{7}{x+1} = \frac{3(x+1)}{(x-2)(x+1)} - \frac{7(x-2)}{(x-2)(x+1)}$$

$$= \frac{3(x+1) - 7(x-2)}{(x-2)(x+1)} = \frac{-4x+17}{(x-2)(x+1)}$$

(d) Since $x^2 - 1 = (x-1)(x+1)$, the lowest common denominator is $x^2 - 1$, and so

$$\frac{4x-1}{x^2-1} - \frac{x+1}{x-1} = \frac{4x-1}{x^2-1} - \frac{(x+1)(x+1)}{(x-1)(x+1)}$$

$$= \frac{4x - 1 - (x^2 + 2x + 1)}{x^2 - 1} = \frac{-x^2 + 2x - 2}{x^2 - 1}$$

try it!

Exercise 19. Simplify by calculating the common denominator.

(a) $\dfrac{x}{x-2} - \dfrac{2x-1}{x-4}$ (b) $\dfrac{3}{x} - \dfrac{2x}{x-1} + \dfrac{4}{(x-1)^2}$ (c) $\dfrac{2x+1}{x^2-5x+6} - \dfrac{1}{x-2} + \dfrac{x}{x-3}$

Example 10. Simplify the following fractions (fractions like these are used to compute derivatives in calculus):

(a) $\dfrac{(2+h)^2 - 4}{h}$ (b) $\dfrac{(-1+h)^3 + 1}{h}$ (c) $\dfrac{\frac{1}{h+2} - \frac{1}{2}}{h}$

Solution.

(a) Using the formula for $(a+b)^2$, we compute $(2+h)^2$, and thus

$$\frac{(2+h)^2 - 4}{h} = \frac{4 + 4h + h^2 - 4}{h} = \frac{4h + h^2}{h} = \frac{h(4+h)}{h} = (4+h)$$

(b) We compute

$$\frac{(-1+h)^3 + 1}{h} = \frac{-1 + 3h - 3h^2 + h^3 + 1}{h} = \frac{3h - 3h^2 + h^3}{h} = \frac{h(3 - 3h + h^2)}{h} = 3 - 3h + h^2$$

To calculate $(-1+h)^3 = (h-1)^3$, we use the cube of the difference formula that we stated on page 25. Alternatively (if we cannot recall the formula) we multiply $h-1$ by itself three times.

(c) We start by simplifying the double fraction and then compute the common denominator:

$$\frac{\frac{1}{h+2} - \frac{1}{2}}{h} = \left(\frac{1}{h+2} - \frac{1}{2} \right) \frac{1}{h} = \left(\frac{2}{2(h+2)} - \frac{h+2}{2(h+2)} \right) \frac{1}{h} = \frac{2 - (h+2)}{2(h+2)} \cdot \frac{1}{h}$$

$$= \frac{-h}{2(h+2)} \cdot \frac{1}{h} = \frac{-1}{2(h+2)}$$

extra

Exercise 20. Compute each expression and simplify as much as possible.

(a) $\dfrac{1}{x-y} + \dfrac{2}{x+y}$ (b) $\dfrac{2a+b}{b} - \dfrac{1}{a+b} + \dfrac{b}{ab+b^2}$ (c) $\dfrac{2}{a+2b} - \dfrac{3}{a-2b} - \dfrac{1}{a^2-4b^2}$

(d) $\dfrac{x^2-y+z}{xy} - \dfrac{x+1}{yz} + \dfrac{y}{xz}$ (e) $\dfrac{x+y}{x-y} + \dfrac{x-y}{x+y}$ (f) $\dfrac{2}{x^2-4} - \dfrac{3}{(x+2)^2} - \dfrac{1}{2x-4}$

(g)* $\dfrac{1}{2} + \dfrac{2}{b-2} - \dfrac{1}{b+4} + \dfrac{b}{b^2+2b-8}$ (h) $\dfrac{1}{y-x} + \dfrac{1}{x-y} - \dfrac{1}{(x-y)^2} + \dfrac{3}{(x-y)^3}$

(i) $\dfrac{1}{x} - \dfrac{1}{x^m}$ $(m > 1)$ (j) $\dfrac{2}{a^x} + \dfrac{1}{a^{x+1}}$ (k) $\dfrac{2}{a^x} - \dfrac{1}{a^{x+1}} - \dfrac{1}{a^{x-2}}$

(l)* $\dfrac{x^3-27}{x^2-9}$ (m)* $\dfrac{x^4-x^2}{2x^2+3x+1}$ (n) $(ab+b^2) \cdot \dfrac{a-b}{a+b} + b^2$

(o) $\dfrac{x-y}{a^2-b^2} \cdot \dfrac{(a+b)^2}{x^2-y^2}$ (p) $\dfrac{2x-4}{x^3+x} \cdot \dfrac{x}{3x-6}$ (q) $\left(\dfrac{1}{a} - \dfrac{1}{b} \right)(a+b)$

(r) $\left(\dfrac{1}{a} + \dfrac{1}{b} \right) \cdot \dfrac{a^2b^3}{b^2-a^2}$ (s) $\dfrac{\frac{a^2b}{5}}{\frac{ab^3}{15}}$ (t) $\dfrac{\frac{a}{b} - \frac{b}{a}}{a+b}$

(u) $\dfrac{\frac{a^x}{b^{x-1}}}{\frac{a^{x+1}}{b^x}}$ (v)* $\dfrac{1 - \frac{3}{x}}{1 - \frac{6}{x} + \frac{9}{x^2}}$ (w)* $\dfrac{1 + \frac{1}{x-1}}{1 - \frac{1}{x-1}}$

(extra) **Exercise 21.** To factor x out of $2x^2 - 7x + 5$ means to write $2x^2 - 7x + 5 = x\left(2x - 7 + \dfrac{5}{x}\right)$. Factor each expression as suggested.

(a)* Factor 6 out of $\dfrac{3}{4}x^4 - 6x^2 - \dfrac{x}{2} - 11$
(b) Factor x^4 out of $3x^4 - 6x^2 - 5x - 12$

(c) Factor x^2 out of $-x^3 - x^2 + x + 11$
(d) Factor $x^{1/2}$ out of $-x^3 + 3x^2 - x - 12$

(e) Factor $\dfrac{1}{x}$ out of $-x^3 - x^2 + x + 11$
(f)* Factor $x^{-3/2}$ out of $-x^3 + 3x^2 - x - 12$

(g) Factor $x^{1/3}$ out of $-2x^{-2/3}(x - 5) + 7x^{1/3}(x - 4)$

(h) Factor $x^{-2/3}(x - 5)$ out of $\dfrac{1}{3}x^{-2/3}(x - 5)^2 + \dfrac{4}{5}x^{1/3}(x - 5)$ and simplify

(i)* Factor $\dfrac{x^{-2/3}(x - 5)}{3}$ out of $\dfrac{1}{3}x^{-2/3}(x - 5)^2 + \dfrac{4}{3}x^{1/3}(x - 5)$ and simplify

(j) Factor x^{-1} out of $\dfrac{1}{3x^3} + \dfrac{4}{x^2} - \dfrac{1}{7x} + 2x - 1$

(k) Factor $x^{-1/2}$ out of $\dfrac{1}{3x^3} + \dfrac{4}{x^2} - \dfrac{1}{7x} + 2x - 1$

(l)* Factor $\sqrt{x}$ out of $x^2 - 3\sqrt{x} - 5 + \dfrac{4}{x} - \dfrac{1}{\sqrt{x}}$.

Division of Polynomials (Long Division)

To divide two polynomials, we imitate the division of numbers; suppose we need to calculate the quotient and the remainder when 37 is divided by 8:

$$\begin{array}{r} 4 \quad\longleftarrow \text{8 divides into 37 approximately 4 times} \\ 8\,\overline{)\,37} \\ \underline{-32} \quad\longleftarrow \text{multiply 4 by 8} \\ 5 \quad\longleftarrow \text{subtract to get the remainder} \end{array}$$

Thus, the quotient is 4 and the remainder is 5. Recalling the general form

$$\frac{\text{dividend}}{\text{divisor}} = \text{quotient} + \frac{\text{remainder}}{\text{divisor}}$$

we write $\dfrac{37}{8} = 4 + \dfrac{5}{8}$.

The quotient of two polynomials is called a *rational function* (we will talk about them a lot more in Section 6). Long division of polynomials is used in several places in calculus (for instance, as a tool to simplify rational functions so that we can compute their integrals).

Long division makes sense only when the degree of the polynomial in the numerator is larger than or equal to the degree of the polynomial in the denominator.

Example 11. Divide the polynomial $x^3 - 2x^2 + x - 4$ by $x + 3$.

Solution. We start as if we are dividing numbers: $x + 3$ divides into $x^3 - 2x^2 + x - 4$ approximately x^2 times. We multiply $x + 3$ by x^2 to get $x^3 + 3x^2$ and then subtract; see below, left. We add the remaining terms to $-5x^2$, to get $-5x^2 + x - 4$; see below, right. Now we repeat the routine: x

divides $-5x^2 + x - 4$ approximately $-5x$ times; we add $-5x$ to the quotient (in the top line), and multiply $x + 3$ by $-5x$, etc.

$$
\begin{array}{r}
x^2 \\
x + 3 \overline{\smash{\big)}\, x^3 - 2x^2 + x - 4} \\
-\underline{(x^3 + 3x^2)} \\
-5x^2
\end{array}
\qquad
\begin{array}{r}
x^2 - 5x + 16 \\
x + 3 \overline{\smash{\big)}\, x^3 - 2x^2 + x - 4} \\
-\underline{(x^3 + 3x^2)} \\
-5x^2 + x - 4 \\
-\underline{(-5x^2 - 15x)} \\
16x - 4 \\
-\underline{(16x + 48)} \\
-52
\end{array}
$$

Repeating this process (see above, right) we obtain the quotient $x^2 - 5x + 16$ and the remainder -52. Thus,

$$
\frac{x^3 - 2x^2 + x - 4}{x + 3} = x^2 - 5x + 16 - \frac{52}{x + 3}
$$

Example 12. Find the quotient $\dfrac{x^2 + 1}{x + 2}$ using long division. Write your answer as in Example 11.

Solution. As in the previous example,

$$
\begin{array}{r}
x - 2 \\
x + 2 \overline{\smash{\big)}\, x^2 + 1} \\
-\underline{(x^2 + 2x)} \\
-2x + 1 \\
-\underline{(-2x - 4)} \\
5
\end{array}
$$

Thus, $\dfrac{x^2 + 1}{x + 2} = x - 2 + \dfrac{5}{x + 2}$.

Exercise 22. Use long division to divide given polynomials, if possible. Write your answer as in Examples 11 and 12.

(a)* $\dfrac{x^3 - 3x + 5}{x - 4}$ (b)* $\dfrac{x^2 + 7x - 2}{x + 1}$ (c) $\dfrac{x^2 + 2}{x^2 + 7}$ (d) $\dfrac{x^4}{x^2 + 1}$

(e) $\dfrac{x^2 + 5x + 7}{x + 2}$ (f) $\dfrac{x}{x - 6}$ (g)* $\dfrac{x^3}{x + 7}$ (h) $\dfrac{x^3}{x^3 + 1}$

In some cases (if we get lucky!), we will be able to divide two polynomials without using long division. To do that, we use a little trick.

Suppose we need to divide x^2 by $x^2 + 3$, i.e., calculate $\frac{x^2}{x^2+3}$. The trick is to expand the numerator so that we can break the fraction into a sum or a difference of two fractions in such a way that one fraction cancels out, i.e., is no longer a fraction but a polynomial.

So, start by adding and subtracting 3 in the numerator (which, of course, does not change its value):

$$\frac{x^2}{x^2+3} = \frac{x^2+3-3}{x^2+3} = \frac{(x^2+3)-3}{x^2+3} = \frac{x^2+3}{x^2+3} - \frac{3}{x^2+3} = 1 - \frac{3}{x^2+3}$$

Done! The quotient is 1 and the remainder is 3.

Another example: to divide $3x+1$ by $x-4$, we subtract and add 12:

$$\frac{3x+1}{x-4} = \frac{3x-12+12+1}{x-4} = \frac{(3x-12)+13}{x-4}$$

$$= \frac{3x-12}{x-4} + \frac{13}{x-4} = \frac{3(x-4)}{x-4} + \frac{13}{x-4} = 3 + \frac{13}{x-4}$$

So, the quotient is 3 and the remainder is 13.

(extra) **Exercise 23.** Divide the following polynomials using the trick we just explained. Check using long division.

(a) $\dfrac{x}{x-6}$ (b) $\dfrac{x^2}{x^2-4}$ (c)* $\dfrac{6x}{2x-5}$ (d)* $\dfrac{2x^2}{x^2+1}$

(e) $\dfrac{3x-1}{3x-4}$ (f) $\dfrac{4x+11}{4x+5}$

We mention next an important fact that might not come up in a calculus course. If you wish, skip it (and the exercise that follows) for now and come back to it if you need it.

Recall that, if $p(x)$ is a polynomial and $p(a) = 0$ for some a (i.e., a is a root of the polynomial), then $x - a$ divides $p(a)$. Using long division, we can then factor (or, at least start factoring) the given polynomial. Here is an example.

Example 13. Factor the polynomial $p(x) = x^3 + x^2 - 10x + 8$.

Solution. We try to identify a root of $p(x)$ by guessing.

Recall that, if $p(x)$ has an integer root, then the root must divide its free term (in this case, must divide 8).

Now it's trial and error: 4 divides 8, but $p(4) = (4)^3 + (4)^2 - 10(4) + 8 = 48 \neq 0$ and shows that 4 is not a root.

However, since $p(1) = (1)^3 + (1)^2 - 10(1) + 8 = 0$ we know that 1 is a root; thus, $x - 1$ must divide $p(x) = x^3 + x^2 - 10x + 8$, i.e.,

$$x^3 + x^2 - 10x + 8 = (x-1)q(x)$$

where the unknown polynomial $q(x)$ is identified using long division:

$$
\begin{array}{r}
x^2 + 2x - 8 \\
x - 1 \overline{\smash{\big)}\ x^3 + x^2 - 10x + 8} \\
\underline{-\ (x^3 - x^2)} \\
2x^2 - 10x + 8 \\
\underline{-\ (2x^2 - 2x)} \\
-8x + 8 \\
\underline{-\ (-8x + 8)} \\
0
\end{array}
$$

The remainder is zero, as it should be. We write

$$\frac{x^3 + x^2 - 10x + 8}{x - 1} = x^2 + 2x - 8$$

i.e., $x^3 + x^2 - 10x + 8 = (x - 1)(x^2 + 2x - 8)$. Factoring the quadratic polynomial (as explained earlier in this section), we obtain $x^2 + 2x - 8 = (x + 4)(x - 2)$, and so

$$x^3 + x^2 - 10x + 8 = (x - 1)(x + 4)(x - 2)$$

try it!   **Exercise 24.**   Factor the polynomial $x^3 + 2x^2 - 11x - 12$.

Rationalizing the Denominator

In some situations, it might be necessary to remove square roots from denominators. The technique that accomplishes that, called *rationalizing the denominator*, is based on using the difference of squares formula $(a - b)(a + b) = a^2 - b^2$ and the fact that $\sqrt{a}\sqrt{a} = a$ for $a > 0$.

Example 14. Rationalize the denominator in:

(a) $\dfrac{2}{\sqrt{17}}$ (b) $\dfrac{1}{\sqrt{5} + \sqrt{6}}$ (c) $\dfrac{1}{\sqrt{x} - 2}$ (d) $\dfrac{1}{\sqrt{x - 2} - \sqrt{x + 3}}$

Solution.

(a) Multiplying and dividing by $\sqrt{17}$, we get

$$\frac{2}{\sqrt{17}} = \frac{2}{\sqrt{17}} \cdot \frac{\sqrt{17}}{\sqrt{17}} = \frac{2\sqrt{17}}{17}$$

(b) Multiply the given fraction by 1, written in the form $(\sqrt{5} - \sqrt{6})/(\sqrt{5} - \sqrt{6})$.

$$\frac{1}{\sqrt{5} + \sqrt{6}} = \frac{1}{\sqrt{5} + \sqrt{6}} \cdot \frac{\sqrt{5} - \sqrt{6}}{\sqrt{5} - \sqrt{6}} = \frac{\sqrt{5} - \sqrt{6}}{5 - 6} = -(\sqrt{5} - \sqrt{6}) = \sqrt{6} - \sqrt{5}$$

To multiply the terms in the denominator, we used the difference of squares formula:

$$(\sqrt{5} + \sqrt{6})(\sqrt{5} - \sqrt{6}) = (\sqrt{5})^2 - (\sqrt{6})^2 = 5 - 6$$

(c) Using the same idea as in (a), we get

$$\frac{1}{\sqrt{x} - 2} = \frac{1}{\sqrt{x} - 2} \cdot \frac{\sqrt{x} + 2}{\sqrt{x} + 2} = \frac{\sqrt{x} + 2}{(\sqrt{x})^2 - 2^2} = \frac{\sqrt{x} + 2}{x - 4}$$

(d) We compute

$$\frac{1}{\sqrt{x - 2} - \sqrt{x + 3}} = \frac{1}{\sqrt{x - 2} - \sqrt{x + 3}} \cdot \frac{\sqrt{x - 2} + \sqrt{x + 3}}{\sqrt{x - 2} + \sqrt{x + 3}}$$

$$= \frac{\sqrt{x - 2} + \sqrt{x + 3}}{(\sqrt{x - 2})^2 - (\sqrt{x + 3})^2}$$

$$= \frac{\sqrt{x - 2} + \sqrt{x + 3}}{x - 2 - (x + 3)}$$

$$= -\frac{\sqrt{x - 2} + \sqrt{x + 3}}{5}$$

(extra) **Exercise 25.** Rationalize the denominator and simplify if possible.

(a)* $\dfrac{4}{\sqrt{7}-3}$

(b) $\dfrac{\sqrt{5}-\sqrt{3}}{\sqrt{5}+\sqrt{3}}$

(c) $\dfrac{2}{\sqrt{x}-1}$

(d)* $\dfrac{4-\sqrt{x}}{2+\sqrt{x}}$

(e) $\dfrac{x}{\sqrt{x+1}-1}$

(f) $\dfrac{\sqrt{x}}{2\sqrt{x}-6}$

(g)* $\dfrac{3}{\sqrt{x}-\sqrt{x-1}}$

(h) $\dfrac{1}{\sqrt{x+2}+\sqrt{x-2}}$

What we just learned can be applied in a slightly different context as well. In calculus, to transform the fraction

$$\frac{\sqrt{3x+1}-\sqrt{2x+1}}{x}$$

into a form more appropriate for a computation of some limits (for instance when x approaches zero or ∞), we write

$$\begin{aligned}
\frac{\sqrt{3x+1}-\sqrt{2x+1}}{x} &= \frac{\sqrt{3x+1}-\sqrt{2x+1}}{x}\cdot\frac{\sqrt{3x+1}+\sqrt{2x+1}}{\sqrt{3x+1}+\sqrt{2x+1}} \\
&= \frac{\left(\sqrt{3x+1}\right)^2-\left(\sqrt{2x+1}\right)^2}{x\left(\sqrt{3x+1}+\sqrt{2x+1}\right)} \\
&= \frac{(3x+1)-(2x+1)}{x\left(\sqrt{3x+1}+\sqrt{2x+1}\right)} \\
&= \frac{x}{x\left(\sqrt{3x+1}+\sqrt{2x+1}\right)} = \frac{1}{\sqrt{3x+1}+\sqrt{2x+1}}
\end{aligned}$$

Answers to quiz questions: **1.** (a) $2x^3-7x^2-4x$ (b) $x^2-8x+16$ (c) $x^6+2x^5+x^4$ (d) x^4-144 (e) x^3+3x^2+3x+1 [see Example 1]. **2.** $(x+7/2)^2-33/4$ [see Exercise 8(d)]. **3.** (a) $6x(x^5-4x+2)$ (b) $(y^3-1)(4y^2-3)$ (c) $(x+2)(x+5)$ [see Example 3]. **4.** $(4x+1)(x+2)$ [see Example 4(c)]. **5.** $5(x-\sqrt{11})(x+\sqrt{11})$ [see Exercise 11(e)]. **6.** (a) $x(x-1)(x+1)(x^2+1)$ (b) $2(2x-5)(2x+5)$ (c) $(x/4-y/7)(x/4+y/7)$ [see Exercise 13(d), (e), (f)]. **7.** $\frac{x^2-x+4}{(x-2)(x-3)}$ [see Exercise 19(c)]. **8.** $x^2+4x+13+\frac{57}{x-4}$ [see Exercise 22(a)]. **9.** $(x+4)(x-3)(x+1)$ [see Exercise 24]. **10.** $\sqrt{6}-\sqrt{5}$ [see Example 14(b)].

3. Basic Facts and Formulas from Geometry

What is in this section?

Basic facts and formulas from plane geometry: triangles, circles, trapezoids, etc.; surface area and volume of three-dimensional solids; review of all geometric formulas that are needed for calculus.

Do I need to read this?

Answer the quiz questions below. If you get all of them right, or make a few smaller mistakes, then you can skip this section. Otherwise, identify what you don't know or are not sure about and read relevant parts of this section (or read all of it!).

Quiz

1. What is the sum of angles in a triangle? rectangle? pentagon?

2. State the Pythagorean Theorem.

3. What is an equilateral triangle? How do we compute its area? State formulas for the area of a rectangle, square, circle, ellipse and trapezoid.

4. State formulas for the volume and surface area of a parallelepiped, cube and sphere.

Over ...

5. What is a frustum of a cone?

6. What is the relation between the volume of a cone and the volume of a cylinder with the same radius and the same height? What is the relation between the volume of a pyramid and the volume of a parallelepiped?

7. What is the relation between the angles α and β in the figure below, left? The triangle ABC is inscribed into a circle in such a way that the side AB is a diameter of the circle (see figure below, right). Is there anything special about the triangle ABC?

 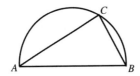

8. Consider a right triangle ABC, with the right angle at C. Draw the height from C to the hypotenuse c (see figure below). Identify a pair of similar triangles.

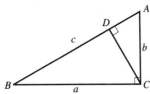

[Answers to this quiz are at the bottom of page 49.]

Plane Geometry

Usually, we use lowercase letters a, b, c, ... to denote the sides (edges), and uppercase letters A, B, C, ... to denote the vertices of a polygon. Lowercase Greek letters α, β, γ, ... are used for angles. Sometimes, we use $\angle A$ to denote the angle at vertex A, $\angle B$ to denote the angle at vertex B, etc. More often, we use $\angle BAC$ to denote the angle in a triangle (or in a polygon, or in some diagram) formed by the sides BA and AC.

In a general triangle (also called a *scalene* triangle; below, left), the sum of the angles $= \angle A + \angle B + \angle C = 180^O$ or π radians (see Section 7 for conversion between degrees and radians). Perimeter $= a + b + c$. Area $= \frac{1}{2}ah$ (h is the height of the triangle from vertex A).

In a *right* triangle (below, right) $\angle C = 90^O$ (or $\pi/2$ radians). Area $= \frac{1}{2}ab$.

The *Pythagorean Theorem* states that, in a right triangle, the sides a and b and the hypotenuse c are related by the formula $c^2 = a^2 + b^2$, or $c = \sqrt{a^2 + b^2}$.

The statement also goes the other way around: if the sides a, b and c in some triangle satisfy $a^2 + b^2 = c^2$, then the triangle is a right triangle, and the right angle is opposite side c.

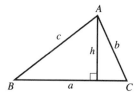 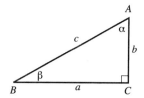

Example 1. Find a formula for the area of the *equilateral* triangle (all sides equal) of side a.

Solution. Draw the height from A, as shown in figure below.

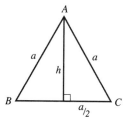

Using the Pythagorean Theorem, we get

$$h = \sqrt{a^2 - \left(\frac{a}{2}\right)^2} = \sqrt{a^2 - \frac{a^2}{4}} = \sqrt{\frac{3a^2}{4}} = \frac{a}{2}\sqrt{3}$$

Thus, the area is

$$A = \frac{1}{2}ah = \frac{1}{2}a\frac{a}{2}\sqrt{3} = \frac{a^2}{4}\sqrt{3}$$

Recall that, in an equilateral triangle, all angles are equal to 60° (or $\pi/3$ radians).

Two triangles are called *similar* if the corresponding angles are equal (in the figure below: $\angle A = \angle A'$, $\angle B = \angle B'$, and $\angle C = \angle C'$). In that case, $\dfrac{a}{a'} = \dfrac{b}{b'} = \dfrac{c}{c'}$.

Note that, to prove the similarity of triangles, it is enough to show that two pairs of angles are equal; say, $\angle A = \angle A'$ and $\angle B = \angle B'$. Since angles in a triangle must add to 180°, it follows that $\angle C = 180^{\circ} - \angle A - \angle B = 180^{\circ} - \angle A' - \angle B' = \angle C'$.

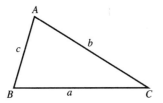 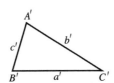

Quite often, we recognize similar triangles in various diagrams, such as the two shown in the figures below. Note that, in either case, the triangles ABC and $A'B'C$ are similar.

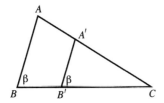 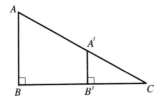

Here is another situation where we meet similar triangles. Consider a right triangle ABC, with the right angle at C. Draw the height from C to the hypotenuse c (see figure below).

The triangles ABC and BCD are similar: they are both right triangles, and $\angle ABC = \angle DBC$. Thus,

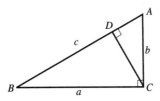

$$\frac{a}{BD} = \frac{b}{CD} = \frac{c}{a}$$

Are triangles ABC and DCA similar?

Yes. Both are right triangles, and have an angle in common: $\angle CAB = \angle CAD$. Thus,

$$\frac{a}{CD} = \frac{b}{AD} = \frac{c}{b}$$

In a *rectangle* with sides a and b (below, left), Perimeter $= 2(a + b)$. Area $= ab$. Diagonal $d = \sqrt{a^2 + b^2}$. In a *square* with side a (below, right), Perimeter $= 4a$. Area $= a^2$. Diagonal $= d = a\sqrt{2}$.

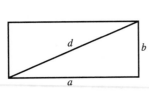

For a *circle* of radius r (below, left), Diameter $= d = 2r$. Circumference $= 2\pi r$. Area of the region (i.e., the disk) bounded by the circle $= \pi r^2$.

Sector of a circle of radius r and angle α (below, centre). Length of the arc is $a = r\alpha$, and area is $A = r^2\alpha/2$ (α must be in radians; if α is in degrees, then multiply α by $\pi/180$. For conversion between radians and degrees, see Section 7.) When $\alpha = 2\pi$, we obtain the circle, and then $a = r\alpha = 2\pi r$ is its circumference, and $A = r^2\alpha/2 = r^2\pi$ is its area.

Annular region bounded by the circles of radius r_1 and r_2, where $r_1 < r_2$ (shaded area in the figure below, right). Area $= \pi r_2^2 - \pi r_1^2 = \pi(r_2^2 - r_1^2)$.

Ellipse with semi-axes a and b (see the figure below). C is the centre of the ellipse. Area $= \pi ab$.

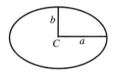

Trapezoid with sides a, b, c and d and height h (below, left). Sides a and c are parallel. Perimeter $= a + b + c + d$. Area $= \frac{1}{2}(a + c)h$; a good way to remember this formula is: sum of the two parallel sides times height divided by 2.

The special case of a trapezoid that has two right angles is shown below, right, in the position that is used in integration in calculus. *Area* $= \frac{1}{2}(a + c)b$.

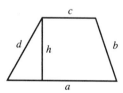
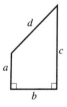

Miscellaneous Facts

The sum of angles in a polygon with n sides is $(n - 2)\pi$ radians or $180(n - 2)$ degrees. So the sum of angles in a triangle is π radians or 180°. In a rectangle, square, trapezoid, or any other polygon with four sides, the sum of angles is 360°. The sum of angles in a pentagon is 540°, etc.

Assume that a line c intersects two parallel lines a and b (see figure below). Then $\alpha = \beta$. Since $\alpha = \alpha'$ and $\beta = \beta'$, it follows that $\alpha = \alpha' = \beta = \beta'$.

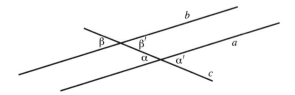

If the same arc subtends angle α and corresponding central angle β (below, left), then $\beta = 2\alpha$.

Assume that the triangle ABC is inscribed into a circle in such a way that the side AB is a diameter of the circle (below, right). In that case, the triangle is the right triangle, i.e., $\angle C = 90^0$. We can rephrase this fact by saying that an angle inscribed in a semicircle is a right angle.

 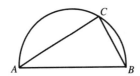

Geometry in Three-Dimensional Space

Parallelepiped (rectangular box) of length a, width b, and height c (below, left). Volume $= abc$. Surface area $= 2(ab + ac + bc)$.

Cube of side a (below, right). Volume $= a^3$. Surface area $= 6a^2$.

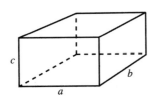 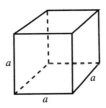

Sphere of radius r (below, left). Volume $= \frac{4}{3}\pi r^3$. Surface area $= 4\pi r^2$.

Ellipsoid with semi-axes a, b and c (below, right). Volume $= \frac{4}{3}\pi abc$.

 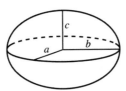

Cylinder of radius r and height h (below, left). Volume $= \pi r^2 h$. Surface area $= 2\pi rh$ (this is also called lateral surface area). If both top and bottom disks are included, then surface area $= 2\pi r^2 + 2\pi rh = 2\pi r(r + h)$; see Example 2 below.

Cylindrical shell: a cylinder of radius r_1 from which a cylinder of radius r_2 (where $r_2 < r_1$) has been removed (see figure below, right). Volume $= \pi r_1^2 h - \pi r_2^2 h = \pi(r_1^2 - r_2^2)h$.

Example 2. Derive the formula for the surface area of a cylinder of height h and radius r.

Solution. To compute the lateral surface area, we cut the cylinder along the dashed line (see below).

When we unroll it, we obtain a rectangle of height h and length equal to the circumference of the circle, $2\pi r$. So the lateral surface area is $2\pi rh$.

The top and the bottom parts are disks of radius r, so each contributes πr^2 towards the total area. So the surface area (top disk plus bottom disk plus lateral surface) is $2\pi r^2 + 2\pi rh = 2\pi r(r + h)$.

Cone of radius r and height h (below, left). Volume $= \frac{1}{3}\pi r^2 h$. The volume of the cone is $1/3$ of the volume of the cylinder with the same radius and the same height.

The segment ℓ is called the *slant height* of a cone. From the Pythagorean Theorem, we get $\ell = \sqrt{r^2 + h^2}$.

  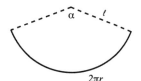

To compute the lateral surface area of a cone, we cut it along one of its slant heights (dashed line in the figure above, centre) and unroll it, to obtain the sector of a circle of radius ℓ and arc length equal to $2\pi r$.

From the [arc length equals angle times radius] formula, we get $2\pi r = \alpha\ell$, and so $\alpha = 2\pi r/\ell$. The area of the sector is [one half times radius squared times angle]

$$\frac{1}{2}\ell^2 \frac{2\pi r}{\ell} = \pi r\ell$$

Thus, the lateral surface area of a cone is $\pi r\ell = \pi r\sqrt{r^2 + h^2}$.

Pyramid of height h whose base is a rectangle with sides a and b (below). Volume $= \frac{1}{3}abh$. The volume of the pyramid is $1/3$ of the volume of the parallelepiped with the same base and the same height.

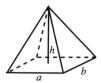

If length is given in specified units, then area is expressed in those same units squared, and volume in those same units cubed.

So if the radius of a sphere is $r = 4$ cm, then its surface area is $4\pi r^2 = 4\pi(4)^2 = 64\pi = 201.06$ cm^2, and its volume $\frac{4}{3}\pi r^3 = \frac{4}{3}\pi(4)^3 = \frac{256}{3}\pi = 268.08$ cm^3.

In other words, the formula $2\pi r$ *cannot* be the formula for the area of a disk of radius r (actually cannot represent the area of anything!). As well, πr^2 *cannot* represent the circumference of a circle.

Another example: assume that a, b and c are measured in metres. Then expressions such as $a^2 b$, abc, or $a^3 + bc^2$ could represent the volume of something (all expressions have units of metres cubed), and $ab + ac + bc$, a^2, or $b^2 + c^2$ could represent area (since all expressions have units of metres squared).

On the other hand, expressions such as $a^2 + b$ (adding units squared to units) or $a^3 + b^2$ (adding units cubed to units squared) have no geometric meaning. Of course, $a^3 + b^2$ could represent something that does make sense; for instance, if $a = 1$ and $b = 2$ (i.e., a and b have no units attached to them) then we can calculate (and possibly interpret) $a^3 + b^2 = (1)^3 + (2)^2 = 5$.

What we do next might, or might not come up in your calculus course. If you wish, skip this for now (i.e., skip the next two examples) and come back when you need it.

Example 3. A *frustum* of a cone is obtained from a cone of radius r_1 and height h_1 by removing a cone of radius r_2 and height h_2 ($h_2 < h_1$) from its top; see the figure below, left.

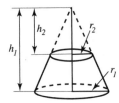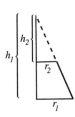

The volume of the frustum is equal to the volume of the larger cone minus the volume of the smaller one that was removed, i.e.,

$$\text{Volume} = \frac{1}{3}\pi r_1^2 h_1 - \frac{1}{3}\pi r_2^2 h_2$$

For various calculations (including the one that follows) we make use of similar triangles shown in the figure above, right; we conclude that $h_1/h_2 = r_1/r_2$.

Let $h = h_1 - h_2$. We will show that the above volume formula can be written as

$$\text{Volume} = \frac{1}{3}\pi h(r_1^2 + r_1 r_2 + r_2^2)$$

We start with the right side, replace h by $h_1 - h_2$, and multiply out:

$$\frac{1}{3}\pi h(r_1^2 + r_1 r_2 + r_2^2) = \frac{1}{3}\pi(h_1 - h_2)(r_1^2 + r_1 r_2 + r_2^2)$$
$$= \frac{1}{3}\pi(h_1 r_1^2 - h_2 r_1^2 + h_1 r_1 r_2 - h_2 r_1 r_2 + h_1 r_2^2 - h_2 r_2^2)$$

Once we show that the four middle terms

$$-h_2 r_1^2 + h_1 r_1 r_2 - h_2 r_1 r_2 + h_1 r_2^2$$

add up to zero, we will be done.

From the similar triangles formula that we deduced above, we get $h_2 = h_1 r_2 / r_1$, and thus

$$-h_2 r_1^2 + h_1 r_1 r_2 - h_2 r_1 r_2 + h_1 r_2^2 = -\frac{h_1 r_2}{r_1} r_1^2 + h_1 r_1 r_2 - \frac{h_1 r_2}{r_1} r_1 r_2 + h_1 r_2^2$$
$$= -h_1 r_2 r_1 + h_1 r_1 r_2 - h_1 r_2^2 + h_1 r_2^2 = 0$$

Example 4. Compute the lateral surface area of the frustum of a cone.

Solution. Recall that the lateral surface area of a cone is equal to π times radius times slant height.

Thus, the lateral surface area of the frustum is equal to the lateral surface area of the larger cone minus the lateral surface area of the smaller cone, i.e.,

$$\text{Area} = \pi r_1 \ell_1 - \pi r_2 \ell_2$$

Let $\ell = \ell_1 - \ell_2$. We will show that the above formula is equal to $\pi(r_1 + r_2)\ell$, which we often find in literature and use, for instance, in integration in calculus.

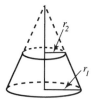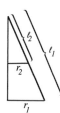

First we identify similar triangles (see figure above, right); thus, $\ell_1 / \ell_2 = r_1 / r_2$.

Now

$$\pi(r_1 + r_2)\ell = \pi(r_1 + r_2)(\ell_1 - \ell_2) = \pi(r_1 \ell_1 + r_2 \ell_1 - r_1 \ell_2 - r_2 \ell_2) = \pi(r_1 \ell_1 - r_2 \ell_2)$$

since the middle two terms cancel (here we use the similar triangles ratio):

$$r_2 \ell_1 - r_1 \ell_2 = r_2 \ell_1 - r_1 \frac{\ell_1 r_2}{r_1} = r_2 \ell_1 - r_2 \ell_1 = 0$$

Answers to quiz questions: **1.** In a triangle, the sum is 180 degrees. The sum of angles in a polygon with n sides is $(n-2)\pi$ radians or $180(n-2)$ degrees. So it is 360 degrees in a rectangle and 540 degrees in a pentagon. **2.** See page 43. **3.** Equilateral triangle: see Example 1. Other formulas: see pages 44–45. **4.** See Geometry in Three-Dimensional Space. **5.** See Example 3. **6.** See page 47. **7.** See Miscellaneous Facts. **8.** See page 44.

4. Equations and Inequalities

What is in this section?

Solving linear and quadratic equations and inequalities; solving equations and inequalities involving absolute value; solving equations using graphs, and solving systems of two equations with two unknowns.

Do I need to read this?

Answer the quiz questions below. If you get all of them right, or make a few smaller mistakes, then you can skip this section. Otherwise, identify what you don't know or are not sure about and read relevant parts of this section (or read all of it!).

Quiz

1. Determine whether $x = -2$ is a solution of the equation $\dfrac{1}{2x+1} - \dfrac{1}{x+1} = 0$.

2. Solve the equation $3.4x - 6.2 = -3.3(2 - 3x)$.

3. Solve the equation $\dfrac{2}{x-2} + \dfrac{1}{2} = \dfrac{3}{2x-4}$.

4. Solve the following equation by factoring: $2x^2 - 5x + 3 = 0$.

5. Solve the following equation by completing the square: $x^2 - 8x + 9 = 0$.

Over ...

6. Solve the following equation using the quadratic formula: $x^2 - 4x + 4 = 0$.

7. Solve the pair of inequalities $3x + 1 \geq x - 5 \geq 1 + 4x$.

8. Solve the inequality $x^2 \leq 16$.

9. Solve the inequality $x^2 + 6x - 7 \geq 0$ both algebraically (i.e., by factoring) and geometrically (i.e., by using graphs).

10. Find all x such that $|x| > 17$.

11. Solve the equation $|2x + 1| = 4$. Find all x such that $|2x + 1| \leq 4$.

[Answers to this quiz are at the bottom of page 71.]

To *solve an equation* means to find *all* values of unknown variable(s) (these values are called solutions) that satisfy the given equation. In other words, a *solution* is a real number that, when substituted into the equation, gives identity.

For example, $x = 3$ is a solution of the equation $x^2 - 4x = 6 - x^2$, since $x^2 - 4x = (3)^2 - 4(3) = -3$ and $6 - x^2 = 6 - (3)^2 = -3$; i.e., both sides are equal to -3. On the other hand, $x = 4$ is not a solution of the above equation; the left side is $x^2 - 4x = (4)^2 - 4(4) = 0$, whereas the right side is $6 - x^2 = 6 - (4)^2 = -10$.

(extra) **Exercise 1.** (a)* Which one of the numbers $x = 1$, $x = -2$ and $x = 0$ is a solution of the equation $\dfrac{1}{2x+1} - \dfrac{1}{x+1} = 0$?

(b) Which of the numbers $x = 11$, $x = 1$, $x = 0$ and $x = -3$ is a solution of the equation $x^3 - 5x + 11 = -1$?

(c) Identify two numbers among $x = -4$, $x = -2$, $x = 0$, $x = 2$ and $x = 3$ which are solutions of the equation $x^4 + 2x^3 - 13x^2 - 14x + 24 = 0$.

Linear Equations

We start with the simplest possible equation.

> The linear equation $ax + b = 0$ (where $a \neq 0$) has one solution, $x = -b/a$.

Note: If $a = 0$, we don't really have an equation!

Example 1. Solve the equation $3(x + 4) = -4(2 - 2x)$.

Solution. We simplify

$$3(x + 4) = -4(2 - 2x)$$
$$3x + 12 = -8 + 8x$$

and then gather like terms together

$$3x - 8x = -8 - 12$$
$$-5x = -20$$

Dividing by (-5), we get $x = \frac{-20}{-5} = 4$.

Example 2. Solve the equation $\dfrac{4x - 1}{3} + \dfrac{x}{4} = -2$.

Solution. Multiplying the equation by 12 (12 is the lowest common denominator), we get

$$4(4x - 1) + 3(x) = -2(12)$$
$$16x - 4 + 3x = -24$$
$$19x = -20$$
$$x = -\frac{20}{19}$$

(try it!)   **Exercise 2.** Solve each linear equation.

(a) $4(3x - 0.5) + 11 = -3(x + 2)$ (b) $\dfrac{3}{4}x - \dfrac{7}{13} = 1$

(c) $3.4x - 6.2 = -3.3(2 - 3x)$ (d) $\sqrt{3}\,x - 3 = 2\sqrt{3}$

Example 3. Solve the equation $\dfrac{4}{x - 3} = \dfrac{5}{x + 2}$.

Solution. The lowest common denominator of $x - 3$ and $x + 2$ is their product $(x - 3)(x + 2)$. Multiplying by $(x - 3)(x + 2)$, we get

$$\frac{4}{x - 3}(x - 3)(x + 2) = \frac{5}{x + 2}(x - 3)(x + 2)$$
$$4(x + 2) = 5(x - 3)$$

(in other words, we "cross-multiplied" the equation). Thus,

$$4x + 8 = 5x - 15$$
$$x = 23$$

We can check that our solution is correct. Substituting $x = 23$ into the left side, we get $\frac{4}{x-3} = \frac{4}{23-3} = \frac{4}{20} = \frac{1}{5}$; substituting it into the right side, we get $\frac{5}{x+2} = \frac{5}{23+2} = \frac{5}{25} = \frac{1}{5}$.

(try it!)   **Exercise 3.** Solve each linear equation.

(a) $\dfrac{4x - 2}{5} - \dfrac{3x - 11}{4} = 0$ (b) $\dfrac{-2}{2x - 1} + \dfrac{4}{x + 3} = 0$ (c) $\dfrac{\sqrt{5}}{x} = \dfrac{2\sqrt{5}}{x + 1}$

(!!) In solving equations, it is important to check whether our solution is valid. The following example serves as warning.

Example 4. Solve the equation $\dfrac{x}{x + 2} - 1 = \dfrac{8}{x^2 - 4}$.

Solution. Since $x^2 - 4 = (x - 2)(x + 2)$, it follows that $x^2 - 4$ is the lowest common denominator. Multiplying the given equation by $x^2 - 4$ we get

$$\frac{x}{x + 2}(x - 2)(x + 2) - 1(x^2 - 4) = \frac{8}{x^2 - 4}(x^2 - 4)$$
$$x^2 - 2x - x^2 + 4 = 8$$
$$-2x = 4$$
$$x = -2$$

However, $x = -2$ is not a solution, since neither of the two fractions is defined in that case. Thus, the given equation does not have any solutions.

(extra)   **Exercise 4.** For extra practice, solve the following equations.

(a)* $\dfrac{2}{x} - \dfrac{5}{2x} + \dfrac{4}{3x} = \dfrac{1}{2}$ (b)* $\dfrac{x}{x - 3} = \dfrac{x + 3}{x + 5}$ (c)* $\dfrac{2}{x - 2} + \dfrac{1}{2} = \dfrac{3}{2x - 4}$

(d) $0.6(2x - 0.1) = 0.35(3.4x + 1.5)$

(e) $\dfrac{3x + 1}{12} = \dfrac{-4x - 1}{3} - 1$

(f) $\dfrac{11}{-2x + 1} - \dfrac{3}{3x - 1} = 0$

(g) $4(-5x + 3) - 3(1 - x) = -2(x - 1) + 13x$

Quadratic Equations

We start with the equation $x^2 = a$, where a is a real number.

> If $a > 0$, the solutions of $x^2 = a$ are $x = \pm\sqrt{a}$ (or, $x = \sqrt{a}$ and $x = -\sqrt{a}$).
>
> If $a = 0$, then the solution of $x^2 = 0$ is $x = 0$.
>
> If $a < 0$, the equation $x^2 = a$ does not have solutions.

"Does not have solutions" above means that there are no real numbers that satisfy the equation.

Example 5. Solve each equation.

(a) $x^2 = 13$ (b) $x^2 = \frac{13}{4}$ (c) $(x - 4)^2 = 9$ (d) $(x - 4)^2 = 5$ (e) $x^2 = -2$

Solution.

(a) $x = \pm\sqrt{13}$ (b) $x = \pm\sqrt{\frac{13}{4}} = \pm\frac{\sqrt{13}}{2}$

(c) Computing the square root of both sides, we get $x - 4 = \pm\sqrt{9}$; i.e., $x - 4 = \pm 3$ and so $x = 4 \pm 3$. The solutions are $x = 7$ and $x = 1$.

(d) Proceeding as in (c), we obtain $x - 4 = \pm\sqrt{5}$; i.e., $x = 4 \pm \sqrt{5}$. So, the solutions are $x = 4 + \sqrt{5}$ and $x = 4 - \sqrt{5}$.

(e) Since the square of a real number cannot be negative, the equation has no solutions.

(extra) **Exercise 5.** Solve each equation.

(a) $x^2 = \sqrt{2}$ (b)* $x^2 = \sqrt[3]{2}$ (c) $(x + 1)^2 = -4$ (d) $(3x + 1)^2 = 4$ (e)* $(2x - 5)^2 = 2$

The general quadratic equation $ax^2 + bx + c = 0$ can be solved by:

- factoring,
- completing the square, or
- using the quadratic formula.

We discuss all three methods now.

When solving any equation (not just quadratic) by factoring, we use the following:

> If $A \cdot B = 0$, then $A = 0$ or $B = 0$.

If the product of two quantities A and B is zero, then one of A or B, or both, must be zero. Note that this works for the product equal to zero only! For instance, if $A \cdot B = 1$, we cannot say anything about the values of A or B.

What about quotients? Remember that the only way to make a fraction equal to zero is to make its numerator equal to zero. Assuming that $B \neq 0$,

$$\frac{A}{B} = 0 \text{ if and only if } A = 0.$$

"If and only if " — what does that mean? (Quick answer here; details are provided in Section 9.) It means that the above statement actually consists of two statements, which we obtain by reading from left to right and then from right to left. So it is a short way of saying

$$\text{if } \frac{A}{B} = 0 \text{ then } A = 0 \quad \text{and} \quad \text{if } A = 0 \text{ then } \frac{A}{B} = 0$$

To convince yourself that the first statement is true, start with $\frac{A}{B} = \frac{0}{1}$ and cross-multiply. The second statement says that, if the numerator (A) of a fraction is zero, then the fraction ($\frac{A}{B}$) is zero. Division by 0 is not defined, i.e., $\frac{A}{0}$ is not a real number (that is why B in the above is assumed to be non-zero).

Here we see a few examples involving fractions and zero. The solution of the equation

$$\frac{3x - 4}{x^2 + x - 1} = 0$$

is given by $3x - 4 = 0$, or $x = 4/3$. Likewise,

$$\frac{x^2 - 6}{x - 1} = 0$$

implies $x^2 - 6 = 0$, so the solutions are $x = \pm\sqrt{6}$. The equation

$$\frac{17}{4x - 11} = 0$$

does not have any solutions.

Example 6. Solve each equation by factoring.

(a) $x^2 + 5x - 24 = 0$ (b) $2x^2 - 5x + 3 = 0$

Solution.

(a) From

$$x^2 + 5x - 24 = (x - 3)(x + 8) = 0$$

it follows that either $x - 3 = 0$ (in which case $x = 3$), or $x + 8 = 0$ (and thus $x = -8$). So, the solutions are $x = -8$ and $x = 3$.

(b) Factoring, we get

$$2x^2 - 5x + 3 = (2x - 3)(x - 1) = 0$$

Thus, $2x - 3 = 0$, i.e., $x = 3/2$, or $x - 1 = 0$, i.e., $x = 1$. We conclude that the solutions are $x = 3/2$ and $x = 1$.

 Exercise 6. Solve each equation.

(a) $x^2 = -4$ (b) $(x - 6)^2 = 12$ (c) $x^2 + 10x = -24$ (d) $3x^2 = x + 4$

Example 7. Solve the following equations by completing the square. (If you need to, look at Section 2 to review how to complete the square.)

(a) $x^2 - 8x + 9 = 0$ 　　　　　　(b) $3x^2 - 2x - 4 = 0$

Solution.

(a) We add and subtract the square of one half of the coefficient of x, which is $(-8/2)^2 = 16$, and write $x^2 - 8x + (16 - 16) + 9 = 0$, i.e.,

$$(x^2 - 8x + 16) - 16 + 9 = 0$$

Next, we recall that the square term involves one half of the coefficient of x (i.e., one half of -8)

$$(x - 4)^2 - 7 = 0$$

and so $(x - 4)^2 = 7$. Thus, $x - 4 = \pm\sqrt{7}$. There are two solutions, $x = 4 + \sqrt{7}$ and $x = 4 - \sqrt{7}$.

(b) Factor 3 out first.

$$3\left(x^2 - \frac{2}{3}x\right) - 4 = 0$$

(One half of the coefficient of x is $\left(-\frac{2}{3}\right)\frac{1}{2} = -\frac{1}{3}$, so we add and subtract $\frac{1}{9}$.)

$$3\left(x^2 - \frac{2}{3}x + \frac{1}{9} - \frac{1}{9}\right) - 4 = 0$$

$$3\left(\left(x - \frac{1}{3}\right)^2 - \frac{1}{9}\right) - 4 = 0$$

$$3\left(x - \frac{1}{3}\right)^2 - \frac{1}{3} - 4 = 0$$

$$3\left(x - \frac{1}{3}\right)^2 = \frac{13}{3}$$

Thus, $\left(x - \frac{1}{3}\right)^2 = \frac{13}{9}$, and $x - \frac{1}{3} = \pm\sqrt{\frac{13}{9}} = \pm\frac{\sqrt{13}}{3}$. There are two solutions, $x = \frac{1}{3} \pm \frac{\sqrt{13}}{3}$.

try it! **Exercise 7.** Solve each equation by completing the square.

(a) $x^2 - x + 5 = 0$ 　　　(b) $2x^2 - 2x - 7 = 0$ 　　　(c) $3x^2 - x - 5 = 0$

Next, we introduce the *quadratic formula*:

> The solutions of $ax^2 + bx + c = 0$ are given by
> $$x = \frac{-b \pm \sqrt{b^2 - 4ac}}{2a}$$

The expression $D = b^2 - 4ac$ is called the *discriminant*. If $D > 0$, the equation has two distinct real solutions; if $D = 0$, it has one real solution, and if $D < 0$, the equation has no real solutions.

Note: saying "no real solutions" is correct; however, many times we will just say "no solutions," since in the context of calculus we consider real numbers only (and not complex numbers).

Example 8. Solve the following equations using the quadratic formula.

(a) $x^2 + 2x - 2 = 0$ (b) $x^2 - 4x + 4 = 0$ (c) $x^2 + x + 1 = 0$

Solution.

(a) We compute

$$x = \frac{-2 \pm \sqrt{4+8}}{2} = \frac{-2 \pm \sqrt{12}}{2} = \frac{-2 \pm 2\sqrt{3}}{2} = -1 \pm \sqrt{3}$$

In the above computation, we simplified $\sqrt{12}$ using $\sqrt{12} = \sqrt{4 \cdot 3} = \sqrt{4} \cdot \sqrt{3} = 2\sqrt{3}$.

(b) Similarly, $x = \dfrac{4 \pm \sqrt{16 - 16}}{2} = \dfrac{4 \pm 0}{2} = 2$. So, there is one solution.

(c) We compute

$$x = \frac{-1 \pm \sqrt{1-4}}{2} = \frac{-1 \pm \sqrt{-3}}{2}$$

There are no solutions, since the square root of a negative number is not a real number. Alternatively, we could have said: the discriminant $D = -3$ is negative, so there are no solutions.

Example 9. Solve the equation $1 + \sqrt{2 - x} = 2x$.

Solution. Rearrange the terms first: $\sqrt{2 - x} = 2x - 1$. Squaring both sides, we get

$$2 - x = 4x^2 - 4x + 1$$

$$4x^2 - 3x - 1 = 0$$

Thus,

$$x = \frac{3 \pm \sqrt{9 + 16}}{8} = \frac{3 \pm 5}{8}$$

So, $x = (3 + 5)/8 = 1$ and $x = (3 - 5)/8 = -1/4$ are candidates for solutions.

We have to check whether they really give solutions. Substituting $x = 1$ into the left side, we get $1 + \sqrt{2 - 1} = 2$. The right side is $2(1) = 2$, so $x = 1$ is a solution.

Substituting $x = -1/4$ into the left side of the given equation, we get $1 + \sqrt{2 + 1/4} = 1 + \sqrt{9/4} = 1 + 3/2 = 5/2$. Since the right side gives $2(-1/4) = -1/2$, we conclude that $x = -1/4$ is not a solution.

Why did we have to check solutions in Example 9, but not in Example 8?

Before we refer to Example 9, let us look at a simpler case. Consider the equation $2x = 4$. Clearly, the solution is $x = 2$. Now square the equation to get $4x^2 = 16$, i.e., $x^2 = 4$. There are now two solutions, $x = 2$, and $x = -2$. But $x = -2$ is not the solution to the equation $2x = 4$ we started with!

This example illustrates the fact that, starting with an equation, squaring it and then solving it could create solutions that are not the solutions of the original equation.

Now we understand the answer to our question: to get rid of the square root in Example 9, we squared the equation! And it turned out that one of the solutions of the squared equation, $x = -1/4$, was not the solution of the original equation. We did not square anything in Example 8.

We always need to check the solutions, as in Example 9, when a function is not defined for all real numbers. This function could be a square root or it could be a different function such as a fraction.

To make this a bit more clear: without even solving the equation $\sqrt{x} + x^2 = 3$, we know that $x = -2$ cannot be a solution, because $\sqrt{-2}$ is not defined; likewise, $x = 3$ cannot be a solution of the equation $\frac{2}{x-3} = 4x$.

Note: this was not the case in our example (for both $x = 1$ and $x = -1/4$ the square root $\sqrt{2-x}$ is defined), but it could happen when we are solving some other equation involving a square root.

There was no need to check solutions in Example 8, since all expressions involved are defined for all real numbers x.

extra **Exercise 8.** Solve each quadratic equation using an appropriate method.

(a)* $x^2 - 18x + 81 = 0$

(b)* $\dfrac{2}{x^2 - 9} = \dfrac{1}{x + 3} + \dfrac{3}{x - 3}$

(c) $(3x - 14)^2 - 16 = 0$

(d)* $\sqrt{2x + 4} = \sqrt{6x + 1} - 1$ [hint: square, simplify, then square again]

(e)* $\dfrac{3}{x + 1} - \dfrac{2}{x - 1} = -1$

(f) $5x^2 + \dfrac{11x}{2} - 3 = 0$

(g) $2x^2 - 6x + 5 = 0$

(h) $2x^2 - 3x = 5$

(i) $x^2 - \dfrac{5}{4}x + \dfrac{1}{4} = 0$

(j) $2x^2 + \dfrac{5x}{2} - \dfrac{3}{4} = 0$

The quadratic formula can help us factor quadratic trinomials. Remember:

> If x_1 and x_2 are solutions of the equation $ax^2 + bx + c = 0$,
> then $ax^2 + bx + c = a(x - x_1)(x - x_2)$.

Example 10. Factor each quadratic trinomial.

(a) $3x^2 + x - 2$

(b) $2x^2 - x - 5$

Solution.

(a) Using the quadratic formula, we compute $x = \dfrac{-1 \pm \sqrt{1 + 24}}{6} = \dfrac{-1 \pm 5}{6}$.
Thus, the solutions are $x_1 = 4/6 = 2/3$ and $x_2 = -6/6 = -1$, and we factor
$$3x^2 + x - 2 = 3(x - 2/3)(x + 1)$$

(b) We compute $x = \dfrac{1 \pm \sqrt{1 + 40}}{4} = \dfrac{1 \pm \sqrt{41}}{4}$. Thus,
$$2x^2 - x - 5 = 2\left(x - \frac{1 + \sqrt{41}}{4}\right)\left(x - \frac{1 - \sqrt{41}}{4}\right)$$

extra **Exercise 9.** Factor each quadratic trinomial, if possible.

(a)* $x^2 + x - 1$

(b)* $4x^2 - 4x - 15$

(c)* $2x^2 + 2x - 3$

(d) $x^2 + 2x + 15$

(e) $x^2 - \dfrac{5}{4}x + \dfrac{1}{4}$

(f) $5x^2 + \dfrac{11x}{2}$

(g) $3x^2 - 4x - 1 = 0$

(h) $x^2 + 2x - 15$

Inequalities

Rules for inequalities state that we can apply the same basic rules that we use for equations (i.e., moving term(s) from one side to the other, or multiplying or dividing by a non-zero number), except when we have to multiply or divide an inequality by a negative number. In that case, we reverse the direction of the inequality.

For example, the inequality $3 < 4$, multiplied by (-5), gives $-15 > -20$.

Likewise, dividing $-4 \leq -2x < 6$ by (-2), we get $2 \geq x > -3$.

To solve an inequality means to find all values of the unknown variable that satisfy it. In case of inequalities, the solution usually belongs to an interval (or intervals) of real numbers.

Example 11. Solve the inequality $-(3 + x) < 2(3x + 2)$.

Solution. We simplify first

$$-(3 + x) < 2(3x + 2)$$
$$-3 - x < 6x + 4$$
$$-x - 6x < 4 + 3$$
$$-7x < 7$$

Dividing by (-7), we get $x > -1$. Using interval notation, we write the solution as $(-1, \infty)$.

Example 12. Solve the pair of inequalities $-11 < 3x + 4 \leq 7$.

Solution. We can work with both inequalities at the same time, since there is only one term involving x (compare with the next example). Adding (-4) to all sides and dividing by 3, we get

$$-11 < 3x + 4 \leq 7$$
$$-15 < 3x \leq 3$$
$$-5 < x \leq 1$$

Thus, the solution is the interval $(-5, 1]$.

Sometimes, we have to solve inequalities separately, as in the following example.

Example 13. Solve the pair of inequalities $3x + 1 \geq x - 5 \geq 1 + 4x$.

Solution. Solving $3x + 1 \geq x - 5$, we get $2x \geq -6$ and $x \geq -3$.

Solving $x - 5 \geq 1 + 4x$, we get $-3x \geq 6$ and $x \leq -2$.

It follows that $x \geq -3$ and $x \leq -2$.

Drawing the two intervals $x \geq -3$ and $x \leq -2$ on a number line (see the figure below) we see that the solution is the interval $[-3, -2]$.

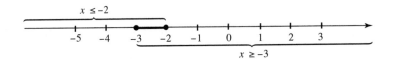

extra **Exercise 10.** Solve the following inequalities.

(a)* $13x - 17 > 4x + 1$ (b)* $1 - x \geq 3 - 2x \geq x - 6$ (c)* $3 \leq 3x - 2 \leq 4$

(d) $\frac{5x}{2} - \frac{1}{3} < -2x + \frac{2}{5}$ (e) $-3 < -2x - 11 < -2$ (f) $2 - 3x \geq x + 2 \geq 4x - 5$

Certain operations that we use with equations can be used with inequalities, but we have to be very careful, as there are restrictions.

If a and b are real numbers and $a \leq b$, is it true that $a^2 \leq b^2$?

If we square $2 \leq 7$, we get $4 \leq 49$, which is true; squaring $0.1 \leq 0.8$, we get $0.01 \leq 0.64$, which is true again. Let's try some negative numbers: from $-2 \leq 5$, we get $4 \leq 25$, which is true. However $-4 \leq -3$ is true, but $16 \leq 9$ is not true! Likewise, $-4 \leq 2$ is true, but $16 \leq 4$ is not true.

So assuming that $a \leq b$, the statement $a^2 \leq b^2$ does not hold for all real numbers.

But it does hold in one case (look at first two cases we examined): if a and b are *positive* and $a \leq b$, then $a^2 \leq b^2$ holds.

Here is how we prove it: multiply $a \leq b$ by a to get $a^2 \leq ab$ (since a is positive, we keep the inequality sign). Now multiply $a \leq b$ by b, to get $ab \leq b^2$ (b is positive, so again we keep the inequality sign); combine the two inequalities, $a^2 \leq ab$ and $ab \leq b^2$, to obtain $a^2 \leq b^2$.

$$\boxed{\begin{array}{c} \text{Rules for Inequalities} \\[4pt] \text{If } a \leq b \text{ and } a \geq 0 \text{ and } b \geq 0 \text{ then } a^2 \leq b^2. \\[6pt] \text{If } 0 < a \leq b \text{ or } a \leq b < 0, \text{ then } \dfrac{1}{a} \geq \dfrac{1}{b}. \end{array}}$$

The second statement says that we can apply the reciprocal to an inequality only when both sides are positive or both sides are negative (and in those cases we have to reverse the sign). The statement no longer holds if one number is positive and the other is negative; for example, $-2 \leq 4$, but $-1/2 \geq 1/4$ is not true.

Methods involving more complicated inequalities are reviewed in the next two examples.

Example 14. Solve the inequality $x^2 + 6x - 7 \geq 0$.

Solution. Factoring, we get $(x - 1)(x + 7) \geq 0$. The solutions of the equation

$$(x - 1)(x + 7) = 0$$

are $x = 1$ and $x = -7$. The numbers -7 and 1 divide the number line into three intervals:

$$(-\infty, -7), (-7, 1) \text{ and } (1, \infty)$$

Since the expression $x^2 + 6x - 7 = (x - 1)(x + 7)$ can change the sign only at -7 and 1, it follows that its sign on each of the intervals is constant.

We check the sign of each factor on each interval and record it in the table below. For example, if x is in $(-7, 1)$, then $x > -7$ and so $x + 7 > 0$; that is why we put the plus sign in the row corresponding to $x + 7$ and in the column for the interval $(-7, 1)$.

	$(-\infty, -7)$	$(-7, 1)$	$(1, \infty)$
$x - 1$	$-$	$-$	$+$
$x + 7$	$-$	$+$	$+$
$(x - 1)(x + 7)$	$+$	$-$	$+$

After filling in the signs in the two rows corresponding to the two linear factors, we calculate the sign of their product in the last row.

It follows that the solution consists of the intervals $(-\infty, -7]$ and $[1, \infty)$, since the value 0 for the product is allowed.

Note that, if the inequality were a strict inequality, i.e., $(x - 1)(x + 7) > 0$, then the solution would have been $(-\infty, -7)$ and $(1, \infty)$.

Alternatively, to fill in the signs in the table, we use test values for each interval. The rationale is that the factors involved do not change their sign within an interval. So if a factor is positive (negative) at one point in the interval, then it is positive (negative) in the whole interval. For example, to test the sign of $x + 7$ in the interval $(-7, 1)$, we can use any number in $(-7, 1)$ — say, $x = -4$. Since $x + 7 = -4 + 7 = 3 > 0$, we conclude that $x + 7$ is positive in the interval $(-7, 1)$.

A slightly different way of solving $x^2 + 6x - 7 = (x - 1)(x + 7) \geq 0$ consists of using test values to check the sign of the whole polynomial at once. Here is how it works.

Test the interval $(-\infty, -7)$: take, for example, $x = -10$; then $x^2 + 6x - 7 = (x - 1)(x + 7) = (-11)(-3) = 33 > 0$. It follows that $(-\infty, -7)$ is part of the solution of $x^2 + 6x - 7 \geq 0$.

Next, take $x = 0$ to test the interval $(-7, 1)$: it follows that $x^2 + 6x - 7 = (x - 1)(x + 7) = (-1)(7) = -7 < 0$; thus, $(-7, 1)$ is not part of the solution.

Analogously, we check the interval $(1, \infty)$.

In the end, we include -7 and 1, since they make the expression $x^2 + 6x - 7$ equal to 0, and the given inequality allows for that possibility.

Near the end of this section, we will solve this inequality by graphing.

Example 15. Solve the inequality $x < -\dfrac{3}{x - 4}$.

Solution. We simplify using a common denominator and then factor:

$$x + \frac{3}{x - 4} < 0$$

$$\frac{x(x - 4)}{x - 4} + \frac{3}{x - 4} < 0$$

$$\frac{x^2 - 4x + 3}{x - 4} < 0$$

$$\frac{(x-3)(x-1)}{x-4} < 0$$

The factors $x-3$, $x-1$ and $x-4$ are zero when $x=3$, $x=1$ and $x=4$, respectively. Thus, we need to examine the intervals $(-\infty, 1)$, $(1, 3)$, $(3, 4)$ and $(4, \infty)$.

	$(-\infty, 1)$	$(1, 3)$	$(3, 4)$	$(4, \infty)$
$x-3$	$-$	$-$	$+$	$+$
$x-1$	$-$	$+$	$+$	$+$
$x-4$	$-$	$-$	$-$	$+$
$\frac{(x-3)(x-1)}{x-4}$	$-$	$+$	$-$	$+$

As in the previous example, we fill in the signs for each of the three linear terms and then calculate the signs for the fraction in the last row.

Thus, the solution consists of two intervals, $(-\infty, 1)$ and $(3, 4)$. Using interval notation, we write it as $(-\infty, 1) \cup (3, 4)$.

Instead of using the table, we could have used test values and checked the whole fraction at once. For instance, to test the interval $(-\infty, 1)$ pick $x = 0$; then $\frac{(x-3)(x-1)}{x-4} = \frac{(0-3)(0-1)}{0-4} = \frac{3}{-4} < 0$, and so $(-\infty, 1)$ is part of the solution.

Similarly, to test the interval $(1, 3)$, we use $x = 2$: $\frac{(x-3)(x-1)}{x-4} = \frac{(2-3)(2-1)}{2-4} = \frac{-1}{-2} > 0$, so interval $(1, 3)$ does not belong to the solution. We continue with the intervals $(3, 4)$ and $(4, \infty)$ in the same way.

Example 16. Solve the inequality $x \le -\dfrac{3}{x-4}$. [Note that we just modified the inequality sign of the previous example.]

Solution. Simplifying as in the previous example, we arrive at
$$\frac{(x-3)(x-1)}{x-4} \le 0$$

This time, we need to include $x = 3$ and $x = 1$ (as they make numerator equal to 0), so the solution is $(-\infty, 1] \cup [3, 4)$.

Example 17. Solve the inequality $\dfrac{x+2}{2x-3} \le 4$.

Solution. We need zero on the right side, so we move 4 to the left first, and then simplify:
$$\frac{x+2}{2x-3} - 4 \le 0$$
$$\frac{x+2}{2x-3} - \frac{4(2x-3)}{2x-3} \le 0$$
$$\frac{x+2-8x+12}{2x-3} \le 0$$
$$\frac{-7x+14}{2x-3} \le 0$$

From $-7x + 14 = 0$ we get $x = 2$, and $2x - 3 = 0$ yields $x = 3/2$. Thus, we need to examine the intervals $(-\infty, 3/2)$, $(3/2, 2)$ and $(2, \infty)$. We use test values for each interval.

$(-\infty, 3/2)$: use $x = 0$, and compute $\frac{-7x+14}{2x-3} = \frac{14}{-3} < 0$.

$(3/2, 2)$: use $x = 1.8$, and compute $\frac{-7x+14}{2x-3} = \frac{-7(1.8)+14}{2(1.8)-3} = \frac{1.4}{0.6} > 0$.

$(2, \infty)$: use $x = 10$, and compute $\frac{-7x+14}{2x-3} = \frac{-7(10)+14}{2(10)-3} = \frac{-56}{17} < 0$.

So, the solution contains the intervals $(-\infty, 3/2)$ and $(2, \infty)$. Since the fraction is allowed to be zero, we must include the value where its numerator $-7x + 14$ is zero, i.e., when $x = 2$. It follows that the solution is $(-\infty, 3/2) \cup [2, \infty)$.

Exercise 11.   Solve the following inequalities.

(a) $x^2 \geq 64$ (b) $x^2 < 64$ (c) $\dfrac{x+2}{x-2} \leq 0$ (d) $\dfrac{x+2}{x-2} \leq 1$

(e) $x^2 > 21 - 4x$ (f) $\dfrac{6}{x-5} \leq 2$ (g) $x^3 - x \leq 0$ (h) $x^2 - x \leq 2$

Example 18.   Solve the inequality $x^2 \leq a$, where a is a positive number.

Solution. Simplify by factoring:

$$x^2 - a \leq 0$$
$$(x - \sqrt{a})(x + \sqrt{a}) \leq 0$$

Since the factors $x - \sqrt{a}$ and $x + \sqrt{a}$ are zero (i.e., change signs) at $x = \pm\sqrt{a}$, we need to examine the intervals $(-\infty, -\sqrt{a})$, $(-\sqrt{a}, \sqrt{a})$ and $(\sqrt{a}, \infty)$.

We do it in a table:

	$(-\infty, -\sqrt{a})$	$(-\sqrt{a}, \sqrt{a})$	$(\sqrt{a}, \infty)$
$x - \sqrt{a}$	$-$	$-$	$+$
$x + \sqrt{a}$	$-$	$+$	$+$
$x^2 - a = (x - \sqrt{a})(x + \sqrt{a})$	$+$	$-$	$+$

We fill out the signs as usual. To calculate the signs for the middle interval $(-\sqrt{a}, \sqrt{a})$, we use $x = 0$ (keep in mind that $\sqrt{a} > 0$).

To analyze the signs on the interval $(-\infty, -\sqrt{a})$, we need a number smaller than $-\sqrt{a}$, for instance $x = -10\sqrt{a}$. Then

$$x - \sqrt{a} = -10\sqrt{a} - \sqrt{a} = -11\sqrt{a} < 0$$

and

$$x + \sqrt{a} = -10\sqrt{a} + \sqrt{a} = -9\sqrt{a} < 0$$

Likewise, to analyze $(\sqrt{a}, \infty)$, we need a number larger than $\sqrt{a}$, such as $2\sqrt{a}$.

Since the product $(x - \sqrt{a})(x + \sqrt{a})$ is allowed to be zero, we need to include $x = \sqrt{a}$ and $x = -\sqrt{a}$ in the solution. Thus, the solution of $x^2 - a \leq 0$, i.e., $x^2 \leq a$, is the interval $[-\sqrt{a}, \sqrt{a}]$.

From the table above, we can read solutions to some other equations.

For instance, the solution of $x^2 - a > 0$, i.e., $x^2 > a$, is $(-\infty, -\sqrt{a}) \cup (\sqrt{a}, \infty)$.

As well, the solution of $x^2 \geq a$ is $(-\infty, -\sqrt{a}] \cup [\sqrt{a}, \infty)$; using inequalities, we write it as $x \leq -\sqrt{a}$ or $x \geq \sqrt{a}$.

Since we will need solutions to inequalities such as $x^2 \leq a$, $x^2 < a$, etc. quite often, we list them all in a table.

> Assume that a is a positive number.
>
> If $x^2 > a$, then $x < -\sqrt{a}$ or $x > \sqrt{a}$;   if $x^2 \geq a$, then $x \leq -\sqrt{a}$ or $x \geq \sqrt{a}$
>
> If $x^2 < a$, then $-\sqrt{a} < x < \sqrt{a}$;   if $x^2 \leq a$, then $-\sqrt{a} \leq x \leq \sqrt{a}$

Near the end of this section, we will use graphs to solve inequalities. Once we understand how it's done, we will see that there is no reason why we need to memorize the statements in the box above.

Equations and Inequalities Involving Absolute Value

Recall that $|a - b|$ calculates the distance between numbers a and b on a number line.

So, for example, we think of $|x - 2|$ as the distance from a real number x to the number 2 on the x-axis.

In working with absolute values, the following statements will be helpful.

> Let A be any expression, and $a \geq 0$.
>
> $|A| = a$ if and only if $A = a$ or $A = -a$.
>
> $|A| < a$ if and only if $-a < A < a$; $|A| \leq a$ if and only if $-a \leq A \leq a$.
>
> $|A| > a$ if and only if $A > a$ or $A < -a$; $|A| \geq a$ if and only if $A \geq a$ or $A \leq -a$.

Again, the geometric approach (using graphs, which we will do soon) will help us understand these statements and remove the need to memorize them.

 Here is a good way of reasoning geometrically about these inequalities: write $|A| = |A - 0|$, i.e., interpret $|A|$ as the distance between A and the origin on a number line. Now $|A - 0| < a$ means that we need all numbers A whose distance from the origin is smaller than some fixed number a; thus, $-a < A < a$, see the figure below.

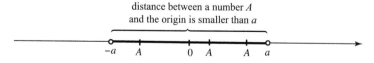

Other inequalities, such as $|A| > a$, $|A| \geq a$, etc. are interpreted similarly.

Example 19. Solve the following inequalities:

(a) $|x| > 17$ (b) $|x - 4| \leq 3$ (c) $|x + 4| \geq 3$

Solution.

(a) Thinking of the given inequality as $|x - 0| > 17$, we realize that we have to identify all numbers x whose distance from 0 (i.e., from the origin) is larger than 17. Thus, $x > 17$ or $x < -17$.

(b) Formula $|x - 4| \leq 3$ says that the distance between x and 4 needs to be smaller than or equal to 3. So, x can be anywhere between 1 and 7, including the two values; see the figure below, left. The answer is $[1, 7]$.

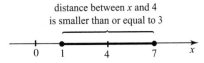 

(c) Rewriting $|x + 4| \geq 3$ as $|x - (-4)| \geq 3$, we interpret it as: the distance between x and -4 must be equal to or larger than 3. Drawing it on the number line (above, right), we see that the solution consists of two intervals, $(-\infty, -7]$ and $[-1, \infty)$.

Exercise 12. Solve each inequality.

(a) $|x + 2| > 3$ (b) $|x + 2| \leq 3$ (c)* $|x - 1| \geq 12$ (d) $|x + 1| > 12$

To practice understanding the relationship between absolute value and distance bit more, we discuss the reversal of the previous example.

Example 20. Find an inequality using absolute value for which the sets below are solutions.

(a) $[-2, 2]$ (b) $[3, 5]$ (c) $(3, 5)$ (d) $(-\infty, -3] \cup [3, \infty)$

Solution.

(a) The interval $[-2, 2]$ contains all numbers whose distance from the origin is 2 or less; thus, the desired inequality is $|x| \leq 2$.

(b) The midpoint of the interval $[3, 5]$ is 4; thus, $[3, 5]$ contains all numbers whose distance from 4 is 1 or less than 1; so, the equation is $|x - 4| \leq 1$.

(c) We reason as in (b), except that the distance is not allowed to be equal to 1; so, the equation is $|x - 4| < 1$.

(d) The given intervals contain numbers whose distance from the origin is 3 or more; thus, the equation is $|x| \geq 3$.

Exercise 13. Find an inequality using absolute value for which each set below is a solution.

(a) $[-8, 8]$ (b) $(3, 4)$ (c) $(-\infty, -1] \cup [1, \infty)$ (d) $(-\infty, 0] \cup [4, \infty)$

Example 21. Solve the equation $|4x - 3| = 2$.

Solution. By the definition of absolute value,

$$|4x - 3| = \begin{cases} 4x - 3 & \text{if } 4x - 3 \geq 0 \\ -(4x - 3) & \text{if } 4x - 3 < 0 \end{cases} = \begin{cases} 4x - 3 & \text{if } x \geq 3/4 \\ -4x + 3 & \text{if } x < 3/4 \end{cases}$$

Thus, the given equation breaks up into two equations:

If $x \geq 3/4$, it reads $4x - 3 = 2$ (and the solution is $x = 5/4$).

If $x < 3/4$, it reads $-4x + 3 = 2$ (and the solution is $x = 1/4$).

Consequently, there are two solutions, $x = 5/4$ and $x = 1/4$.

So we had to use the definition of absolute value and then consider cases. Is there a way to avoid all that?

Yes! Let's adjust the equation $|4x - 3| = 2$ a bit; factor 4 out of the absolute value brackets: $4|x - \frac{3}{4}| = 2$, and then divide by 4 to get

$$\left| x - \frac{3}{4} \right| = \frac{2}{4} = \frac{1}{2}$$

Now, we are in familiar territory: we realize that we are asked to identify all x whose distance from $\frac{3}{4}$ is $\frac{1}{2}$. So, the answers are

$$x = \frac{3}{4} - \frac{1}{2} = \frac{1}{4} \quad \text{and} \quad x = \frac{3}{4} + \frac{1}{2} = \frac{5}{4}$$

Done!

 Exercise 14. Solve each equation algebraically (as in Example 21) and using the distance argument.

(a)* $|2x - 3| = 7$ (b)* $\left| \dfrac{x}{2} - 4 \right| = 3$ (c) $\left| \dfrac{2x}{3} - 1 \right| = 2$ (d) $\left| 2x - \dfrac{5}{3} \right| = 7$

Example 22. Solve the following inequalities.

(a) $|2x + 1| \leq 4$ (b) $|3x - 4| > 1$

Solution.

(a) Let us discuss two approaches — the algebraic first, using the box on page 65. The given inequality is equivalent to the following pair of inequalities:

$$-4 \leq 2x + 1 \leq 4$$
$$-5 \leq 2x \leq 3$$
$$-5/2 \leq x \leq 3/2$$

Now the geometric approach: to interpret the absolute value as distance, we need to get rid of 2 in front of x. So, we factor it out: $2|x + \frac{1}{2}| \leq 4$, then divide the equation by 2 to get $|x + \frac{1}{2}| \leq 2$, and finally rewrite it as $|x - (-\frac{1}{2})| \leq 2$.

So we are looking for all x whose distance from $-\frac{1}{2}$ is 2 or less than 2; visualizing this on a number line, we get the answer: $[-\frac{5}{2}, \frac{3}{2}]$.

(b) The given inequality is equivalent to $3x - 4 > 1$ and $3x - 4 < -1$.

Solving $3x - 4 > 1$, we get $3x > 5$ and $x > 5/3$.

Solving $3x - 4 < -1$, we get $3x < 3$ and $x < 1$.

Thus, the solution consists of two intervals, $(-\infty, 1)$ and $(5/3, \infty)$.

To use the distance argument, simplify the inequality as in part (a), to obtain $|x - \frac{4}{3}| > \frac{1}{3}$. So, we are looking for all x whose distance from $\frac{4}{3}$ is larger than $\frac{1}{3}$.

 Exercise 15. Solve the following inequalities.

(a) $|2x - 3| < 2$ (b) $|3x + 4| \geq 4$ (c) $|3x + 4| < 4$

(d) $3|x - 5| + 2 < 7$ (e) $\frac{2}{3}|x - 5| < 1$ (f) $4 + \left|\dfrac{x + 3}{4}\right| < 12$

Using Graphs To Solve Inequalities

In this subsection, we will need graphs of quadratic functions (parabolas) and of the absolute value function. If you are not familiar with these graphs, read Section 5 (starting at page 83), and Section 6 (for graphs in general; in particular, page 101 for the graph of absolute value).

Example 23. Solve the inequality $x^2 \leq 16$.

Solution. Let us represent this inequality geometrically. The graph of x^2 (we think of it as $y = x^2$) is a parabola with its vertex located at the origin; the graph of 16 (we think of it as $y = 16$) is a horizontal line crossing the y-axis at 16, see below (left).

The two graphs intersect when $x^2 = 16$, i.e., when $x = \pm 4$ (we computed this by combining the two equations).

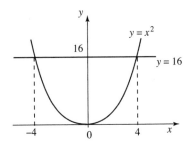 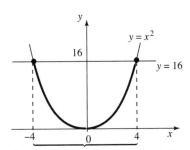

for x values in this interval, the parabola
lies below the horizontal line, or touches it

Now $x^2 \leq 16$ means that we have to identify that part of the graph of $y = x^2$ (i.e, the parabola) that lies below the graph of $y = 16$ (the horizontal line), or touches it (since equality is allowed); see above (right), where that part of the parabola is made thicker. Now all we have to do is to identify corresponding values of x; from the graph, we see that they all belong to the interval $[-4, 4]$.

In the same way, replacing 16 by a, we can solve the inequality $x^2 \leq a$.

This example carries a powerful message, that we now explore further:

> Sometimes, the easiest way to solve an inequality is by graphing!

Example 24. Solve the inequality $x^2 + 6x - 7 > 0$.

Solution. In this case, we need to find all x for which the parabola $y = x^2 + 6x - 7$ lies above the x-axis (since 0, i.e., $y = 0$, represents the x-axis). Let's make a sketch like in the previous example. To graph the parabola, we find its intercepts; from $x^2 + 6x - 7 = (x - 1)(x + 7) = 0$ we get $x = -7$ and $x = 1$. Since the coefficient of x^2 is positive, the parabola opens upwards — that's all we need! See below (left).

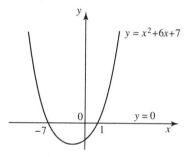 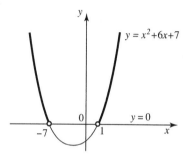

The parts of the parabola that lie strictly above the x-axis (i.e., are not allowed to touch) are drawn thicker in the graph above (right). Corresponding values for x constitute the solution of the inequality: $(-\infty, -7) \cup (1, \infty)$.

To solve the inequality $x^2 + 6x - 7 \geq 0$, all we have to do is to note that, this time, the parabola is allowed to touch the x-axis (so, the two empty dots in the figure above (right) would be filled); thus, the solution is $(-\infty, -7] \cup [1, \infty)$.

Example 25. Solve the inequality $|x| \geq 3$ geometrically.

Solution. As before, we sketch the graphs of $y = |x|$ and $y = 3$. Since $|x| = 3$ implies that $x = \pm 3$, we see that the two graphs intersect at $x = \pm 3$, see below (left).

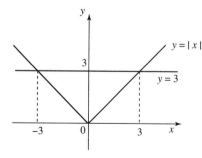 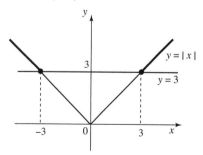

Next, we identify those parts of the graph of $y = |x|$ that lie above the horizontal line $y = 3$, or touch it (shown by the thicker line in the graph above, right), and read the corresponding x values; thus, the solution is $(-\infty, -3] \cup [3, \infty)$.

In the same way, we solve the inequalities such as $|x| \geq a$, $|x| > a$, $|x| < a$, etc. that we discussed on page 65.

extra **Exercise 16.** Solve the following inequalities geometrically.

(a)* $x^2 + x - 20 > 0$ (b)* $x^2 - 2x \leq 0$ (c)* $|x| \leq 2$

(d) $2x - 7 \geq 0$ (e) $3 - x^2 > 0$ (f) $|x| - 1.4 > 0$

Systems of Equations

In the two examples below, we review the most common methods of solving systems of two equations with two unknowns.

Example 26. Solve the system $2x + y = 10$, $4x - y = 2$.

Solution. We use the substitution method (also called the method of elimination). The idea is to eliminate one variable, so that we end up with one equation and one unknown. Computing y from $2x + y = 10$, we get $y = 10 - 2x$. Substituting y into the second equation $4x - y = 2$, we get

$$4x - y = 2$$
$$4x - (10 - 2x) = 2$$
$$6x = 12$$
$$x = 2$$

The corresponding solution for y is $y = 10 - 2x = 10 - 4 = 6$.

Alternatively, adding up the two equations, we get

$$(2x + y) + (4x - y) = 10 + 2$$

Thus, $6x = 12$ and $x = 2$. Using either of the two equations, we get $y = 6$.

Example 27. Solve the system $2x - y = -5$, $y = x^2 + 2$.

Solution. From $2x - y = -5$, we get $y = 2x + 5$. Substituting y into the second equation, we get

$$y = x^2 + 2$$
$$2x + 5 = x^2 + 2$$
$$x^2 - 2x - 3 = 0$$
$$(x - 3)(x + 1) = 0$$

Consequently, there are two solutions for x, $x = -1$ and $x = 3$. From $x = -1$ (by substituting into $y = 2x + 5$) we get $y = 2(-1) + 5 = 3$. Likewise, when $x = 3$, $y = 2(3) + 5 = 11$. Thus, there are two solutions, $x = -1$, $y = 3$ and $x = 3$, $y = 11$.

extra **Exercise 17.** Solve the following systems of equations.

(a)* $2x - y = 13$, $x + 2y = -11$ (b)* $y = x^2 + 2x + 2$, $x - y + 4 = 0$

(c) $-5x - 6y = 1$, $x + 3y = 5/2$ (d) $2x + 10y = 6$, $-x + y - 9 = 0$

(e) $x^2 + y^2 = 10$, $x + y = 2$ (f) $4x + y^2 - 2 = 0$, $2x + y = 0$

Answers to quiz questions: **1.** Not a solution [see Exercise 1(a)]. **2.** $x = 0.4/6.5 = 0.061538$ [see Exercise 2(c)]. **3.** $x = 1$ [see Exercise 4(c)]. **4.** $x = 3/2$ and $x = 1$ [see Example 6(b)]. **5.** $x = 4 \pm \sqrt{7}$ [see Example 7(a)]. **6.** $x = 2$ [see Example 8(b)]. **7.** $[-3, -2]$ [see Example 13]. **8.** $[-4, 4]$ [see Example 23]. **9.** $(-\infty, -7]$ and $[1, \infty)$ [see Example 14 and Example 24]. **10.** $x > 17$ or $x < -17$ [see Example 19(a)]. **11.** Equation: $-\frac{5}{2}, \frac{3}{2}$ Inequality: $[-\frac{5}{2}, \frac{3}{2}]$ [see Example 22(a)].

5. Elements of Analytic Geometry

What is in this section?

Cartesian coordinate system and distance between points; various equations of the line; slope, parallel and perpendicular lines; equations of circles, ellipses, parabolas and hyperbolas.

Do I need to read this?

Answer the quiz questions below. If you get all of them right, or make a few smaller mistakes, then you can skip this section. Otherwise, identify what you don't know or are not sure about and read relevant parts of this section (or read all of it!).

Quiz

1. Find the distance between the points whose coordinates are $(-3, 4)$ and $(4, -2)$.

2. Find an equation of the line that contains the points $(0, 4)$ and $(3, 3)$.

3. Sketch the graph of the equation $2x + y - 4 = 0$.

4. Find an equation of a line that is perpendicular to the line $6x + 2y - 4 = 0$ and goes through $(3, -2)$.

5. Are the lines $x + 2y + 4 = 0$ and $y = -3x + 4$ parallel?

Over ...

6. Show that the equation $x^2 + y^2 + 4x - 6y + 3 = 0$ represents a circle.

7. Describe in words the graph of the equation $4x^2 + 2y^2 = 8$.

8. What curve is the graph of the equation $y = x^2 - 4x + 4$? Find x-intercepts (if they exist), the y-intercept, coordinates of the vertex, and sketch (or describe in words) the graph.

9. Sketch the graph of the equation $2x^2 - 4y^2 = 5$.

10. Sketch the graph of the equation $x = -y^2/3$.

[Answers to this quiz are at the bottom of page 91.]

Cartesian Coordinate System, Distance Between Points

The *Cartesian coordinate system* consists of two number lines that are perpendicular to each other and are placed so that they intersect at the point that represents the number zero for both of them.

The number lines are named x-axis and y-axis, and are usually visualized as in the figure below. Their intersection is called the *origin* (and is denoted by 0).

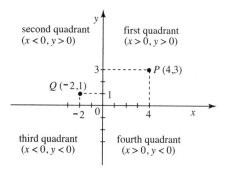

In the figure above, the units along the x- and y-axes are of the same size. There will be situations, however, when it will be more convenient to use a different size unit on each axis. Many times, we will not even indicate the size of a unit, since it is not going to be relevant.

 The position of a point is uniquely determined by specifying the ordered pair (x, y), where x is the x-coordinate and y is the y-coordinate of the point. The coordinates of the point P in the figure above are $(4, 3)$. Point Q has coordinates $(-2, 1)$. The points whose x-coordinate is zero lie on the y-axis. The points whose y-coordinate is zero lie on the x-axis. The origin has coordinates $(0, 0)$.

The x-axis and the y-axis divide the plane into four *quadrants*.

The first quadrant consists of points (x, y) whose coordinates satisfy $x > 0$ and $y > 0$. See the figure above for the location of the second, third and fourth quadrants.

> The *distance* between two points $P_1(x_1, y_1)$ and $P_2(x_2, y_2)$ is
> $$d(P_1, P_2) = \sqrt{(x_2 - x_1)^2 + (y_2 - y_1)^2}.$$

To derive this formula, we draw the right triangle whose hypotenuse is $d(P_1, P_2)$, see below. Recall that the distance between two numbers on a number line is equal to the absolute value of their difference. So, the distance between P_1 and Q is the same as the distance between x_1 and x_2, i.e., equal to $|x_2 - x_1|$. Likewise, the distance between P_2 and Q is $|y_2 - y_1|$. By the Pythagorean Theorem

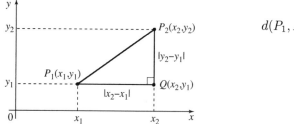

$$d(P_1, P_2)^2 = |x_2 - x_1|^2 + |y_2 - y_1|^2$$
$$= (x_2 - x_1)^2 + (y_2 - y_1)^2$$

(Note: since the quantities are squared, there is no need to keep the absolute value.)

Example 1. The distance between the points $(3, -2)$ and $(-4, -3)$ is

$$\sqrt{(-4 - (3))^2 + (-3 - (-2))^2} = \sqrt{(-7)^2 + (-1)^2} = \sqrt{50} = \sqrt{25 \cdot 2} = 5\sqrt{2}$$

Likewise, the distance between the point $(a, 0)$ on the x-axis and the point $(0, b)$ on the y-axis is $\sqrt{(0 - a)^2 + (b - 0)^2} = \sqrt{a^2 + b^2}$.

(try it!) **Exercise 1.** (a) Find the distance between the points whose coordinates are $(-3, 4)$ and $(4, -2)$.

(b) Which of the points $(-4, 2)$, $(0, 1)$ or $(3, 1)$ is closest to the point $(0, 5)$?

Equations of a Line

A line is uniquely determined by a point that lies on it and by its slope. The *slope* of a line is the ratio of the change in y to the change in x ("rise over run"). The line is characterized by the property that this ratio is constant (i.e., it is the same, no matter where on the line we measure it). If a line passes through the points $P_1(x_1, y_1)$ and $P_2(x_2, y_2)$, and if $x_1 \neq x_2$ (i.e., if the two points do not lie one above the other), then its slope is given by

$$m = \frac{y_2 - y_1}{x_2 - x_1}$$

See the figure below (left). If $x_1 = x_2$, then the line through $P_1(x_1, y_1)$ and $P_2(x_2 = x_1, y_2)$ is vertical, and its equation is $x = x_1$; see the figure below (right).

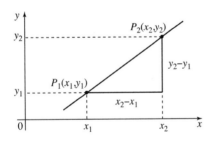 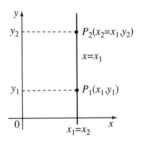

!! The slope of a vertical line is not defined (i.e., it is not a real number). A line parallel to the x-axis (i.e., a horizontal line) has slope zero.

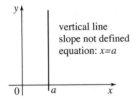 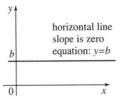

Example 2. The slope of the line through $(2, -7)$ and $(-2, -4)$ is

$$m = \frac{-4 - (-7)}{-2 - (2)} = \frac{-4 + 7}{-4} = -\frac{3}{4}$$

It does not matter in what order we take the points, but the same order must be used for the numerator and the denominator:

$$m = \frac{-7 - (-4)}{2 - (-2)} = \frac{-7 + 4}{2 + 2} = -\frac{3}{4}$$

which is the same as above.

The slope of the line through $(2, 4)$ and $(-3, 4)$ is $m = \frac{4-4}{-3-2} = \frac{0}{-5} = 0$; thus, the line is horizontal and its equation is $y = 4$.

The slope of the line through $(2, -3)$ and $(2, 1)$ is $m = \frac{1-(-3)}{2-2} = \frac{4}{0}$, which is not defined; thus, the line is vertical, and its equation is $x = 2$.

Lines with positive slopes slant upward: the bigger the slope, the more slanted the line is. Lines with negative slopes slant downward, see the figure below, left.

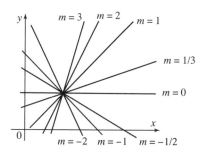 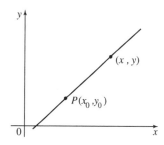

The following equation is known as the *point-slope equation* of a line.

> The equation of a line with slope m that passes through $P(x_0, y_0)$ is $y - y_0 = m(x - x_0)$.

How did we get $y - y_0 = m(x - x_0)$?

Pick any point (x, y) on the line, and use it, together with the given point $P(x_0, y_0)$, to compute the slope (see the figure above, right):

$$m = \frac{y - y_0}{x - x_0}$$

Multiplying by $x - x_0$, we get $y - y_0 = m(x - x_0)$.

Example 3. Find an equation of the line that contains the points $(0, 4)$ and $(3, 3)$.

Solution. The slope is $m = \frac{4-3}{0-3} = -\frac{1}{3}$. Thus, the desired equation is

$$y - 4 = -\frac{1}{3}(x - 0)$$

i.e., $y = -\frac{x}{3} + 4$.

Of course, it does not matter which of the two given points we use for $P(x_0, y_0)$ in the point-slope equation. In the above example, we used $(0, 4)$. Had we used $(3, 3)$, we would have

$$y - 3 = -\frac{1}{3}(x - 3)$$

i.e., $y - 3 = -\frac{x}{3} + 1$, and thus $y = -\frac{x}{3} + 4$.

Exercise 2. Find an equation of the line that contains the points $(1, 3)$ and $(2, -4)$.

When we express y in terms of x, we obtain the *explicit equation* of a line; it is also known as the *slope-intercept equation*.

> The slope-intercept (explicit) equation of a line is
> $y = mx + b$, where m represents the slope, and b is the y-intercept.

 Why is the y-intercept equal to b?

When we substitute $x = 0$ into $y = mx + b$, we get $y = b$; thus, the line goes through the point $(0, b)$ on the y-axis.

The horizontal line that crosses the y-axis at b has the explicit equation $y = b$ (since its slope is zero). The vertical line that crosses the x-axis at a cannot be written in the form $y = mx + b$ (its slope m is not defined!); we write its equation as $x = a$.

> An equation of the form $ax + by + c = 0$,
> where at least one of a or b is not zero, is called a *linear equation*.

 The linear equation $ax + by + c = 0$ always represents a line. How do we show that?

If $b \neq 0$, then we solve for y: from $by = -ax - c$, we get $y = -\frac{a}{b}x - \frac{c}{b}$, so it is a line of slope $-\frac{a}{b}$ and y-intercept $-\frac{c}{b}$.

If $b = 0$, the equation $ax + by + c = 0$ reads $ax = -c$, and so, dividing by a, we get $x = -\frac{c}{a}$; this is a vertical line that crosses the x-axis at $-\frac{c}{a}$. (Note: by assumption, only one of a or b can be zero; since we assumed that $b = 0$, it follows that $a \neq 0$, so we were allowed to divide by a!)

Example 4. (a) Sketch the graph of the equation $2x + y - 4 = 0$.

(b) Find the slope-intercept equation of the line in the figure below, right.

Solution.

(a) Solving the given equation for y, we get $y = -2x + 4$. Thus, the graph is a line of slope -2 and y-intercept 4 (below, left).

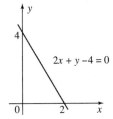   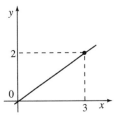

Alternatively, we argue as follows: the given equation $2x + y - 4 = 0$ is linear, so its graph is a line (and all we need are two points, because two points uniquely determine a line). From $2x + y - 4 = 0$, using $x = 0$, we get $2(0) + y - 4 = 0$, i.e., $y = 4$, so $(0, 4)$ lies on the line. Substituting $y = 0$ into $2x + y - 4 = 0$ we get $x = 2$; so $(2, 0)$ is another point on the line.

(b) The line goes through $(0, 0)$ and $(3, 2)$, so its slope is $m = \frac{2-0}{3-0} = \frac{2}{3}$. Since the y-intercept is zero, we conclude that the required equation is $y = \frac{2}{3}x + 0 = \frac{2}{3}x$.

try it! **Exercise 3.** Sketch, or describe in words, the graphs of the following equations

(a) $-x - 2y = 0$ (b) $3x + 2y - 4 = 0$ (c) $x + 2 = 0$

> **Slopes of Parallel and Perpendicular Lines**
> Parallel lines have equal slopes.
> Two lines with slopes m_1 and m_2 are perpendicular if and only if $m_2 = -1/m_1$, i.e., if and only if $m_1 m_2 = -1$.

Example 5. Find an equation of a line that is

(a) parallel to the line $6x + 2y - 4 = 0$ and goes through the origin

(b) perpendicular to the line $6x + 2y - 4 = 0$ and goes through $(3, -2)$

Solution.

(a) First, we need to find the slope of the given line. Solving $6x + 2y - 4 = 0$ for y, we get $y = -3x + 2$. Thus, the slope of the given line (and, consequently, the slope of the line we are looking for) is -3. Using the point-slope equation, we get $y - 0 = -3(x - 0)$; i.e., $y = -3x$.

(b) Because the slope of the given line is -3 (we know that from (a)), we conclude that the slope of a line perpendicular to it is $-\frac{1}{-3} = \frac{1}{3}$. We now use the point-slope form to get the desired equation:

$$y - (-2) = \frac{1}{3}(x - 3); \text{ i.e., } y = \frac{1}{3}x - 3$$

try it! **Exercise 4.** Answer the following questions.

(a) Are the lines $x + 2y + 4 = 0$ and $y = -3x + 4$ parallel?

(b) Find an equation of a line perpendicular to the line $2x + y - 4 = 0$ that goes through the point $(1, -2)$.

(c) Show that the lines $3x - 2y = 6$ and $2x + 3y - 12 = 0$ are perpendicular.

try it! **Exercise 5.** Find an equation of the line going through $(3, -4)$, which is

(a) parallel to the x-axis

(b) parallel to the y-axis

(c) parallel to the line $x - 3y - 7 = 0$

(d) perpendicular to the line $x - 3y - 7 = 0$

Exercise 6. Find the slope (or say it does not exist) and y-intercept of the following lines.

(a) $x + y = 0$ (b) $2x + 3 = 0$ (c) $y + 4 = 0$ (d) $3x - 5y - 1 = 0$

Example 6. Find the coordinates (x_M, y_M) of the *midpoint* M of the line segment joining the points $P_1(x_1, y_1)$ and $P_2(x_2, y_2)$; see the figure below.

From $d(P_1, M) = d(M, P_2)$ (M is the midpoint!) and the fact that the corresponding angles are equal, we conclude that the triangles P_1AM and MCP_2 are congruent. Thus,

$$d(P_1, A) = d(M, C) = d(A, B)$$

i.e., x_M is the midpoint of the interval from x_1 to x_2, and thus $x_M = (x_1 + x_2)/2$ (recall that we did the midpoint of an interval in Section 1).

Arguing in a similar way, we get $y_M = (y_1 + y_2)/2$.

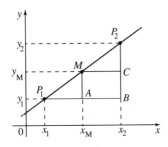

> The midpoint M of the line segment
> joining $P_1(x_1, y_1)$ and $P_2(x_2, y_2)$
> has coordinates $\left(\dfrac{x_1 + x_2}{2}, \dfrac{y_1 + y_2}{2} \right)$.

The equation

$$\frac{x}{a} + \frac{y}{b} = 1$$

is a linear equation and thus represents a line (we could solve for y, to obtain $\frac{y}{b} = 1 - \frac{x}{a}$, so $y = b - \frac{bx}{a} = -\frac{b}{a}x + b$; slope is $-b/a$, and the y-intercept is b).

The reason we mention this special form $\frac{x}{a} + \frac{y}{b} = 1$ is that it allows us to read off intercepts: when $x = 0$, from $\frac{y}{b} = 1$ we get $y = b$, i.e., b is the y-intercept; likewise, if $y = 0$, then $\frac{x}{a} = 1$ implies $x = a$, i.e., a is the x-intercept. In other words, the denominators in $\frac{x}{a} + \frac{y}{b} = 1$ are (respective) intercepts.

Thus, the equation $x/3 - y/4 = 1$ represents the line whose x-intercept is 3 and y-intercept is -4. (Since we needed the plus sign between the x and the y terms, we rewrote the equation as

$$\frac{x}{3} + \frac{y}{-4} = 1$$

That's why the y-intercept is -4).

Keep in mind that we can do this only if the equation is reduced to the form $\frac{x}{a} + \frac{y}{b} = 1$. So, if $x + 3y = 4$, we need to divide by 4, to get $\frac{x}{4} + \frac{3y}{4} = 1$, and simplify to the form

$$\frac{x}{4} + \frac{y}{4/3} = 1$$

So the x-intercept is 4 and the y-intercept is $4/3$.

To further practice the concepts we have covered so far, work on the following exercises.

(extra) **Exercise 7.** (a) Find the distance between the points $(-1, -2)$ and $(-3, 4)$.

(b) Find the lengths of the sides of the triangle with vertices at $(-1, 2)$, $(3, 8)$ and $(-5, -2)$.

(c)* Arrange the following points from the closest to the farthest from the origin: $A = (0, -3.3)$, $B = (2, 3.2)$, $C = (-2, 2.8)$, and $D = (-2.8, -2.3)$.

(d) Find the midpoint of the line segment joining $(-3.4, 1)$ and $(-12, 4.6)$.

(e) The midpoint of the line segment from $(4, -3)$ to (a, b) is $(6, 11)$. Find a and b.

(f)* The midpoint of the line segment from $(x, 9)$ to $(-4, y)$ is $(-2, -1)$. Find x and y.

(extra) **Exercise 8.** For each line, idenify the slope (or say that it is not defined) and the y-intercept (or say that it does not exist).

(a) $-x - y - 3.4 = 0$ (b)* $y - \dfrac{9}{7} = 0$ (c) $-3x = 14$ (d) $\dfrac{x}{2} - \dfrac{y}{5} = 7$

(e) $4y = 7.6$ (f)* $\dfrac{x}{3} = \dfrac{4}{7}$ (g) $\dfrac{x}{4} + \dfrac{y}{6} = 1$ (h)* $\dfrac{3x}{2} - \dfrac{2y}{5} = 5$

(extra) **Exercise 9.** Arrange the following lines from the one with the largest slope to the one with the smallest slope.

(a) $3x - y + 4 = 0$ (b) $3x + y - 4 = 0$ (c) $3y + 4 = 0$ (d) $3x - 2y + 5 = 0$

(extra) **Exercise 10.** In each case find the slope-intercept equation (if possible; otherwise, use an appropriate form).

(a) The line which passes through the points $(2, 1)$ and $(3.3, 2.3)$.

(b) The line whose x-intercept is $x = 3$ and the y-intercept is $y = -2$.

(c) The line with passes through the origin and $(-2, -5)$.

(d)* The line which passes through the points $(-4, 2)$ and $(-4, 4)$.

(e) The line which passes through the points $(3, -2)$ and $(-3, -2)$.

(f) The line through the point $(-8, 2)$ and parallel to the line $x - y - 3 = 0$.

(g) The line through the point $(-2.7, 4.5)$ and parallel to the y-axis.

(h)* The line through the point $(-4, 1)$ and perpendicular to the line $x - y - 3 = 0$.

(i) The line through the point (x_0, y_0), and parallel to the line $y = m$.

(j) The line through the point (x_0, y_0), and parallel to the line $x = n$.

(k)* The line through the point (x_0, y_0), and parallel to the line $ax + by + c = 0$ (where $b \neq 0$).

(l) The line through the point (x_0, y_0), and perpendicular to the line $ax + by + c = 0$ (where $b \neq 0$).

(extra) **Exercise 11.** Sketch the graph of each equation.

(a) $2x - \dfrac{y}{4} = 12$ (b)* $4x + 5y = 1$ (c) $4x = -2$ (d) $\dfrac{y}{2} = \dfrac{4}{3}$

Circle

Recall that the distance between an arbitrary point (x, y) and a given fixed point (p, q) can be calculated from the expression $\sqrt{(x-p)^2 + (y-q)^2}$. So all points (x, y) whose distance from (p, q) is equal to a positive number r satisfy

$$\sqrt{(x-p)^2 + (y-q)^2} = r$$

Of course, these points lie on the circle of radius r centred at the point (p, q). Hence, by squaring both sides, we obtain

> The *equation of the circle* of radius r centred at (p, q) is
> $$(x-p)^2 + (y-q)^2 = r^2$$

In particular, the equation $x^2 + y^2 = r^2$ represents the circle of radius r centred at the origin.

Example 7. The equation $(x+3)^2 + y^2 = 7$ represents the circle of radius $\sqrt{7}$ with the centre at $(-3, 0)$. The equation $x^2 + y^2 = 1$ describes the circle of radius 1 centred at the origin.

In some cases, we need to do calculations in order to recognize the centre and the radius of a circle.

Example 8. Show that the equation $x^2 + y^2 + 4x - 6y + 3 = 0$ represents a circle.

Solution. We first group the x terms and the y terms together

$$x^2 + 4x + y^2 - 6y = -3$$

and then complete the square:

$$x^2 + 4x + 4 - 4 + y^2 - 6y + 9 - 9 = -3$$
$$(x^2 + 4x + 4) + (y^2 - 6y + 9) = -3 + 4 + 9$$
$$(x+2)^2 + (y-3)^2 = 10$$

Thus, the given equation represents the circle of radius $\sqrt{10}$ centered at $(-2, 3)$.

Exercise 12. In each case, find the centre and the radius of the circle.

(a) $x^2 + y^2 - 5x + 1 = 0$ (b) $x^2 + y^2 - 2x + 8y = 4$ (c) $2x^2 + 2y^2 - 6 = 0$

Ellipse

The equation

$$\frac{x^2}{a^2} + \frac{y^2}{b^2} = 1$$

(where $a > 0$ and $b > 0$) represents an *ellipse* centred at the origin with semi-axes a and b (see the figure next page). It is symmetric with respect to both x and y axes (and also with respect to the origin, i.e., with respect to its centre).

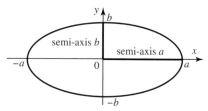

Substituting $x = 0$ into $\frac{x^2}{a^2} + \frac{y^2}{b^2} = 1$ we get $y^2 = b^2$ and $y = \pm b$. In words, the y-intercepts are b and $-b$. Similarly, $y = 0$ implies $x^2/a^2 = 1$ and $x^2 = a^2$; thus $x = a$ and $x = -a$ are the x-intercepts.

? Is a circle also an ellipse?

Yes. If we divide both sides of the equation of the circle $x^2 + y^2 = r^2$ by r^2, we get $\frac{x^2}{r^2} + \frac{y^2}{r^2} = 1$. Thus, a circle is a special case of an ellipse (whose semi-axes a and b are both equal to r).

Example 9. Describe in words the graph of the equation $4x^2 + 2y^2 = 8$.

Solution. Dividing the given equation by 8, we get

$$x^2/2 + y^2/4 = 1$$

From $a^2 = 2$ we get $a = \sqrt{2}$ (keep in mind that a and b must be positive) and from $b^2 = 4$ we get $b = 2$. Thus, the given equation represents an ellipse with semi-axes $a = \sqrt{2}$ and $b = 2$, centred at the origin. Its x-intercepts are $\pm a = \pm\sqrt{2}$, and its y-intercepts are $\pm b = \pm 2$.

(try it!) **Exercise 13.** Describe in words the curve defined by each equation.
(a) $x^2 + 3y^2 = 9$ (b) $x^2 + y^2 - 2x - 6y = 0$ (c) $2x^2 + 3y^2 = 4$ (d) $x^2 + y^2 - y = 0$

Parabola

The graph of the equation $y = ax^2 + bx + c$ is a *parabola*.

Consider a special case $y = ax^2$ first. By plotting points, we obtain the following picture that shows the graphs of $y = ax^2$ for $a = 2$, $a = 1$, $a = 1/3$ and $a = -2$.

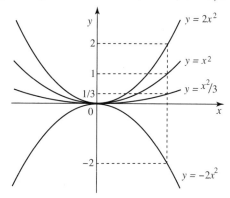

The parabola $y = ax^2$ goes through the origin. It opens upward if $a > 0$ and it opens downward if $a < 0$. It is symmetric with respect to the y-axis. The lowest point on a parabola opening upwards, or the highest point of a parabola opening downwards, is called a *vertex*. The vertex of a parabola $y = ax^2$ is at the origin.

Next, consider a general parabola $y = ax^2 + bx + c$, where a, b and c are real numbers and $a \neq 0$. Again, it opens upward if $a > 0$ and it opens downward if $a < 0$. The x-intercepts (if they exist) are given as solutions of the quadratic equation $y = ax^2 + bx + c = 0$.

The x-coordinate of the vertex is $x = -b/2a$; if x-intercepts exist, then the x-coordinate of the vertex is located half-way between them (see next example, part (a)).

Example 10. Sketch the graph of each equation.

(a) $y = -x^2 + 5x - 6$ (b) $y = x^2 + x + 2$

Solution. (a) Since $a = -1$, the parabola opens downward. Solving

$$-x^2 + 5x - 6 = -(x^2 - 5x + 6) = -(x - 2)(x - 3) = 0$$

we get $x = 2$ and $x = 3$ for the x-intercepts. The x-coordinate of the vertex is $x = \frac{-b}{2a} = \frac{-5}{-2} = \frac{5}{2}$; so, as mentioned earlier, the vertex is half-way (i.e., the midpoint) between x-intercepts 2 and 3. The y-coordinate of the vertex is

$$y = -x^2 + 5x - 6 = -\left(\tfrac{5}{2}\right)^2 + 5\left(\tfrac{5}{2}\right) - 6 = \tfrac{1}{4}$$

The y-intercept (substitute $x = 0$ into $y = -x^2 + 5x - 6$) is $y = -6$. So we need to draw a parabola that opens downward, whose vertex is at $(5/2, 1/4)$, that crosses the x-axis at 2 and at 3, and that crosses the y-axis at -6; see figure below, left.

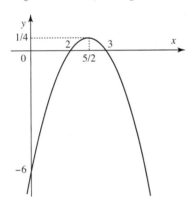
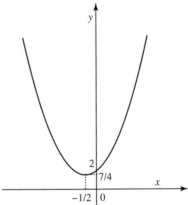

(b) The parabola $y = x^2 + x + 2$ opens upward. The discriminant (see page 57) of the equation $y = x^2 + x + 2 = 0$ is $D = 1 - 8 = -7 < 0$, which means that it has no real solutions (i.e., there are no x-intercepts). Since the parabola opens upward, we conclude that it must lie above the x-axis. The x-coordinate of the vertex is $x = -b/2a = -1/2$. The y-coordinate of the vertex is

$$y = x^2 + x + 2 = (-1/2)^2 + (-1/2) + 2 = 7/4$$

The y-intercept is 2; see the figure above, right.

Exercise 14.   Find x-intercepts (if they exist), the y-intercept, coordinates of the vertex, and sketch (or describe in words) the graphs of each equation.

(a) $y = x^2 + 6x + 3$ (b) $y = x^2 - 4x + 4$ (c) $y = -x^2 - 1$

Switching x and y (i.e., reflecting the graph with respect to the line $y = x$) we obtain the graphs of the parabolas $x = ay^2$. See the figures below.

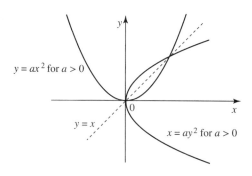
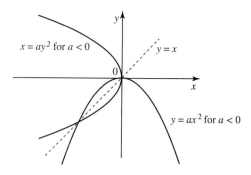

To convince yourself that switching x and y amounts to symmetry with respect to the line $y = x$, plot a few points, say, $(0, 2)$, $(-1, 1)$, $(1, 4)$, $(-4, -1)$, and $(2, 2)$, and then plot the corresponding points $(2, 0)$, $(1, -1)$, $(4, 1)$, $(-1, -4)$, and $(2, 2)$.

Note the relationship between a point and its corresponding point with regards to the line $y = x$; see below, left.

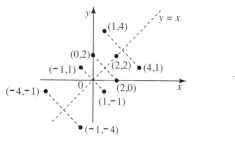
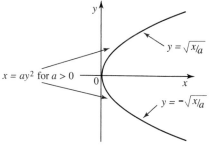

As mentioned, the equation $x = ay^2$ for $a > 0$ represents a parabola that opens towards the x-axis; see the figure above, right. Solving for y, we get $y^2 = x/a$ and $y = \pm\sqrt{x/a}$.

Since $\sqrt{x/a}$ is positive, $y = \sqrt{x/a}$ represents the part of the parabola above the x-axis (including the origin). Likewise, the equation $y = -\sqrt{x/a}$ represents the part of the parabola below the x-axis, including the origin; see the figure above, right.

Thus, the same geometric object (in our case, parabola) can be described in two different ways: either as $x = ay^2$, or as a pair of equations $y = \sqrt{x/a}$ and $y = -\sqrt{x/a}$.

Hyperbola
The equation

$$\frac{x^2}{a^2} - \frac{y^2}{b^2} = 1$$

(where $a > 0$ and $b > 0$) represents a *hyperbola*. The x-intercepts are found by substituting $y = 0$ into $x^2/a^2 - y^2/b^2 = 1$, resulting in $x^2/a^2 = 1$ and $x = \pm a$. There are no y-intercepts, since $-y^2/b^2 = 1$ implies $y^2 = -b^2 < 0$.

The hyperbola consists of two branches that approach the lines $y = \pm\frac{b}{a}x$. See the figure below, left. The lines $y = \pm\frac{b}{a}x$ are called the *asymptotes*.

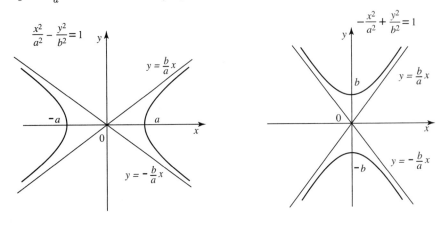

The equation

$$-\frac{x^2}{a^2} + \frac{y^2}{b^2} = 1$$

is also a hyperbola. This time, there are no x-intercepts (since $-x^2/a^2 = 1$ implies that $x^2 = -a^2 < 0$). The y-intercepts are $y = \pm b$. The asymptotes are given by $y = \pm\frac{b}{a}x$. See the figure above, right.

Example 11. Sketch the graph of the equation $2x^2 - 4y^2 = 5$.

Solution. We need 1 on the right side, so we divide by 5:

$$\frac{2x^2}{5} - \frac{4y^2}{5} = 1$$

Next, we simplify

$$\frac{x^2}{5/2} - \frac{y^2}{5/4} = 1$$

so that we can read off the values: $a^2 = 5/2$, so $a = \sqrt{5}/\sqrt{2}$ and $b^2 = 5/4$, so $b = \sqrt{5}/2$ (recall that a and b must be positive). Because there is a minus sign on the left side, the curve involved is a hyperbola, whose asymptotes are

$$y = \pm\frac{b}{a}x = \pm\frac{\frac{\sqrt{5}}{2}}{\frac{\sqrt{5}}{\sqrt{2}}}x = \pm\frac{\sqrt{5}}{2} \cdot \frac{\sqrt{2}}{\sqrt{5}}x = \pm\frac{\sqrt{2}}{2}x$$

The asymptotes divide the xy-plane into four regions, and we know that the hyperbola is either in the left and the right regions, or in the top and the bottom regions. How do we find out where (besides memorizing)?

The quickest way is to check for the intercepts. If $x = 0$, then from $2x^2 - 4y^2 = 5$ we get $-4y^2 = 5$, and $y^2 = -5/4$; so, there are no y-intercepts. It follows that the hyperbola is located in the regions to the left and right of its asymptotes (see the figure next page, left). In particular, from $2x^2 - 4y^2 = 5$, by substituting $y = 0$, we know that the x-intercepts are $x = \pm\sqrt{5}/\sqrt{2}$.

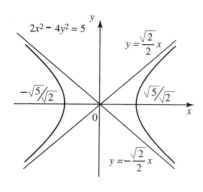

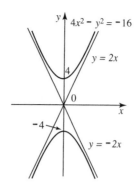

Example 12. Sketch the graph of the equation $4x^2 - y^2 = -16$.

Solution. Dividing both sides of the equation by -16, we get

$$-\frac{x^2}{4} + \frac{y^2}{16} = 1$$

Because one of the signs is a minus, the equation represents a hyperbola. From $a^2 = 4$, we get $a = 2$; from $b^2 = 16$, we get $b = 4$. It follows that the asymptotes are given by $y = \pm\frac{b}{a}x = \pm 2x$.

Substituting $y = 0$ into the given equation (we are looking for x-intercepts) we get $-\frac{x^2}{4} = 1$, i.e., $x^2 = -4$. Since this equation has no solutions, there are no x-intercepts. Substituting $x = 0$, we get $\frac{y^2}{16} = 1$, i.e., $y^2 = 16$, and $y = \pm 4$. So, there are two y-intercepts, 4 and -4. The hyperbola lies in the regions above and below its asymptotes; see the figure above, right.

Exercise 15. Sketch the graphs of these equations.
(a) $-3x^2 + y^2/2 = 4$ (b) $2x^2 - y^2/3 = 11$ (c) $x = 3y^2$ (d) $x = -y^2/3$

Summary

To review — in this section, we studied the following graphs generated by quadratic expressions.

Equations and Graphs
$(x - p)^2 + (y - q)^2 = r^2$ circle centred at (p, q) of radius r
$\dfrac{x^2}{a^2} + \dfrac{y^2}{b^2} = 1$ ellipse with semi-axes a and b
$-\dfrac{x^2}{a^2} + \dfrac{y^2}{b^2} = 1$ hyperbola in regions above and below its asymptotes $y = \pm\dfrac{b}{a}x$
$\dfrac{x^2}{a^2} - \dfrac{y^2}{b^2} = 1$ hyperbola in regions to the left and right of its asymptotes $y = \pm\dfrac{b}{a}x$
$y = ax^2 + bx + c$ parabola that opens up or down
$x = ay^2$ parabola that opens to the left or to the right

We will study more graphs in the sections that follow.

Algebraic equations represent geometric objects (lines, circles, parabolas, etc.), and vice versa, geometric objects can be represented algebraically in terms of equations.

In an example where algebra represents geometry, the equation $2x - 3y = 7$ represents a line, and the equation $x^2 + y^2 = 25$ describes a circle of radius 5. Vice versa (geometry represented using algebra), the line parallel to the y-axis going through $(-2, 8)$ has the equation $x = -2$; an ellipse with semi-axes 3 and 2 can be described as $x^2/9 + y^2/4 = 1$.

An equation can be thought of as being a way of checking whether or not a given point belongs to the curve described by that equation. Consider, for instance, the circle $x^2 + y^2 = 25$ and pick the point $(-3, 4)$. Since $x^2 + y^2 = (-3)^2 + (4)^2 = 9 + 16 = 25$, we conclude that the point $(-3, 4)$ belongs to the given circle. Likewise, $(\sqrt{17}, -\sqrt{8})$ belongs to the circle, since $x^2 + y^2 = 17 + 8 = 25$. On the other hand, because $(2)^2 + (-6)^2 = 4 + 36 = 40 \neq 25$, we know that the point $(2, -6)$ does not belong to the circle.

In some cases, it might be difficult to visualize the given curve geometrically. However, we can still apply algebra to check whether or not a given point lies on the curve. As an example, consider the curve defined by the equation $x^3 + 4xy - y^3 + 2y^4 = 33$. It does not go through the origin, since $x^3 + 4xy - y^3 + 2y^4 = (0)^3 + 4(0)(0) - (0)^3 + 2(0)^4 = 0 \neq 33$. The point $(1, -2)$ belongs to the curve because $x^3 + 4xy - y^3 + 2y^4 = (1)^3 + 4(1)(-2) - (-2)^3 + 2(-2)^4 = 1 - 8 + 8 + 32 = 33$.

For more practice, work on the following exercises.

(extra)   **Exercise 16.**   Identify the centre and the radius of each circle.
(a) $x^2 + 8x + y^2 - 8y = 4$ (b) $x^2 + y^2 + x = 0$ (c) $2x^2 + 2y^2 - 7y = 5$

(d) $x^2 + y^2 - \dfrac{2x}{5} + \dfrac{3y}{2} = 1$ (e)* $\dfrac{x^2 + y^2}{4} - x - 3y = 1$

(extra)   **Exercise 17.**   The equation $\dfrac{(x-p)^2}{a^2} + \dfrac{(y-q)^2}{b^2} = 1$ where $a > 0$ and $b > 0$ represents an ellipse centred at (p, q) with semi-axes a and b. Identify the centre and the semi-axes of each ellipse.

(a) $x^2 + 3x + 4y^2 - 6y = 2$ (b)* $2x^2 + y^2 + x = 1$ (c) $x^2 + \dfrac{y^2}{5} - 2x = 1$

(extra)   **Exercise 18.**   Describe in words, or sketch the graph of each parabola.

(a) $y = x^2 - 6x - 7$ (b) $y = 2x^2 - 3x + 6$ (c) $y = -\dfrac{x^2}{2} - x + 1$

(d)* $x = -\dfrac{y^2}{4}$ (e) $y = -3x^2 - 11$ (f) $x = 3y^2$

(extra)   **Exercise 19.**   Identify the asymptotes and the intercepts of each hyperbola. Where does the graph lie with respect to its asymptotes?

(a) $-x^2 + 5y^2 = 5$ (b)* $x^2 - 5y^2 = 2$ (c) $3x^2 - 4y^2 = 12$ (d) $-3x^2 + 4y^2 = 1$

(e) $\dfrac{x^2}{12} - 2y^2 = 1$ (f)* $-\dfrac{x^2}{3} + \dfrac{y^2}{7} = 7$

(extra) **Exercise 20.** Describe in words, or sketch the graph of the curve given by each equation.

(a) $6x^2 + y^2 = 3$

(b) $y = x^2 + \dfrac{3x}{2} - 1$

(c) $6x^2 + 6y^2 = 3$

(d) $-3x^2 + 4y^2 = 48$

(e)* $\dfrac{x^2}{3} + \dfrac{y^2}{3} - 3x = 1$

(f) $x^2 + 5x + y^2 - y = 0$

(g) $x = -y^2$

(h) $x = -y^2 + 1$

(i) $3x^2 - 4y^2 = 1$

(j)* $x^2 + 6x + 8y^2 = 0$ [see Exercise 17]

(k) $x^2 + 5x + 4y^2 - y = 0$ [see Exercise 17]

As mentioned earlier–all points whose coordinates satisfy an algebraic equation belong to the graph of that equation. Thus, in order to find all points which are common to two curves (i.e., where the two curves intersect) we need to combine their equations. In other words, we need to solve a system of equations representing these curves (see end of Section 4).

(extra) **Exercise 21.** Determine whether or not the given points belong to the graph of the given curve.

(a) $x^2 + y^2 - 2x + 4y - 4 = 0$; $(1, 1)$, $(0, 1)$, $(2, 0)$

(b) $-x^2 + y^3 - 2x - 11y = 0$; $(0, 0)$, $(2, 1)$, $(-1, -1)$

(c)* $y = x^3 - x + 12$; $(1, 0)$, $(1, 12)$, $(-1, 12)$

(extra) **Exercise 22.** In each case, identify the curves and find their intersection, if any (i.e., identify all points common to both curves, or else say that such points do not exist).

(a) $x - 2y + 4 = 0$, $-4x - y = 12$

(b) $y = -3x + 1$, $y + 3x - 6 = 0$

(c) $\dfrac{y}{2} - x = 1$, $2y - 4x = 4$

(d) $\dfrac{x}{3} + \dfrac{y}{5} = 0$, $\dfrac{x}{2} - \dfrac{y}{3} = 2$

(e) $y = 2x + 3$, $y = -2x + 3$

(f)* $y = -6x + 11$, $y = -6x + 12$

(g) $x^2 + y^2 = 14$, $y = -x$

(h) $x^2 + y^2 = 25$, $x = -4$

(i)* $x^2 - y^2 = 1$, $x - 2y = 0$

(j) $-x^2 + 2y^2 = 4$, $y = x + 1$

(k) $2x^2 + y^2 = 3$, $y = 5$

(l) $2x^2 + y^2 = 3$, $y = 1$

(m)* $4x^2 + 3y^2 = 1$, $x + y = 1$

(n) $2x^2 - y^2 = 10$, $y = 0$

Curves in Applications

In math, when we work within abstract contexts, it is common practice to use x and y to denote variables: x is the independent variable, and is represented by a horizontal number line (called the x-axis) in the xy-coordinate system; y is the dependent variable, and is represented by a vertical number line (called the y-axis) in the xy-coordinate system.

In applications, however, we use all kinds of symbols (usually because they remind us of the quantities we study). For instance, we use t to represent time, P to denote population, m to denote mass, and so on.

In these cases, we need to identify which symbols denote the independent and the dependent variables. There are several ways to do this. Sometimes we simply say "A is the independent variable and B is the dependent variable." More often, we convey the same information using phrases such as "In the AB-coordinate system" or "In the B versus A coordinate system" or "Plot B vs A" or "In the AB-space" or "With B on the vertical axis and A on the horizontal axis."

Once we identify the independent and dependent variables, all remaining symbols (if any) denote constants (real numbers).

For example, in the PQ-coordinate system, the equation $Q = aP - 5$ represents the line of slope a and Q-intercept equal to -5. In the x_1x_2-coordinate system, the circle centred at the origin of radius K is represented by the equation $x_1^2 + x_2^2 = K^2$.

Example 13. In the z_1z_2-space, sketch the graph of the equation $2z_1^2 + 5z_2 = 3$.

Solution. The convention we just mentioned suggests that we place z_1 on the horizontal axis and z_2 on the vertical axis. Solving for z_2, we obtain $5z_2 = -2z_1^2 + 3$ and

$$z_2 = -\frac{2}{5}z_1^2 + \frac{3}{5}$$

We recognize this curve as a parabola. (If you prefer, translate into x and y, by taking $z_1 = x$ and $z_2 = y$, in which case the equation reads $y = -\frac{2}{5}x^2 + \frac{3}{5}$.) The minus sign in front of z_1^2 term forces the parabola to open downward.

Solving for z_1 (horizontal) intercepts, we substitute $z_2 = 0$ to obtain $-\frac{2}{5}z_1^2 + \frac{3}{5} = 0$, and thus $-2z_1^2 + 3 = 0$ and $z_1^2 = \frac{3}{2}$. So $z_1 = \frac{\sqrt{3}}{\sqrt{2}}$ and $z_1 = -\frac{\sqrt{3}}{\sqrt{2}}$.

To find a z_2-intercept we substitute $z_1 = 0$, and obtain $z_2 = 3/5$.

Since the vertex is half-way between the intercepts, we conclude that the vertex is at $z_1 = 0$.

Alternatively, we can use transformations of graphs (as explained in Section 6: start with the graph of $z_2 = z_1^2$, scale it by a factor of $2/5$ (to obtain $z_2 = \frac{2}{5}z_1^2$), then reflect across the z_1-axis (to obtain $z_2 = -\frac{2}{5}z_1^2$), and finally move up by $3/5$ units). See the figure below.

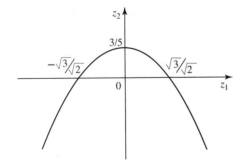

For extra practice, work on the following exercises.

(extra) **Exercise 23.** (a) What curve is represented by $2P - 3Q - 4 = 0$ in the PQ-space?

(b)* In the P vs. t coordinate system, what is the graph of $P = 2t^2 + 1.4$?

(c) Plot x_2 vs. x_1 if $3x_1 - 2x_2 - 1 = 0$.

(d) What curve is represented by $aM + bN + c = 0$ $(b \neq 0)$ in the MN-coordinate system?

(e)* With z_2 on the vertical axis, what is the graph of $z_2 - 2z_1 = 0$?

(f) Find the intersection of the lines $3P - Q/2 = 0$ and $P - 2Q = 4$ in the PQ-space.

(g) Sketch the graph of P as a function of t if $3P^2 - t = 0$.

(h) Sketch the following lines in the x_1x_2-space: $x_1 - x_2 = 0$, $x_1 = -4$, and $x_2 = 1$.

(i)* Sketch, or describe in words, the graph of $P^2 + 4Q^2 = 5$ with Q on the vertical axis.

(j)* Sketch, or describe in words, the graph of $P^2 + 4Q^2 = 5$ with P on the vertical axis.

(k) Assume that $a > 0$. What curve is represented by the equation $\dfrac{X^2}{a} + \dfrac{Z^2}{a} = 1$ in the XZ-coordinate system?

(l) What curve is represented by $\dfrac{p^2}{2} - \dfrac{q^2}{3} = 1$ in the q vs. p coordinate system?

Answers to quiz questions: **1.** $\sqrt{85}$ [see Exercise 1(a)]. **2.** $y = -\frac{x}{3} + 4$ [see Example 3]. **3.** Line of slope -2 and y-intercept 4 [see Example 4(a)]. **4.** $y = \frac{1}{3}x - 3$ [see Example 5(b)]. **5.** No [see Exercise 4(a)]. **6.** Reduce to $(x + 2)^2 + (y - 3)^2 = 10$; circle of radius $\sqrt{10}$ centred at $(-2, 3)$ [see Example 8]. **7.** Ellipse with semi-axes $a = \sqrt{2}$ and $b = 2$, centred at the origin [see Example 9]. **8.** Parabola; x-intercept at $x = 2$; y-intercept at $y = 4$; vertex at $(2, 0)$; points upward [see Exercise 14(b)]. **9.** See Example 11. **10.** Parabola, vertex is at the origin, opens towards the negative x-axis [see Exercise 15(d)].

6. Functions

What is in this section?

Definition of a function, domain and range; graph of a function; creating new functions from old, algebraically (composition) and geometrically (shifts and scaling); inverse functions.

Definition, Domain, Range and Graph

Reading the definition below, keep in mind that the key word is "unique."

> A *function* f is a rule that assigns, to each real number x in a set D a unique real number $f(x)$. The set D is called the *domain* of f, and the set of values $f(x)$ for all x in D is called the *range* of f.

The number x is called the *independent variable*, and $f(x)$ is called the corresponding *value of the function* f. The value $f(x)$ is also denoted by y; hence the usual notation $y = f(x)$. We use the symbols D for the domain and R for the range of a function.

> Depending on the context, we think of a function algebraically (i.e., as a formula, such as $f(x) = x^4 + 2$, or $y = 1/x$, etc.), geometrically (as a graph) or numerically (as a table of values).

Numerous examples of each of the above will appear in this and in all remaining sections.

 If the domain of a function f is not given explicitly, then it is assumed that the domain of f consists of all real numbers for which the formula for f makes sense (i.e., defines a real number). This domain is sometimes called a *natural domain*.

For instance, if $f(x) = 1/x$ and no other information is given, then we assume that the domain consists of all real numbers x such that $x \neq 0$. The natural domain of $y = x^3 - 2x^2 + 4x - 1$ is the set of all real numbers.

However, if the domain of a function is given explicitly, then that's what we work with (and we say that we work with a *given domain* of the function).

For example, consider $g(x) = 1/x$, where $x > 0$. Then $g(1) = 1$, $g(7) = 1/7$, but $g(-2)$ is not defined. Likewise, assume that $h(x) = x^2$, where $1 \leq x \leq 5$. Then $h(2) = 2^2 = 4$, and $h(3.3) = 3.3^2 = 10.89$, but $h(0.9)$ or $h(-2)$ are not defined.

> (Natural) domain of a Function: What Is Not Allowed?
> - Dividing by zero
> - Taking the square (or fourth, or sixth, or any even) root of a negative number

 Why are these not allowed?

Keep in mind that, in calculus, we deal with *real numbers* only. Dividing a number by zero does not give a real number. Exactly what we do get when we divide by zero ("infinity") is explained precisely and unambiguously in a calculus course using the concept of the limit of a function.

The square root or any even root of a negative number is not a real number. It is a complex number. Thus, the domain of the function $y = x^{1/4} = \sqrt[4]{x}$ consists of all $x \geq 0$, whereas the domain of $y = x^{1/5} = \sqrt[5]{x}$ is the set of all real numbers.

Example 1. Find the domain of each function.

(a) $f(x) = \dfrac{1}{x+4}$ (b) $y = \dfrac{1}{\sqrt{x+4}}$ (c) $y(x) = \dfrac{x+2}{x^2 - 2x}$ (d) $g(x) = \sqrt{1 - x^2}$

Solution.

(a) Since division by zero is not allowed, it follows that all x in the domain of f must satisfy $x+4 \neq 0$, i.e., $x \neq -4$. Thus, the domain is $D = \{x \mid x \neq -4\}$. Quite often, we drop the set notation and say that the domain consists of all real numbers x such that $x \neq -4$. More colloquially, we say that the domain is $x \neq -4$.

(b) To calculate the square root, we need $x + 4 \geq 0$. But since the square root is in the denominator, we have to make sure that it is not zero, hence $x + 4 \neq 0$. Combining the two requirements, we get $x + 4 > 0$, i.e., $x > -4$. So, the domain is the set of all real numbers such that $x > -4$.

(c) As in (a), we require that $x^2 - 2x \neq 0$. Because it is usually easier to work with equations, we will solve the equation $x^2 - 2x = 0$ and then remove the solutions from the set of real numbers to form the domain. Since

$$x^2 - 2x = x(x - 2) = 0$$

implies that $x = 0$ or $x = 2$, we conclude that $D = \{x \mid x \neq 0 \text{ and } x \neq 2\}$. Quite often, we write $x \neq 0, 2$ instead of using notations for sets. This also may be written in interval notation as $(\infty, 0) \cup (0, 2) \cup (2, \infty)$.

(d) The square root function is not defined for negative numbers; thus, all x in the domain of g must satisfy $1 - x^2 \geq 0$, or $x^2 \leq 1$. From here (look at Section 4), we conclude that $-1 \leq x \leq 1$.

To review a bit: we can solve $1 - x^2 \geq 0$ in several ways (try them all!):

• Multiply both sides by (-1), to get $x^2 - 1 \leq 0$; factor, to get

$$(x - 1)(x + 1) \leq 0$$

and then analyze the signs of factors (as done in Section 4).

• Simplify to the form $x^2 \leq 1$ and use the table on page 65 or use the graph, as done on page 68.

• Avoid formalities, and solve $x^2 \leq 1$ by asking the following question: what numbers, when squared, are smaller than or equal to 1?

Answer: the square of any number between 0 and 1 is smaller than 1, and so is the square of any number between -1 and 0. The square of 1 is 1, and the square of -1 is 1. The square of a number larger than 1 or smaller than -1 is larger than 1.

So, only numbers between -1 and 1 (and all those numbers, including -1 and 1) when squared, give a number smaller than or equal to 1.

Therefore, the solution to $x^2 \leq 1$ is $-1 \leq x \leq 1$, or $[-1, 1]$.

Exercise 1. Find the domain of each function.

(a) $f(x) = -3x^4 + x^2 - 13$ (b) $y = \dfrac{x^2 - 1}{x - 2}$ (c)* $h(x) = \dfrac{x^2 - 1}{x^2 + 1}$

(d) $y = \dfrac{x - 4}{\sqrt{x}}$ (e) $h(x) = \dfrac{x - 4}{\sqrt[3]{x}}$ (f) $y = \sqrt{\dfrac{x + 5}{x^2 + 1}}$

(g)* $f(x) = \dfrac{1}{\sqrt[4]{x - 2}}$ (h)* $g(x) = \dfrac{x}{x^3 - x}$ (i)* $h(x) = \left(1 - \dfrac{1}{x}\right)^{1/6}$

Recall that the *range* of a function $y = f(x)$ consists of all numbers (i.e., the y values) that are obtained when f is applied to all real numbers x in its domain. We can find the range either from the graph, or by using algebraic reasoning. We soon explain how to do both.

The *graph* of a function $y = f(x)$ is the set of points $(x, f(x))$ for all values of x in the domain of f. In other words, the graph of f consists of points, and each point carries two pieces of data: the value of the independent variable x and the corresponding value $y = f(x)$ of the function f at x; see figure below (left).

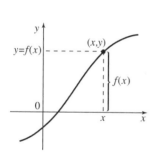
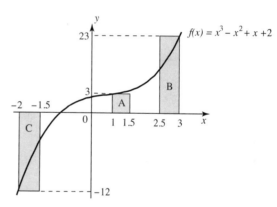

So, given x, the distance from the x-axis to the graph is the value of the function, if the graph lies above the x-axis (as in the figure above, left). If the graph lies below the x-axis, the value of the function is minus the distance.

Example 2. The graph above (right) represents the function $f(x) = x^3 - x^2 + x + 2$. Compute the areas of rectangles A, B and C. (This type of question appears (and is quite important!) when we study definite integrals in calculus.)

Solution. Area of a rectangle equals base times height. All three rectangles have base length equal to 0.5, so all we have to do is to determine their heights.

The height of rectangle A is equal to the value of the function at $x = 1$; since $f(1) = (1)^3 - (1)^2 + (1) + 2 = 3$, it follows that the area of the rectangle A is $0.5 \cdot 3 = 1.5$.

Likewise, $f(3) = (3)^3 - (3)^2 + (3) + 2 = 23$ is the height of rectangle B. Its area is $0.5 \cdot 23 = 11.5$.

Since $f(-2) = (-2)^3 - (-2)^2 + (-2) + 2 = -12$, we conclude that the height of rectangle C is 12, and so its area is $0.5 \cdot 12 = 6$.

Why is the base length of rectangle C equal to 0.5?

Recall that the distance between two points a and b on a number line is equal to $|a - b| = |b - a|$. Thus, the base length of C is $|-2 - (-1.5)| = |-0.5| = 0.5$.

Now we start drawing graphs. Keep in mind the following:

> The graph of a function $y = f(x)$ is a curve. An elementary way of sketching the graph is by plotting points.

The fact that a function assigns a *unique* value y to each x in its domain means that its graph cannot contain two or more points that have the same x-coordinate. In other words, every vertical line that crosses the graph must cross it exactly once (this is known as the *vertical line test*).

The curve in (a) in the figure below satisfies the vertical line test, and therefore represents the graph of some function. So does the curve in (c); note that it is not necessary that *all* vertical lines cross the curve–but those that do, must cross it exactly once.

Even if a single line crosses the curve more than once (as in (b)), then that curve cannot be the graph of a function.

(a) 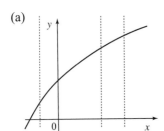   (b) 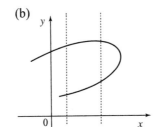   (c)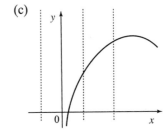

We have already seen a few graphs of functions. For example, the graph of $y = mx + b$ is a line of slope m and y-intercept b; the graph of the function $y = ax^2 + bx + c$ is a parabola.

A circle or an ellipse are not graphs of functions — the vertical line test does not work. However, circle and ellipse are graphs of *equations*.

Given the graph of a function, we can determine some of its features, such as domain and range (as will be done in many examples to follow).

Example 3. Sketch the graph of the function $y = x^3 + x + 1$.

Solution. In some cases, graphing amounts to recognizing the curve involved (such as a line, or a parabola). Later in this section we will list some important graphs (which we should remember, as they appear very often).

However, if the graph is not one of those we know (or a modification, as discussed later in this section), we go back to the basic routine–plotting points.

We choose (convenient) values for x and compute corresponding values for y. For example, when $x = 0$, we get $y = 1$; thus, the point $(0, 1)$ belongs to the graph. In the same way, we can compute as many points as we wish. The table below (right) shows some of them.

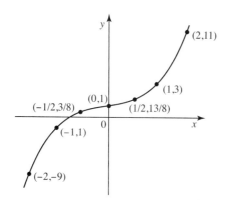

x	$y = x^3 + x + 1$	point on the graph
-2	-9	$(-2, -9)$
-1	-1	$(-1, -1)$
$-1/2$	$3/8$	$(-1/2, 3/8)$
0	1	$(0, 1)$
$1/2$	$13/8$	$(1/2, 13/8)$
1	3	$(1, 3)$
2	11	$(2, 11)$

Now we use these points (the more points we have, the better the picture will look) to produce the graph (above, left).

(extra) **Exercise 2.** Sketch the graph of each function by plotting points.

(a) $y = \dfrac{1}{x - 2}$.   (b) $y = \sqrt{x + 3}$ (c) $y = \dfrac{x}{x - 4}$ (d) $y = \dfrac{1}{\sqrt{x}}$

(try it!) **Exercise 3.** Sketch the graph of the function $y = \sqrt{x^3 + 1}$ by plotting points.

Example 4. Find the range of the functions whose graphs are shown below.

(a)
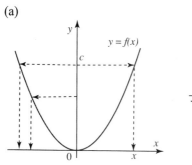

(b)
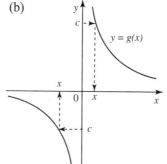

(c)
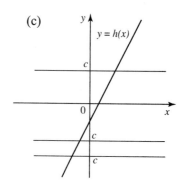

We claim that the range of $y = f(x)$ is the set $y \geq 0$, or $[0, \infty)$. How do we justify that? Pick a number $c \geq 0$ on the y-axis, as shown in figure (a) above. Following the arrows, we find corresponding x, i.e., the number such that $f(x) = c$. (Note that there is another value for x (negative) for which $f(x) = c$; however, this is not relevant — all we need is to find *one* x for which $f(x) = c$.)

The same construction can be repeated no matter which $c \geq 0$ we take (if $c = 0$, then $x = 0$), so we proved our claim.

Similarly, we see that any $c \neq 0$ is in the range of the function $y = g(x)$ shown in (b) above. The range can also be written $(-\infty, 0) \cup (0, \infty)$.

By looking at the two cases we have done so far, we obtain the following geometric way of testing whether or not a number belongs to the range of a function:

> A number c (on the y-axis) is in the range of a function if the horizontal line through c intersects the graph of the function (once, or several times, does not matter).

Clearly, a horizontal line through any value c intersects the graph of $y = h(x)$ above (figure (c)). So, the range of h consists of all real numbers.

(try it!) **Exercise 4.** Find the range of the functions whose graphs are shown below.

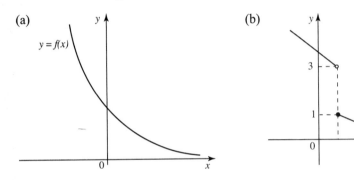

Next, we illustrate how to find the range algebraically.

Consider the linear function $f(x) = 2x + 7$. Since $f(2) = 2(2) + 7 = 11$, we conclude that 11 belongs to the range of f.

Is 19 in the range of f? If we plan to say yes, we need to find a number such that f evaluated on it gives 19. In symbols, we need to find x so that $f(x) = 19$. Thus, $2x + 7 = 19$, and so $2x = 12$ and $x = 6$. So, that number is 6. Check: $f(6) = 2(6) + 7 = 19$; i.e., 19 is in the range of f.

One more: to show that -11.4 is in the range of f, we set $f(x) = 2x + 7 = -11.4$, and solve for x: $2x = -18.4$, and so $x = -9.2$. Thus, $f(-9.2) = -11.4$.

Clearly, we cannot proceed like this, by checking individual real numbers. So, we pick a real number c and ask: is there a number x such that $f(x) = c$? From $f(x) = 2x + 7 = c$ we get $2x = c - 7$ and $x = \frac{c-7}{2}$.

Thus, no matter which c we pick, we can always find an x (in this case, x is equal to $\frac{c-7}{2}$) such that $f(x) = c$. Consequently, c is in the range of f. Since no assumptions on c were made, c can be any real number, and so the range of f consists of all real numbers.

Example 5. Find the range of the following functions, and justify your answer algebraically.

(a) $f(x) = x^2$ (b) $g(x) = \dfrac{2}{x}$ (c) $h(x) = \sqrt{x}$

Solution.

(a) The square of any non-zero number is positive, and the square of zero is zero. Thus, the range of f consists of all y satisfying $y \geq 0$, i.e., $R = [0, \infty)$.

Alternatively, we pick a number c and try to find x such that $f(x) = x^2 = c$. Solving for x, we get $x = \pm\sqrt{c}$. So, $f(\pm\sqrt{c}) = c$. Since $\sqrt{c}$ is defined for $c \geq 0$, we conclude that, by evaluating f, we can only obtain positive numbers and 0. Thus, $R = [0, \infty)$.

(b) Pick a real number c and try to find x such that $g(x) = 2/x = c$. From $2/x = c$ we get $x = 2/c$ (which makes sense when $c \neq 0$). So, if we pick $x = 2/c$, and $c \neq 0$, we get $g(2/c) = \frac{2}{2/c} = c$. This statement proves that any nonzero number c is in the range of g. We write

$$R = \{y \mid y \neq 0\} = \mathbb{R} - \{0\}$$

(c) From Section 1 we know that $\sqrt{x} \geq 0$; i.e., the square root of a number is positive or zero. But can we get *any* positive number or zero this way? To check that, take $c \geq 0$. From $h(x) = \sqrt{x} = c$ we get $x = c^2$; i.e., $h(c^2) = c$. Thus, we showed that c is in the range of h. Consequently, $R = [0, \infty)$.

(try it!) **Exercise 5.** Sketch the graphs of the functions f, g and h from Example 5 and check geometrically that their range is as claimed. (To recall graphs, if you need it, check the next subsection.)

(extra) **Exercise 6.** Find the domain and the range for the following functions. Justify your answer for the range by providing an algebraic argument.

(a) $f(x) = x + 6$ (b) $y = -2x$ (c) $g(x) = 3x - 14$ (d) $g(x) = x^2 + 4$

(e) $y = -x^2$ (f)* $f(x) = x^3$ (g) $f(x) = x^3 - 7$ (h) $g(x) = \dfrac{2}{x - 3}$

(i)* $g(x) = \dfrac{1}{x^2}$ (j)* $h(x) = |x|$ (k) $y = |x| - 3$ (l) $f(x) = |x + 2|$

List of Important Functions

For each function, we draw the graph and state its domain D and range R.

(1) $f(x) = c$ (c is a real number) is a *constant function*. It assigns the same number c to all real values x. Its domain consists of all real numbers. The range consists of the single value c. The graph (below, left) shows the constant function $f(x) = 2$.

(2) $f(x) = mx + b$ is a *line* of slope m and y-intercept b. If $m = 0$, the line is horizontal, so it represents a constant function $f(x) = b$. If $m \neq 0$, then $D = \mathbb{R}$, $R = \mathbb{R}$. The special case $f(x) = x$ represents the line of slope 1 going through the origin (below, right).

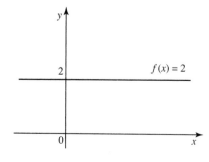
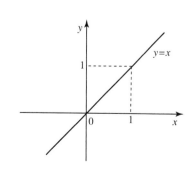

(3) $f(x) = x^2$; $D = \mathbb{R}$, $R = [0, \infty)$; the graph is a *parabola* with the vertex located at the origin, symmetric with respect to the y-axis; see figure below (left). The graphs of x^n, where $n = 4, 6, 8, \ldots$, look similar to the graph of $f(x) = x^2$.

(4) $f(x) = x^3$; $D = \mathbb{R}$, $R = \mathbb{R}$; the graph is symmetric with respect to the origin (below, right). The graphs of x^n, where $n = 5, 7, 9, \ldots$, look similar to the graph of $f(x) = x^3$.

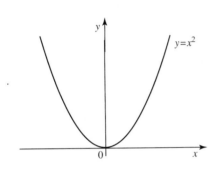 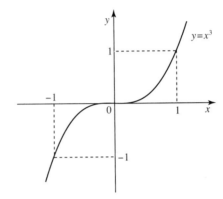

(5) $f(x) = 1/x$; $D = \{x \mid x \neq 0\} = (-\infty, 0) \cup (0, \infty)$, $R = \{y \mid y \neq 0\} = (-\infty, 0) \cup (0, \infty)$; the graph is a *hyperbola*, whose asymptotes are the x-axis and the y-axis. It is symmetric with respect to the origin (below, left).

(6) $f(x) = 1/x^2$; $D = \{x \mid x \neq 0\} = (-\infty, 0) \cup (0, \infty)$, $R = \{y \mid y > 0\} = (0, \infty)$; the graph lies above the x-axis, and its asymptotes are the x-axis and the y-axis. It is symmetric with respect to the y-axis (below, right).

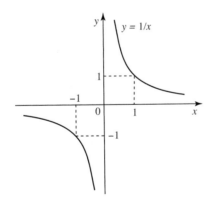 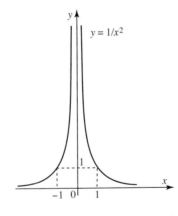

Why is the range of $f(x) = 1/x^2$ equal to $R = (0, \infty)$?

Recall that a number (on the y-axis) is in the range of a function if a horizontal line through it crosses the graph. Clearly, neither the x-axis nor any horizontal line below it cross the graph of $1/x^2$. Only the horizontal lines through positive numbers cross it.

(7) $f(x) = \sqrt{x}$; $D = [0, \infty)$, $R = [0, \infty)$; the graph has a shape of a *parabola* (below, left).

(8) $f(x) = \sqrt[3]{x}$; $D = \mathbb{R}$, $R = \mathbb{R}$; the graph has a shape of a *cubic parabola* (below, right).

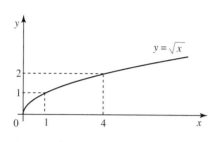 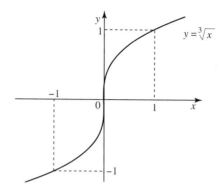

The fact that the domain of $f(x) = \sqrt[3]{x}$ is $\mathbb{R}$ reflects the fact that we can compute a cube root of any real number; for instance, $\sqrt[3]{-27} = -3$, $\sqrt[3]{0} = 0$, $\sqrt[3]{1000} = 10$.

(9) $f(x) = |x|$; $D = \mathbb{R}$, $R = [0, \infty)$.

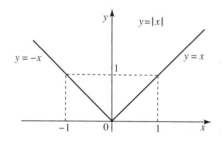

Recall that

$$|x| = \begin{cases} x & \text{if } x \geq 0 \\ -x & \text{if } x < 0 \end{cases}$$

Functions such as $|x|$ defined in the box above or the one in the following example, are said to be *defined piecewise*.

Example 6. Sketch the graph of the function

$$f(x) = \begin{cases} 2x + 1 & \text{if } x < 1 \\ -x + 2 & \text{if } x \geq 1 \end{cases}$$

Solution. When $x < 1$, then $y = 2x + 1$. This is a line of slope 2 and y-intercept 1. (Alternatively, we could compute two points that lie on it (say, $(0, 1)$ and $(-1, -1)$) and join them with a straight line.) When $x \geq 1$, then $y = -x + 2$. This is a line of slope -1 and y-intercept 2.

The graph of f is drawn below.

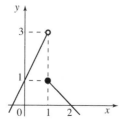

Note that one of the dots is filled, but the other one is not. Why?

The filled dot in the graph indicates that the value of f at $x = 1$ is $y = -x + 2 = -1 + 2 = 1$. The empty dot indicates that a point does not belong to the graph. (Note that two filled dots, one above the other, would violate the vertical line test.)

Example 7. Sketch the graph of the function $f(x) = |3x - 2|$.

Solution. One way to do this is to rewrite f; replacing x by $3x - 2$ in the definition of the absolute value (see box on page 101), we get

$$|3x - 2| = \begin{cases} 3x - 2 & \text{if } 3x - 2 \geq 0 \\ -(3x - 2) & \text{if } 3x - 2 < 0 \end{cases}$$

Now simplify

$$|3x - 2| = \begin{cases} 3x - 2 & \text{if } x \geq 2/3 \\ -3x + 2 & \text{if } x < 2/3 \end{cases}$$

and realize that we are asked to graph a function defined piecewise, as in the previous exercise. In words, the graph of f consists of the line of slope -3 and y-intercept 2 for all $x < 2/3$, and of the line $y = 3x - 2$ for x greater than or equal to $2/3$; see below.

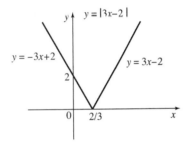

 Exercise 7. Sketch the graphs of the following functions.

(a)* $f(x) = -4$ \qquad\qquad (b)* $y = -x^2$ \qquad\qquad (c)* $f(x) = |x| + x$

(d) $y = |2x - 1|$ \qquad\qquad (e)* $f(x) = \dfrac{|x|}{x}$ \qquad\qquad (f) $g(x) = \dfrac{2|x| - x}{3x}$

(g) $f(x) = \begin{cases} 3 & \text{if } x < -1 \\ -2x + 1 & \text{if } x \geq -1 \end{cases}$

New Functions from Old (Part I)

Two functions can be added, subtracted, multiplied and divided (as long as the one in the denominator is not zero) to form new functions.

Combining constant functions and positive integer powers of x using addition, subtraction and multiplication, we obtain *polynomials* (for instance, $2x^3 - 4.7x^2 + 11$, $3 - x/2 - 4x^4 + 1.5x^2$, and 7 are polynomials). Dividing polynomials we obtain *rational functions*.

A *polynomial* of degree n is a function of the form $f(x) = a_0 + a_1 x + a_2 x^2 + \cdots + a_n x^n$, where $a_0, a_1, a_2, \ldots, a_n$ are real numbers and $a_n \neq 0$. A quotient $f(x)/g(x)$ of two polynomials $f(x)$ and $g(x)$ is called a *rational function*.

The domain of a polynomial consists of all real numbers. The domain of a rational function depends on the polynomial in the denominator (see Example 1(a),(c)).

Recall that we have already worked with polynomials, as well as with rational functions (long division, for example) in Section 2.

Examples of rational functions:

$$\frac{x^2 - 13}{x^6 + 3.7x - 43} \qquad \frac{7}{x^4} \qquad \frac{x^3 - 1}{5} \qquad \frac{1 - x}{1 + 2x}$$

A function that can be obtained using elementary algebraic operations and by taking roots is called an *algebraic function*. For example,

$$\sqrt{x} \qquad \frac{x^4 + \sqrt[3]{x - 1}}{x^2 + \sqrt{x}} \qquad \frac{x^2 - 1}{x^6 + x - 1} \qquad \sqrt[5]{\frac{1 - \sqrt{x}}{x}}$$

are algebraic functions. The functions that are not algebraic are called *transcendental*.

Trigonometric, logarithmic and exponential functions are examples of transcendental functions. We will study such functions in the forthcoming two sections.

We now introduce an important operation on functions.

Composition of functions f and g is the function $g \circ f$, defined by

$$(g \circ f)(x) = g(f(x))$$

 In words, we take an x and apply f to it, thus getting $f(x)$. Then we apply g to $f(x)$, to get the value $g(f(x))$ of the composition $g \circ f$ at x. It is important to pay attention to the order in which the functions are composed. In general, $g \circ f \neq f \circ g$, as the following example shows.

Example 8. Let $f(x) = 1/x$ and $g(x) = x + 4$. Compute $g \circ f$ and $f \circ g$.

Solution. By definition,

$$(f \circ g)(x) = f(g(x)) = f(x + 4) = \frac{1}{x + 4}$$

On the other hand,

$$(g \circ f)(x) = g(f(x)) = g\left(\frac{1}{x}\right) = \frac{1}{x} + 4$$

Clearly, $g \circ f \neq f \circ g$.

The composition of three (or more) functions is computed analogously.

Example 9. Let $f(x) = \sqrt{x}$, $g(x) = 1 - \sqrt{x}$ and $h(x) = x^2 + 1$. Compute

(a) $f \circ g$ (b) $g \circ f \circ h$ (c) $f \circ h \circ f$

Solution.

(a) By definition,

$$(f \circ g)(x) = f(g(x)) = f(1 - \sqrt{x}) = \sqrt{1 - \sqrt{x}}$$

(b) As in the case of a composition of two functions,

$$(g \circ f \circ h)(x) = g(f(h(x))) = g(f(x^2 + 1)) = g(\sqrt{x^2 + 1}) = 1 - \sqrt{\sqrt{x^2 + 1}} = 1 - \sqrt[4]{x^2 + 1}$$

Why is the square root of the square root equal to the fourth root?

Take $a \geq 0$, so that the square root is defined. Then

$$\sqrt{\sqrt{a}} = \sqrt{a^{1/2}} = \left(a^{1/2}\right)^{1/2} = a^{(1/2)(1/2)} = a^{1/4} = \sqrt[4]{a}$$

By the law of exponents, $(a^m)^n = a^{mn}$. That's why the step $\left(a^{1/2}\right)^{1/2} = a^{(1/2)(1/2)}$ above is correct.

(c) Similarly,

$$(f \circ h \circ f)(x) = f(h(f(x))) = f(h(\sqrt{x})) = f((\sqrt{x})^2 + 1) = f(x + 1) = \sqrt{x + 1}$$

(try it!)   **Exercise 8.**   Let $f(x) = 3x + 4$ and $g(x) = x/2$. Compute

(a) $f \circ g$ (b) $f \circ f$ (c) $g \circ f$

(try it!)   **Exercise 9.**   Let $f(x) = x^5$ and $g(x) = x^2 + x + 1$. Compute

(a) $f \circ g$ (b) $f \circ f$ (c) $g \circ f$

Inverse Functions

Recall that a function f is a rule that assigns, to each x in the domain of f a unique real number y in the range of f. The idea of an *inverse function* is to reverse (or, undo) this process. Given f, we will denote its inverse function by f^{-1}.

For instance, if f takes $x = 2$ and assigns 11 to it (i.e., $f(2) = 11$), then f^{-1} will take 11 and assign 2 to it, i.e., $f^{-1}(11) = 2$. Likewise, if $f(-4) = 2.5$, then $f^{-1}(2.5) = -4$. As well, if we know that $f^{-1}(-3) = 17$, then $f(17) = -3$.

> definition of inverse function: if $f(a) = b$, then $f^{-1}(b) = a$

From the definition, we conclude that the domain of f^{-1} is the range of f, and the range of f^{-1} is the domain of f. As well,

$$(f^{-1} \circ f)(a) = f^{-1}(f(a)) = f^{-1}(b) = a$$

and

$$(f \circ f^{-1})(b) = f(f^{-1}(b)) = f(a) = b$$

In words, the composition of f and its inverse f^{-1} (in either order) will not change the value of the number (this sounds reasonable: if we take a number, apply f to it, and then un-apply f (i.e., apply f^{-1}) we should get our number back).

Why did we use a and b in the above, and not x and y?

Because we are used to x representing the independent variable (domain) and y representing the dependent variable (range). But here, we are switching their roles, and have therefore decided to use "neutral" names for variables: a is in the domain of f, and b is in the domain of f^{-1}.

However, now we will adopt the usual practice of using x to denote a number in the domain of *any* function, and will write $f(f^{-1}(x)) = x$ and $f^{-1}(f(x)) = x$ (of course, we still keep in mind that x in $f(f^{-1}(x)) = x$ belongs to the domain of f^{-1}, whereas x in $f^{-1}(f(x)) = x$ belongs to the domain of f).

> **How Do We Recognize Inverse Functions?**
> If two functions $f(x)$ and $g(x)$ satisfy $f(g(x)) = x$ and $g(f(x)) = x$, then they are the inverse of each other.

So, inverse functions come in pairs: if f is inverse to g, then g is inverse to f as well.

Not every function has an inverse function. Take for instance, $f(x) = x^2$. Since $f(3) = 9$, and $f(-3) = 9$, what number should f^{-1} assign to 9? 3 or -3? Recall that, in order to have a function, we need uniqueness of assignment; in situations where we cannot achieve that uniqueness, we say that the function does not have an inverse. Looking at the graph, we see that $f(3)$ and $f(-3)$ have the same height; i.e., a horizontal line through 9 on the y-axis crosses the graph at two points, $(3, 9)$ and $(-3, 9)$. See figure below, left.

We conclude that, if some horizontal line crosses the graph of a function twice (or three times; actually, more than once), then that function does not have an inverse (such as the function $f(x)$ in the figure below, middle).

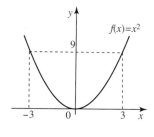
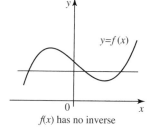
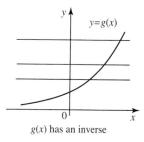

$f(x)$ has no inverse $g(x)$ has an inverse

However, if every horizontal line crosses the graph of a function exactly once (or does not cross it at all), then the function has an inverse (such as the function $g(x)$ in the figure above, right).

> *Horizontal Line Test*
> If every horizontal line crosses the graph of a function $f(x)$ at most once, then $f(x)$ has an inverse function.

Let us look at some graphs we drew in this section and apply the test to them: the functions $y = x$, $y = x^3$, $y = 1/x$, $y = \sqrt{x}$, $y = \sqrt[3]{x}$, have inverse functions, whereas the functions $y = c$ (constant function), $y = x^2$, $y = x^4$, $y = 1/x^2$, $y = |x|$ do not have inverse functions.

Recall that a function assigns a unique y to each x in its domain. Algebraically, a function is a formula that expresses y in terms of x. To find the inverse function, we have to find the rule that undoes this, i.e., we need to express x in terms of y.

Example 10. Find the inverse function for each of the following functions:

(a) $f(x) = 3x - 11$ 　　　　　 (b) $f(x) = \sqrt{x - 2} + 3$ 　　　　　 (c) $f(x) = \dfrac{x - 1}{x + 1}$

Solution.

(a) Rewrite $f(x) = 3x - 11$ as $y = 3x - 11$, and solve for x, resulting in $3x = y + 11$, and so $x = \frac{y+11}{3}$. Using functional notation, we write $f^{-1}(y) = \frac{y+11}{3}$. Although this is correct, in many situations we prefer to use x as independent variable; so, we write

$$f^{-1}(x) = \frac{x + 11}{3}$$

Another (very common!) way of calculating inverse function (basically the same as above but with a slight difference in how we write it) is this: start with $y = 3x - 11$, switch x and y to get $x = 3y - 11$, and then solve for y; so, we obtain $y = \frac{x+11}{3}$. Now we need to replace y as follows.

Important note: y in $y = 3x - 11$ represents $f(x)$, whereas y in $y = \frac{x+11}{3}$ represents $f^{-1}(x)$. So, the answer is $f^{-1}(x) = \frac{x+11}{3}$.

(b) Rewrite the formula for $f(x)$ as $y = \sqrt{x - 2} + 3$ and solve for x:

$$\sqrt{x - 2} = y - 3$$
$$x - 2 = (y - 3)^2$$
$$x = (y - 3)^2 + 2$$

Thus, $f^{-1}(x) = (x - 3)^2 + 2$.

(c) Using the second method explained in (a) we start with $y = \dfrac{x - 1}{x + 1}$, and switch x and y to get $x = \dfrac{y - 1}{y + 1}$. We now solve for y as follows. Cross multiply, and then gather y terms together:

$$xy + x = y - 1$$
$$xy - y = -x - 1$$
$$y(x - 1) = -x - 1$$
$$y = \frac{-x - 1}{x - 1} = \frac{x + 1}{-x + 1}$$

In the last step, we multiplied both numerator and denominator by (-1), to get rid of a couple of minus signs. So, $f^{-1}(x) = \dfrac{x + 1}{-x + 1}$.

 Exercise 10. Find the inverse function for each of the following functions:

(a) $f(x) = \dfrac{2}{x - 4}$ 　　　　 (b) $f(x) = 4\sqrt[7]{2 - x} - 1$ 　　　　 (c) $f(x) = 1 - x^3$

How do we find f^{-1} if f is given as graph?

Assume that, for some function, $f(3) = 0$; this means that the point $(3, 0)$ belongs to its graph. But then $f^{-1}(0) = 3$, i.e., the point $(0, 3)$ belongs to the graph of f^{-1}. As well, if the point $(5, 1)$ belongs to the graph of f, then the point $(1, 5)$ will belong to the graph of f^{-1}. What is the geometric relation between $(3, 0)$ and $(0, 3)$ or between $(5, 1)$ and $(1, 5)$? Looking at the figure below (left), we see that the relation is symmetry with respect to the line $y = x$.

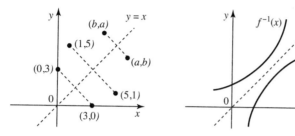

Thus, to draw an inverse, we reflect the given graph across the diagonal line $y = x$, as shown in figure above (right). To conclude:

> **How Do You Find the Inverse of a Function $f(x)$?**
> If the function is given as a formula $y = f(x)$, then we solve for x in terms of y. If the function is given as a graph, then we reflect it with respect to the line $y = x$.

Example 11. (a) Show that $f(x) = \sqrt[3]{x - 1}$ is the inverse of the function $g(x) = x^3 + 1$.

(b) Find the inverse function of the function $f(x) = x^2$, $x \geq 0$.

Solution.

(a) Of course, we could use the procedure just explained in the box to find the inverse of $g(x)$.

Instead, we recall the box "How Do We Recognize Inverse Functions?" on page 105 and verify that $f(g(x)) = x$ and $g(f(x)) = x$:

$$f(g(x)) = f(x^3 + 1) = \sqrt[3]{(x^3 + 1) - 1} = \sqrt[3]{x^3} = x$$
$$g(f(x)) = g(\sqrt[3]{x - 1}) = (\sqrt[3]{x - 1})^3 + 1 = (x - 1) + 1 = x$$

In the above calculations we used the fact that the functions x^3 and $\sqrt[3]{x}$ are the inverse of each other (so that $(\sqrt[3]{x})^3 = x$ and $\sqrt[3]{x^3} = x$).

(b) It is true that $y = x^2$ does *not* have an inverse — when we think of it as having the set of all real numbers as its domain. However, here we are dealing with the function $f(x) = x^2$, defined for $x \geq 0$, i.e., the domain is $[0, \infty)$. Its graph is the part of the parabola $y = x^2$ in the first quadrant, together with the origin; see figure below, left.

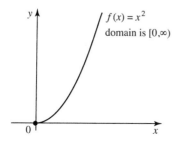 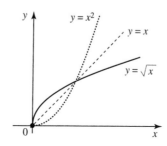

Clearly, the function satisfies the horizontal line test, so it must have an inverse. Solving $y = x^2$ for x, we get $x = \pm\sqrt{y}$. Because $x \geq 0$, we must choose the plus sign, and so $x = \sqrt{y}$; thus, the inverse of $f(x)$ is $f^{-1}(x) = \sqrt{x}$.

Geometrically, we reflect the graph of $f(x) = x^2$ with respect to $y = x$ to obtain the graph of $y = \sqrt{x}$; see the figure above, right.

For extra practice with compositions and inverses, work on the following exercises.

(extra) **Exercise 11.** Compute the compositions $f \circ g$, $g \circ f$, and $f \circ f$ in each case.

(a) $f(x) = -x + 4$, $g(x) = 4x - 12$ (b)* $f(x) = -5$, $g(x) = 4 - 3x$

(c) $f(x) = \dfrac{1}{x}$, $g(x) = \dfrac{x}{2}$ (d) $f(x) = \sqrt{x+1}$, $g(x) = \dfrac{5}{2x^2}$

(e)* $f(x) = \dfrac{6}{x}$, $g(x) = |x + 13|$ (f) $f(x) = \dfrac{x+1}{x-1}$, $g(x) = \dfrac{1}{x}$

(g) $f(x) = \sqrt[3]{x + 12}$, $g(x) = x^3 - 12$ (h)* $f(x) = \sqrt{x^2 + 1}$, $g(x) = x^2$

(extra) **Exercise 12.** Let $f(x) = x^4$ and $g(x) = x^7$. Show that the compositions $f \circ g$ and $g \circ f$ are equal. (So, it could happen that $f \circ g = g \circ f$, even though f and g are not inverse to each other.)

(extra) **Exercise 13.** Find the inverse function of each function, or else say that it does not exist.

(a) $f(x) = 11 - \dfrac{x}{4}$ (b) $f(x) = -13x$ (c)* $f(x) = 4$ (d) $g(x) = \dfrac{2}{3x}$

(e) $f(x) = \sqrt[5]{2x - 9}$ (f) $y = -x^4$ (g) $y = \dfrac{7x - 1}{1 - x}$ (h)* $f(x) = \sqrt[4]{x - 4} - 11$

(i) $f(x) = x^3 - 14$ (j)* $h(x) = |x| + 3$ (k) $f(x) = 4x^{-3}$ (l) $y = x^{-2} + 6$

(m)* $f(x) = x^2$, $x < 0$ (n) $f(x) = x^6$, $x \geq 0$

(extra) **Exercise 14.** Show that $f(g(x)) = x$ and $g(f(x)) = x$ if $f(x) = \dfrac{2x}{x+3}$ and $g(x) = \dfrac{3x}{2-x}$. What does this mean for the functions f and g?

New Functions from Old (Part II)

Shifts. Assume that $c > 0$ is a constant. The function $y = f(x) + c$ is obtained by adding c to every value of $f(x)$; geometrically, it means that the points on the graph of $y = f(x) + c$ are obtained by moving points on the graph of $y = f(x)$ up for c units.

Similarly, the graph of $y = f(x) - c$ is obtained by moving the graph of $f(x)$ c units down, see figure below (left).

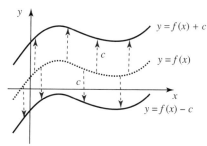 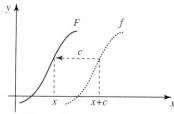

The new function F at x has to be the same as the old function f at $x+c$.

Given the graph of a function f, we define a new function F by $F(x) = f(x+c)$. What is the relation between the graphs of f and F?

The formula $F(x) = f(x+c)$ says that the value of the new function F at x is the same as the value of f at $x + c$ (note that $x + c$ is c units to the right of x); see figure above (right). So, starting with f, we obtain the graph of F by moving f to the *left* for c units.

The case $F(x) = f(x - c)$ is argued analogously.

Let $c > 0$; to obtain the graph of
$y = f(x) + c$,　move the graph of $y = f(x)$　c units up
$y = f(x) - c$,　move the graph of $y = f(x)$　c units down
$y = f(x + c)$,　move the graph of $y = f(x)$　c units to the left
$y = f(x - c)$,　move the graph of $y = f(x)$　c units to the right

Example 12. Starting with a known graph, sketch the graphs of the following functions.

(a) $y = (x - 1)^2 + 2$　　　(b) $y = \sqrt{x} + 1$　　　(c) $y = \dfrac{1}{x - 4}$

Solution.

(a) Consider $y = x^2$. Replacing x by $x - 1$, we get $y = (x - 1)^2$. Adding 2, we get the function $y = (x - 1)^2 + 2$ that we are asked to sketch.

So we start with $y = x^2$ and then replace x by $x - 1$, moving the function one unit to the right. Then add 2 to the function, moving it 2 units up. See figure below (left).

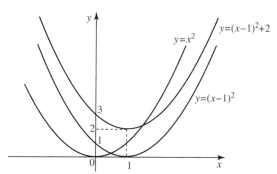 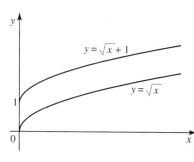

(b) The graph of $y = \sqrt{x} + 1$ is obtained from the graph of $y = \sqrt{x}$ by moving it one unit up; see figure above (right).

(c) The given graph is obtained from $y = 1/x$ by replacing x by $x - 4$; thus, all we need to do is to move the graph of $y = 1/x$ four units to the right; see figure below.

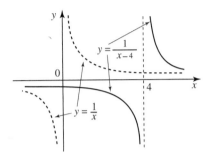

extra   **Exercise 15.** Starting with a known graph, sketch, or describe in words, the graph of each function.

(a)* $y = (x + 2)^2 + 3$ (b)* $y = \sqrt{x - 4} - 2$ (c)* $y = \dfrac{1}{(x - 1)^2} + 2$

(d) $f(x) = |x - 11| - 10$ (e) $y = \dfrac{1}{x + 4} + 4$ (f) $y = (x - 5)^3 - 5$

(g) $f(x) = x^2 + 6x - 11$ [Hint: Complete the square.]

Scaling. Take a function $f(x)$ and form the function $F(x) = cf(x)$ for a *positive* constant c. To obtain the value of F at x, we take the value of f at x and multiply it by c. In other words, we scale the graph vertically (which amounts to stretching, if $c > 1$, and compressing if $c < 1$).

In the figure on the below (left) we show the graphs of $f(x)$, $2f(x)$ and $f(x)/3$.

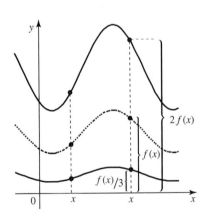
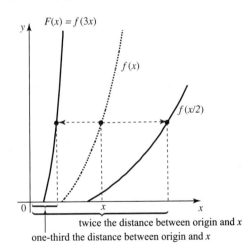

We say that the graph of $f(x)$ needs to be scaled vertically by the factor of 2 (or, stretched vertically by the factor of 2) to produce the graph of $2f(x)$.

As well, the graph of $f(x)$ has to be scaled vertically by the factor of $1/3$ (or, compressed vertically by the factor of 3) to obtain the graph of $f(x)/3$.

What about $f(cx)$? Given the graph of a function f, we define a new function F by $F(x) = f(cx)$, where c is a positive constant. What is the relation between the graphs of f and F?

Assume, for the sake of argument, that $c = 3$, i.e., consider $F(x) = f(3x)$.

The value of the function F at x is the same as the value of f at $3x$ (which is three times farther away from the origin than x). So, starting with f, we obtain the graph of F by compressing it horizontally by the factor of 3.

Likewise, to obtain $f(x/2)$, we stretch the graph of $f(x)$ horizontally by the factor of 2; see figure above (right).

To obtain the graph of	
$y = cf(x),\ c > 1,$	stretch (expand) the graph of $y = f(x)$ vertically by a factor of c
$y = cf(x),\ 0 < c < 1,$	compress the graph of $y = f(x)$ vertically by a factor of $1/c$
$y = f(cx),\ c > 1,$	compress the graph of $y = f(x)$ horizontally by a factor of c
$y = f(cx),\ 0 < c < 1,$	stretch (expand) the graph of $y = f(x)$ horizontally by a factor of $1/c$

We noticed that, when $0 < c < 1$, the transformation (compression or expansion) is by the factor of $1/c$. Why $1/c$ and not c?

It is a matter of how we refer to expansion and compression.

Consider the case of $f(x/2)$ (i.e., $c = 1/2$) that we discussed above; we argued that the graph of $f(x/2)$ is an expansion of the graph of $f(x)$.

How do we quantify the size of the expansion? Saying "expansion by the factor of $c = 1/2$" actually suggests compression; so, we say "expansion by the factor of $1/c = 1/(1/2) = 2$."

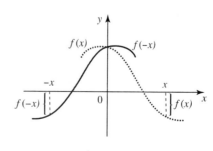

Reflections. How do we get the graph of $-f$ from the graph of f?

Noting that $f(x)$ and $-f(x)$ lie across the x-axis from one another (see figure below, left), we conclude that the graph of $-f(x)$ is the mirror image of the graph of $f(x)$ with respect to the x-axis.

Since x and $-x$ lie symmetrically on opposite sides of the origin, it follows that the graph of $f(-x)$ is the mirror image of the graph of $f(x)$ with respect to the y-axis (see figure below, right).

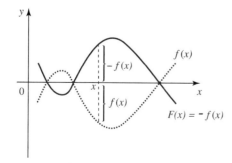
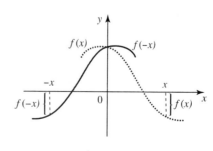

> To obtain the graph of
>
> $y = -f(x)$, reflect the graph of $f(x)$ with respect to x-axis
>
> $y = f(-x)$, reflect the graph of $f(x)$ with respect to y-axis

Next, we discuss two examples of constructing graphs using the geometric rules we described. You can find more examples in the two forthcoming sections.

Example 13. Sketch the graphs of the following functions.

(a) $y = -2\sqrt{x}$ (b) $y = 2|x - 1|$

Solution.

(a) Take the graph of $y = \sqrt{x}$, expand it vertically by a factor of 2 (to get $2\sqrt{x}$) and then reflect with respect to the x-axis (to get $-2\sqrt{x}$); see figure below, left.

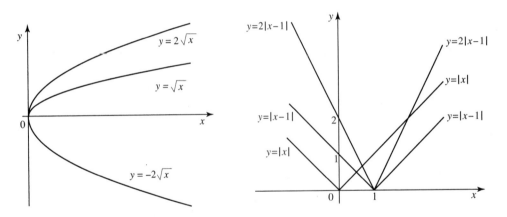

(b) Start with the graph of $y = |x|$, move it 1 unit to the right (that will draw the function $|x - 1|$) and then expand it vertically by a factor of 2; see figure above, right.

Example 14. Given below, left, is the graph of a function $f(x)$. Sketch the graph of $|f(x)|$.

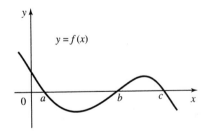
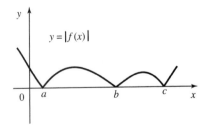

Solution. We start by using the definition of absolute value:

$$|f(x)| = \begin{cases} f(x) & \text{if } f(x) \geq 0 \\ -f(x) & \text{if } f(x) < 0 \end{cases}$$

Now all we have to do is to interpret this. The first line says that whenever $f(x) \geq 0$, i.e., when the graph of f lies above the x-axis or touches it, the function $|f(x)|$ is the same as $f(x)$. The second line says: when $f(x) < 0$, i.e., when the graph of f lies below the x-axis, the function $|f(x)|$ is the same as $-f(x)$.

So, to obtain the graph of $|f|$ from f, we keep the parts of the graph of f that are above the x-axis or touch it, and reflect (across the x-axis) those parts of the graph of f that lie below the x-axis; see figure above, right.

extra **Exercise 16.**   Describe in words, or sketch the graphs of the following functions. In each case, start with a known graph.

(a)* $y = -x^3/2$

(b) $y = -2x^3 - 1$

(c) $y = 2(x-1)^3 + 1$

(d)* $y = 3\sqrt{x+4} + 1$

(e) $y = -3\sqrt{x+4}$

(f)* $y = -\sqrt{x+4} - 3$

(g) $y = \dfrac{2}{x}$

(h) $y = -\dfrac{2}{x-4}$

(i) $y = 3 + \dfrac{2}{x-4}$

(j)* $y = 1 - |x|$

(k) $y = |1 - x|$

(l)* $y = 2|x-4| + 3$

In the sections that follow, we study commonly used (and very important!) functions, such as trigonometric, exponential and logarithmic functions.

7. Trigonometric Functions

What is in this section?

Trigonometric ratios and trigonometric functions; graphs; basic trigonometric identities and trigonometric equations; inverse trigonometric functions.

You will find a large selection of extra practice problems at the end of the section.

Angles, Degrees and Radians

Recall that a *positive angle* is measured counterclockwise from the direction of the positive x-axis. If it is measured clockwise, it is *negative*; see the figures below.

The units commonly used to measure angles are *degrees* (^{O}) and *radians* (rad). Unless stated otherwise, in calculus and elsewhere in mathematics, we use radians. For example, $\sin 1$ denotes the value of the trigonometric function sine for 1 radian (using a calculator, we find $\sin 1 \approx 0.841471$). By definition,

$$360^O = 2\pi \text{ rad, i.e., } 180^O = \pi \text{ rad}$$

In words, one full revolution equals $360^O = 2\pi$ rad. Dividing by 360, we get $1^O = 2\pi/360 = \pi/180$ rad (so, to convert from degrees to radians, we multiply by $\pi/180$). Conversely, one radian equals $180/\pi$ degrees (and in order to convert radians into degrees, we multiply by $180/\pi$).

For example, $90^O = 90\frac{\pi}{180} = \frac{\pi}{2}$ rad; as well, $\frac{5\pi}{4}$ rad $= \frac{5\pi}{4}\frac{180}{\pi} = 225^O$, etc.

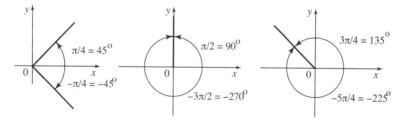

 It is a fairly common practice to omit the word "radians"(but not "degrees"); i.e., if no unit is specified, we mean radians. However, for many calculators, the default unit is degrees. So, we need to be careful in evaluating expressions that involve angles.

The most common angles are:

degrees	radians
0	0
30	$\pi/6$
45	$\pi/4$
60	$\pi/3$
90	$\pi/2$

degrees	radians
120	$2\pi/3$
135	$3\pi/4$
150	$5\pi/6$
180	π
210	$7\pi/6$
225	$5\pi/4$

degrees	radians
240	$4\pi/3$
270	$3\pi/2$
300	$5\pi/3$
315	$7\pi/4$
330	$11\pi/6$
360	2π

Example 1. Using a calculator, convert 71 degrees into radians, and 2.3 radians into degrees.

Solution. 71° equals $71\dfrac{\pi}{180} \approx 1.23918$ rad. As well, 2.3 rad equals $2.3\dfrac{180}{\pi} \approx 131.78029^{\circ}$.

Exercise 1.

(a) Express 225 degrees in radians.

(b) Express $7\pi/6$ radians in degrees.

(c) Express 76 degrees in radians.

(d) Express 3.7 radians in degrees.

Trigonometric Ratios

For an *acute* angle, the trigonometric ratios are defined as ratios of lengths of sides in a right triangle.

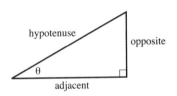

> **Basic Trigonometric Ratios (Acute Angles)**
>
> sine: $\sin\theta = \dfrac{\text{opposite}}{\text{hypotenuse}}$
>
> cosine: $\cos\theta = \dfrac{\text{adjacent}}{\text{hypotenuse}}$
>
> tangent: $\tan\theta = \dfrac{\sin\theta}{\cos\theta} = \dfrac{\text{opposite}}{\text{adjacent}}$

The remaining three ratios are usually defined as the reciprocals of $\sin\theta$, $\cos\theta$ and $\tan\theta$.

> **Trigonometric Ratios for Acute Angles**
>
> cosecant: $\csc\theta = \dfrac{1}{\sin\theta} = \dfrac{\text{hypotenuse}}{\text{opposite}}$
>
> secant: $\sec\theta = \dfrac{1}{\cos\theta} = \dfrac{\text{hypotenuse}}{\text{adjacent}}$
>
> cotangent: $\cot\theta = \dfrac{1}{\tan\theta} = \dfrac{\text{adjacent}}{\text{opposite}}$

Example 2. Assume that $\cos\theta = 3/5$, where $0 < \theta < \pi/2$. Find the values of the remaining five trigonometric ratios.

Solution. Since secant is the reciprocal of cosine, we know right away that $\sec\theta = 1/\cos\theta = 5/3$. To find the remaining ratios, we draw a right triangle, and label one of its (non-right) angles with θ; see below. Using the fact that $\cos\theta$ is the ratio of the adjacent side to the hypotenuse, we label the sides in the triangle as follows:

By the Pythagorean theorem, $a = \sqrt{5^2 - 3^2} = 4$. Thus, $\sin\theta = a/5 = 4/5$ and $\tan\theta = a/3 = 4/3$. Finally, $\csc\theta = 1/\sin\theta = 5/4$, and $\cot\theta = 1/\tan\theta = 3/4$.

Exercise 2. If $0 < \theta < \pi/2$, and $\csc\theta = 3$, find the values of $\sin\theta$, $\cos\theta$ and $\tan\theta$.

For obtuse or negative angles, the above definition does not apply, and we proceed as follows. Let θ be an angle defined by the x-axis and a line ℓ; see the figure below.

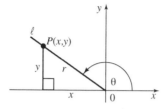

Choose a point P anywhere on the line ℓ (as long as it is not the origin), and denote by (x,y) its coordinates. Let r be the distance between P and the origin; thus, $r = \sqrt{x^2 + y^2} > 0$.

Trigonometric Ratios for General Angles
$\sin\theta = \dfrac{y}{r} \qquad \cos\theta = \dfrac{x}{r} \qquad \tan\theta = \dfrac{y}{x}$
$\csc\theta = \dfrac{1}{\sin\theta} = \dfrac{r}{y} \qquad \sec\theta = \dfrac{1}{\cos\theta} = \dfrac{r}{x} \qquad \cot\theta = \dfrac{1}{\tan\theta} = \dfrac{x}{y}$

Keep in mind that x and y are coordinates of a point, and thus can be positive or negative.

The ratios $\sin\theta$ and $\cos\theta$ are always defined, since r is never zero.

The ratios $\tan\theta$ and $\sec\theta$ are not defined when $x = 0$. In that case, P lies on the positive or negative y-axis, i.e., the angle is $\theta = \pi/2, 3\pi/2, 5\pi/2, \ldots, -\pi/2, -3\pi/2, -5\pi/2, \ldots$. So, $\tan\theta$ and $\sec\theta$ are not defined when $\theta = \pi/2 + k\pi$, where k is an integer.

The ratios $\cot\theta$ and $\csc\theta$ are not defined when $y = 0$, i.e., when P is on the x-axis. Thus, they are not defined when $\theta = 0, \pi, 2\pi, 3\pi, \ldots, -\pi, -2\pi, -3\pi, \ldots = k\pi$, where k is an integer.

Note that, for an acute angle (i.e., when $P(x,y)$ is in the first quadrant), the two definitions (the one for acute angles, and the one for general angles in the box above) agree.

 We compute

$$\sin^2\theta + \cos^2\theta = \frac{y^2}{r^2} + \frac{x^2}{r^2} = \frac{x^2 + y^2}{r^2} = 1$$

since $x^2 + y^2 = r^2$. Thus, we obtained the basic trigonometric identity:

$$\boxed{\sin^2\theta + \cos^2\theta = 1}$$

It is also possible (and useful!) to use the unit circle to define trigonometric ratios. Let P be the point of intersection of a circle of radius 1 and the line whose angle (positive or negative) with respect to the x-axis is θ; see the top figure on page 118. By definition, the coordinates of P are $(\cos\theta, \sin\theta)$.

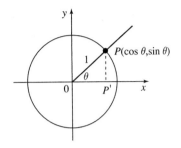

> **Unit Circle Definition**
> $\cos\theta = x$-coordinate of P
> $\sin\theta = y$-coordinate of P

Values of Trigonometric Ratios for Special Angles

(1) $\theta = 0$ (radians). There is no triangle, so we use the unit circle definition. The point P lies on the intersection of the unit circle and the x-axis, so its coordinates are $(1, 0)$. In other words,

$$\cos 0 = 1 \quad \text{and} \quad \sin 0 = 0$$

Thus, $\tan 0 = \sin 0 / \cos 0 = 0$, and $\sec 0 = 1/\cos 0 = 1$. The ratios $\cot 0$ and $\csc 0$ are not defined.

(2) $\theta = \pi/2$ (radians). The coordinates of P are $(0, 1)$, since this time P is the intersection of the unit circle and the y-axis. Thus,

$$\cos\frac{\pi}{2} = 0 \quad \text{and} \quad \sin\frac{\pi}{2} = 1$$

It follows that $\tan\frac{\pi}{2}$ and $\sec\frac{\pi}{2}$ are not defined. Finally, $\cot\frac{\pi}{2} = \cos\frac{\pi}{2} / \sin\frac{\pi}{2} = 0/1 = 0$ and $\csc\frac{\pi}{2} = 1/\sin\frac{\pi}{2} = 1$.

(3) $\theta = \pi$ (radians). For a change, we use the definition for general angles: pick a point $P(x = -1, y = 0)$ on the negative y-axis; we get $r = \sqrt{(-1)^2 + 0^2} = 1$, see figure below, left.

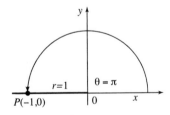

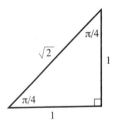

It follows that

$$\cos\pi = x/r = -1/1 = -1 \quad \text{and} \quad \sin\pi = y/r = 0/1 = 0$$

Consequently, $\tan\pi = 0$ and $\sec\pi = -1$. The ratios $\cot\pi$ and $\csc\pi$ are not defined.

(4) $\theta = \pi/4$ (radians). Consider the triangle, above right, with two equal sides. Each of the acute angles is 45° or $\pi/4$ radians. The values of the trigonometric ratios can be read from the triangle. Using the definition for acute angles, we get

$$\sin\frac{\pi}{4} = \frac{\text{opposite}}{\text{hypotenuse}} = \frac{1}{\sqrt{2}} \qquad \cos\frac{\pi}{4} = \frac{\text{adjacent}}{\text{hypotenuse}} = \frac{1}{\sqrt{2}} \qquad \tan\frac{\pi}{4} = \frac{\text{opposite}}{\text{adjacent}} = 1$$

If needed, we rationalize the denominator in sine and cosine: $\frac{1}{\sqrt{2}} = \frac{1}{\sqrt{2}} \cdot \frac{\sqrt{2}}{\sqrt{2}} = \frac{\sqrt{2}}{2}$.

(5) $\theta = \pi/6$ and $\theta = \pi/3$ (radians). The values of trigonometric ratios can be read from the triangle below.

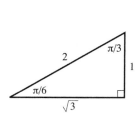 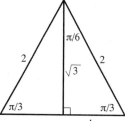

From the definition for acute angles, we get

$$\sin\frac{\pi}{6} = \frac{\text{opposite}}{\text{hypotenuse}} = \frac{1}{2} \qquad \cos\frac{\pi}{6} = \frac{\text{adjacent}}{\text{hypotenuse}} = \frac{\sqrt{3}}{2} \qquad \tan\frac{\pi}{6} = \frac{\text{opposite}}{\text{adjacent}} = \frac{1}{\sqrt{3}}$$

Similarly, $\sin\frac{\pi}{3} = \sqrt{3}/2$, $\cos\frac{\pi}{3} = 1/2$ and $\tan\frac{\pi}{3} = \sqrt{3}$.

 An easy way to remember the triangle that we used here is to start with an equilateral triangle of side 2 (all angles are equal to $\pi/3$) and drop the height from one of the vertices (above, right). The height is computed from the Pythagorean theorem: $\sqrt{2^2 - 1^2} = \sqrt{3}$.

Example 3. Find the values of $\sin\theta$, $\cos\theta$ and $\tan\theta$ for

(a) $\theta = 3\pi/4$ (b) $\theta = 2\pi/3$

Solution.

(a) We use the definition for general angles. The line that makes the angle of $\theta = \frac{3\pi}{4}$ radians with respect to the x-axis is a line with slope -1. Thus, we choose the point $(x = -1, y = 1)$ as P.

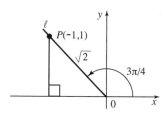

In that case, $r = \sqrt{1+1} = \sqrt{2}$, and it follows that

$$\sin\frac{3\pi}{4} = \frac{y}{r} = \frac{1}{\sqrt{2}} \qquad \cos\frac{3\pi}{4} = \frac{x}{r} = -\frac{1}{\sqrt{2}} \qquad \tan\frac{3\pi}{4} = \frac{y}{x} = -1$$

Of course, we could have used any other point on the line. For instance, had we taken $(-5, 5)$ for P, we would have $r = \sqrt{25 + 25} = \sqrt{50} = \sqrt{25 \cdot 2} = 5\sqrt{2}$, and thus

$$\sin\frac{3\pi}{4} = \frac{y}{r} = \frac{5}{5\sqrt{2}} = \frac{1}{\sqrt{2}}$$

$\cos\frac{3\pi}{4} = \frac{x}{r} = \frac{-5}{5\sqrt{2}} = -\frac{1}{\sqrt{2}}$, etc.

(b) We use the definition for general angles. Placing the triangle that we used in (5) to compute the ratios for $\pi/6$ and $\pi/3$, we see that we can use the point $(x = -1, y = \sqrt{3})$ as P; see figure on page 120.

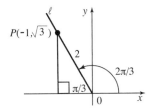

It follows that $r = \sqrt{x^2 + y^2} = \sqrt{1+3} = 2$, and thus, $\sin\frac{2\pi}{3} = y/r = \sqrt{3}/2$, $\cos\frac{2\pi}{3} = x/r = -1/2$ and $\tan\frac{2\pi}{3} = -\sqrt{3}$.

(try it!) **Exercise 3.** Find the values of $\sin\theta$, $\cos\theta$ and $\tan\theta$ for (a) $\theta = 5\pi/6$ and (b) $\theta = -\pi/6$.

(try it!) **Exercise 4.**   Find the values of $\sin\theta$, $\cos\theta$, $\tan\theta$ and $\sec\theta$ for $\theta = -3\pi/2$ using the unit circle definition.

Below is a table of values of trigonometric ratios (we have already calculated some entries; pick a few more entries and convince yourself that the values in the table are correct).

deg	rad	$\sin x$	$\cos x$	$\tan x$	$\csc x$	$\sec x$	$\cot x$
0	0	0	1	0	undefined	1	undefined
30	$\pi/6$	$1/2$	$\sqrt{3}/2$	$1/\sqrt{3}$	2	$2/\sqrt{3}$	$\sqrt{3}$
45	$\pi/4$	$1/\sqrt{2}$	$1/\sqrt{2}$	1	$\sqrt{2}$	$\sqrt{2}$	1
60	$\pi/3$	$\sqrt{3}/2$	$1/2$	$\sqrt{3}$	$2/\sqrt{3}$	2	$1/\sqrt{3}$
90	$\pi/2$	1	0	undefined	1	undefined	0
120	$2\pi/3$	$\sqrt{3}/2$	$-1/2$	$-\sqrt{3}$	$2/\sqrt{3}$	-2	$-1/\sqrt{3}$
135	$3\pi/4$	$1/\sqrt{2}$	$-1/\sqrt{2}$	-1	$\sqrt{2}$	$-\sqrt{2}$	-1
150	$5\pi/6$	$1/2$	$-\sqrt{3}/2$	$-1/\sqrt{3}$	2	$-2/\sqrt{3}$	$-\sqrt{3}$
180	π	0	-1	0	undefined	-1	undefined
210	$7\pi/6$	$-1/2$	$-\sqrt{3}/2$	$1/\sqrt{3}$	-2	$-2/\sqrt{3}$	$\sqrt{3}$
225	$5\pi/4$	$-1/\sqrt{2}$	$-1/\sqrt{2}$	1	$-\sqrt{2}$	$-\sqrt{2}$	1
240	$4\pi/3$	$-\sqrt{3}/2$	$-1/2$	$\sqrt{3}$	$-2/\sqrt{3}$	-2	$1/\sqrt{3}$
270	$3\pi/2$	-1	0	undefined	-1	undefined	0
300	$5\pi/3$	$-\sqrt{3}/2$	$1/2$	$-\sqrt{3}$	$-2/\sqrt{3}$	2	$-1/\sqrt{3}$
315	$7\pi/4$	$-1/\sqrt{2}$	$1/\sqrt{2}$	-1	$-\sqrt{2}$	$\sqrt{2}$	-1
330	$11\pi/6$	$-1/2$	$\sqrt{3}/2$	$-1/\sqrt{3}$	-2	$2/\sqrt{3}$	$-\sqrt{3}$
360	2π	0	1	0	undefined	1	undefined

Trigonometric Functions

Let x denote an angle. Using the general method of defining trigonometric ratios, we can compute the values of the functions $y = \sin x$ and $y = \cos x$ for all real numbers x (keep in mind that x represents an angle in radians).

Since the angles x and $x+2\pi$ are the same (think of an angle and what it looks like one full revolution later), it follows that

$$\boxed{\begin{array}{c} \sin x \text{ and } \cos x \text{ are periodic functions} \\[4pt] \sin(x + 2\pi) = \sin x \qquad \cos(x + 2\pi) = \cos x \end{array}}$$

These formulas state that the values of sin and cos repeat after 2π radians. In other words, $\sin x$ and $\cos x$ are *periodic* with a period equal to 2π.

 By definition, the *period* is the length of the *smallest* interval over which we can define a function (draw a graph), that, by repetition, generates the function in its entire domain (generates the whole graph). In the case of sin and cos, that interval is of length 2π; see the graphs of the two functions below.

We draw the graphs by plotting points. Given below is the graph of $y = \sin x$.

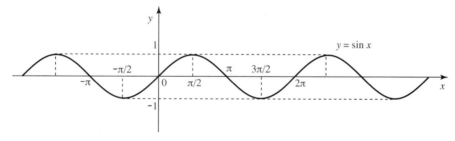

The part of the graph of $\sin x$ on the interval $[0, 2\pi]$ is called the *main period*. By repeating that part in both directions we produce the whole graph.

Note that $\sin x = 0$ when $x = \ldots, -2\pi, -\pi, 0, \pi, 2\pi, \ldots$. In words, $\sin x = 0$ when x is an integer multiple of π, i.e., when $x = k\pi$ (k is an integer).

$$\boxed{\sin x = 0 \quad \text{if and only if} \quad x = k\pi \ (k = \text{integer})}$$

Given below is the graph of $y = \cos x$.

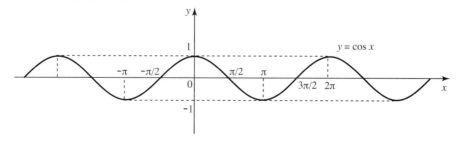

Note that $\cos x = 0$ when $x = \ldots, -3\pi/2, -\pi/2, \pi/2, 3\pi/2, \ldots$. In words, $\cos x = 0$ at $\pi/2$ and all points that are a multiple of π away from it. Thus,

$$\boxed{\cos x = 0 \quad \text{if and only if} \quad x = \tfrac{\pi}{2} + k\pi \ (k = \text{integer})}$$

The part of the graph of $\cos x$ over the interval $[0, 2\pi]$ is called the *main period*. That part is repeated in both directions to produce the whole graph.

By looking at the graphs of $\sin x$ and $\cos x$ we determine their range:

$$\boxed{-1 \le \sin x \le 1 \quad \text{and} \quad -1 \le \cos x \le 1}$$

In other words, the range of both $\sin x$ and $\cos x$ is the interval $[-1, 1]$.

Recall the basic trigonometric identity:

$$\boxed{\sin^2 x + \cos^2 x = 1}$$

Example 4. Sketch the graphs of $y = \sin x$, $y = \sin 2x$ and $y = \sin(x/2)$ in the same coordinate system.

Solution. How is the graph of $\sin 2x$ obtained from the graph of $\sin x$? By compression — recall that replacing x by $2x$ forces us to compress the graph of the original function horizontally by the factor of 2. Thus, the main period of $\sin 2x$ is the interval $[0, \pi]$, i.e., it is of length π.

Replacing $2x$ by ax in the above argument, we conclude that the period of $\sin(ax)$ is $2\pi/a$.

Likewise, the graph of $\sin(x/2)$ is obtained from the graph of $\sin x$ by expansion along the x-axis by the factor of 2. The period of $\sin(x/2)$ is (in this case, $a = 1/2$!) $2\pi/a = 2\pi/(1/2) = 4\pi$. See the figure below.

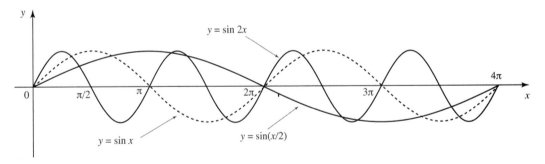

Arguing as in the example above, we show that the period of $\cos(ax)$ is $2\pi/a$.

$$\boxed{\text{The period of both } \sin(ax) \text{ and } \cos(ax) \text{ is } 2\pi/a.}$$

Example 5. Starting with the graph of $\sin x$, sketch the graphs of the functions $f(x) = -2\sin x$, $g(x) = \sin(x + \pi)$ and $h(x) = \sin x + \pi$.

Solution. To obtain the graph of $f(x) = -2\sin x$, we stretch the graph of $\sin x$ vertically by the factor of 2 (thus obtaining the graph of $2\sin x$), and then reflect it with respect to the x-axis; see figure at the top of the next page (only the main period is shown).

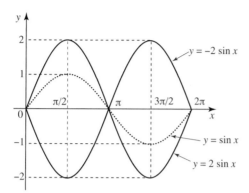

The function $\sin(x + \pi)$ is obtained from $\sin x$ by replacing x by $x + \pi$; thus, the graph of $g(x) = \sin(x + \pi)$ is obtained by shifting the graph of $\sin x$ π units to the left (see below, left).

The graph of $h(x) = \sin x + \pi$ is a vertical shift (by π units) of the graph of $\sin x$; see below, right.

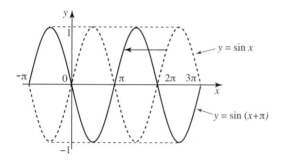
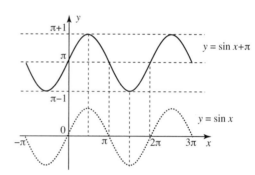

 Exercise 5. Explain how to obtain

(a) the graphs of $y = \cos 3x$ and $y = \cos 0.5x$ from the graph of $y = \cos x$

(b) the graphs of $y = -4 \cos x$ and $y = -\cos x - 4$ from the graph of $y = \cos x$

Example 6. Sketch the graph of the function $f(x) = 3\cos(2x + \pi) - 4$. Looking at the graph, determine the range of f.

Solution. We start with the graph of $\cos 2x$ (recall that $\cos 2x$ is a compressed version of $\cos x$, whose period is of length π).

Now how do we obtain the graph of $\cos(2x + \pi)$ from the graph of $\cos(2x)$? In other words, what should replace x in $2x$ to give $2x + \pi$?

If x is replaced by $x + \pi$, then $2x$ becomes $2(x + \pi) = 2x + 2\pi$, which is not what we need. So the reasoning — because π is added, it is a left shift for π units — is not correct.

Factor 2 out: $2x + \pi = 2(x + \pi/2)$. Thus, to obtain $\cos(2x + \pi)$ from $\cos 2x$ we need to replace x by $x + \pi/2$! So, the graph of $\cos 2x$ needs to be moved $\pi/2$ units to the left.

Next, we stretch the graph vertically by the factor of 3, and finally shift it down 4 units; see the figure on the next page.

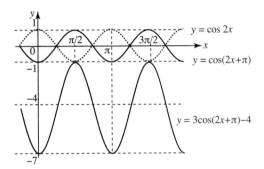

Looking at the graph, we see that the range of $f(x) = 3\cos(2x + \pi) - 4$ consists of all numbers between -7 and -1.

Note that we can calculate the range without looking at the graph. Since $\cos x$ is always between -1 and 1, we start with

$$-1 \leq \cos(2x + \pi) \leq 1$$

and then multiply by 3 and subtract 4 :

$$-3 \leq 3\cos(2x + \pi) \leq 3$$

$$-7 \leq \cos(2x + \pi) - 4 \leq -1$$

Thus, the range is $[-7, -1]$.

 Exercise 6. Sketch the graph of the function $f(x) = 2\sin(3x - \pi)$ and determine its range.

Consider the following triangle, where $0 < x < \pi/2$.

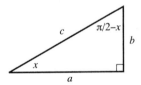

Using the definition of sin and cos, we get

$$\cos x = \frac{a}{c} \qquad \sin\left(\frac{\pi}{2} - x\right) = \frac{a}{c} \qquad \sin x = \frac{b}{c} \qquad \cos\left(\frac{\pi}{2} - x\right) = \frac{b}{c}$$

We have thus obtained the following formulas (for complementary angles):

$$\boxed{\sin\left(\tfrac{\pi}{2} - x\right) = \cos x \qquad \cos\left(\tfrac{\pi}{2} - x\right) = \sin x}$$

 There are many formulas in trigonometry, but fortunately, we usually use (and need to memorize) a very small number of them. A good way of memorizing formulas is to remember the way they have been derived, and/or the pictures or graphs involved. For instance, remembering what a $\pi/3$, $\pi/6$ triangle looks like (see (5) on page 119) we can recover values of all trig ratios for those angles; from the graph of $\sin x$, we can identify the range and period or list x-intercepts, etc.

The following picture will help us relate the values of sin and cos for angles x and $-x$. We use the unit circle definitions.

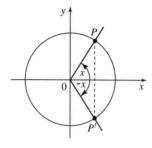

$$\boxed{\sin(-x) = -\sin x \qquad \cos(-x) = \cos x}$$

Why are the two formulas in the box correct?

Since both P and P' have the same x-coordinate, it follows that $\cos(-x) = \cos x$. The y-coordinates of P and P' are of opposite signs, and thus $\sin(-x) = -\sin x$.

The fact that $\cos(-x) = \cos x$ means that its graph is symmetric with respect to the y-axis (such functions are called *even functions*).

The graph of $\sin x$ is symmetric with respect to the origin (and is an example of an *odd function*).

Next, we list several useful formulas involving $\sin x$ and $\cos x$; we will illustrate their use in examples and exercises later in this section.

$$\boxed{\begin{array}{c} \text{Addition and Subtraction Formulas} \\ \sin(x \pm y) = \sin x \cos y \pm \cos x \sin y \\ \cos(x \pm y) = \cos x \cos y \mp \sin x \sin y \\[4pt] \text{Double Angle Formulas} \\ \sin 2x = 2 \sin x \cos x \\ \cos 2x = \cos^2 x - \sin^2 x = 2 \cos^2 x - 1 = 1 - 2 \sin^2 x \end{array}}$$

The function $y = \tan x = \sin x / \cos x$ is not defined when $\cos x = 0$; i.e., it is not defined when $x = \frac{\pi}{2} + k\pi$. The graph of $y = \tan x$ is given below.

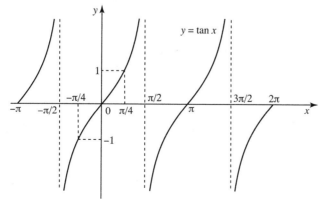

The function $y = \tan x$ is periodic, with period π. The part of the graph over the interval $(-\pi/2, \pi/2)$ is defined as its main period.

We see that $y = \tan x = 0$ whenever $\sin x = 0$; thus, zeros of $\tan x$ are $x = k\pi$, where k is an integer.

(try it!) **Exercise 7.** What is the period of $\tan(ax)$, where $a > 0$?

The function $y = \sec x = 1/\cos x$ has the same domain as $\tan x$. It is periodic, with period 2π. The picture below shows the graphs of both $\cos x$ and $\sec x$, obtained by plotting points.

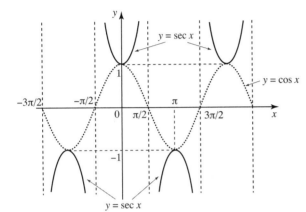

x	$\cos x$	$\sec x$
0	1	1
$\pi/4$	$1/\sqrt{2}$	$\sqrt{2}$
$\pi/2$	0	undefined
$3\pi/4$	$-1/\sqrt{2}$	$-\sqrt{2}$
π	-1	-1
...	...	...

Note that the range of $\sec x$ consists of two intervals, $(-\infty, -1]$ and $[1, \infty)$.

There is a useful relationship between tangent and secant, given by

$$\boxed{\tan^2 x + 1 = \sec^2 x}$$

This formula can be obtained by dividing the basic trig identity $\sin^2 x + \cos^2 x = 1$ by $\cos^2 x$:

$$\frac{\sin^2 x}{\cos^2 x} + \frac{\cos^2 x}{\cos^2 x} = \frac{1}{\cos^2 x} \quad \text{and so} \quad \tan^2 x + 1 = \sec^2 x$$

The graph of $\csc x = 1/\sin x$ is given below.

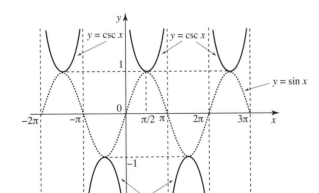

x	$\sin x$	$\csc x$
0	0	undefined
$\pi/4$	$1/\sqrt{2}$	$\sqrt{2}$
$\pi/2$	1	1
$3\pi/4$	$1/\sqrt{2}$	$\sqrt{2}$
π	0	undefined
...	...	...

The range of $\csc x$ consists of two intervals, $(-\infty, -1]$ and $[1, \infty)$.

The graph of $\cot x = 1/\tan x = \cos x / \sin x$ is given below (check by plotting points!).

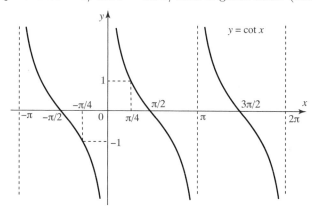

Since both have $\sin x$ in the denominator, the domains of $\csc x$ and $\cot x$ consist of all x such that $x \neq k\pi$ (k is an integer). The range of $\cot x$ consists of all real numbers.

How do we prove an identity?

We start with one side (usually the one that looks more complicated) and keep simplifying until we obtain the other side. Examples follow.

Example 7. Using formulas that we listed in this section, prove the following identities.

(a) $\sin(\pi - x) = \sin x$ (b) $(\sin x + \cos x)^2 = 1 + \sin 2x$

(c) $\dfrac{1}{1 - \sin x} + \dfrac{1}{1 + \sin x} = \dfrac{2}{\cos^2 x}$

Solution.

(a) Using the subtraction formula for the sine function, we simplify the left side as

$$\sin(\pi - x) = \sin \pi \cos x - \cos \pi \sin x = 0 \cdot \cos x - (-1)\sin x = \sin x$$

Recall that $\sin \pi = 0$ and $\cos \pi = -1$.

(b) We square the left side,

$$(\sin x + \cos x)^2 = \sin^2 x + 2\sin x \cos x + \cos^2 x$$

use the identity $\sin^2 x + \cos^2 x = 1$ and then the double angle formula for $\sin 2x$:

$$= 1 + 2\sin x \cos x = 1 + \sin 2x$$

(c) Computing the common denominator on the left side, we get

$$\frac{1}{1 - \sin x} + \frac{1}{1 + \sin x} = \frac{1 + \sin x}{(1 - \sin x)(1 + \sin x)} + \frac{1 - \sin x}{(1 - \sin x)(1 + \sin x)}$$

$$= \frac{1 + \sin x}{1 - \sin^2 x} + \frac{1 - \sin x}{1 - \sin^2 x} = \frac{2}{1 - \sin^2 x} = \frac{2}{\cos^2 x}$$

Recall that $(1 - \sin x)(1 + \sin x) = 1 - \sin^2 x$ by the difference of squares formula. In the last step, we used the identity $\sin^2 x + \cos^2 x = 1$, written as $\cos^2 x = 1 - \sin^2 x$.

try it! **Exercise 8.** Prove the following identities.

(a) $\sin(\pi/2 + x) = \cos x$ (b) $\cot^2 x + 1 = \csc^2 x$

(c) $\sin^2 x - \tan^2 x + \sin^2 x \tan^2 x = 0$

Example 8. Using addition formulas from page 125, prove the following identities.

(a) $\sin 2x = 2 \sin x \cos x$ (b) $\cos 2x = 1 - 2 \sin^2 x$

Solution.

(a) Write $2x = x + x$, and so

$$\sin 2x = \sin(x + x) = \sin x \cos x + \cos x \sin x = 2 \sin x \cos x$$

(b) As in (a),

$$\cos 2x = \cos(x + x) = \cos x \cos x - \sin x \sin x$$
$$= \cos^2 x - \sin^2 x$$

(now we use the identity $\sin^2 x + \cos^2 x = 1$ written as $\cos^2 x = 1 - \sin^2 x$)

$$= (1 - \sin^2 x) - \sin^2 x$$
$$= 1 - 2 \sin^2 x$$

Example 9. Show that $\cos 3x = 4 \cos^3 x - 3 \cos x$.

Solution. Write $3x = 2x + x$, and start with the addition formula for the cosine function:

$$\cos 3x = \cos(2x + x)$$
$$= \cos 2x \cos x - \sin 2x \sin x$$

Use the double angle formulas and simplify:

$$= (2 \cos^2 x - 1) \cos x - (2 \sin x \cos x) \sin x$$
$$= 2 \cos^3 x - \cos x - 2 \cos x \sin^2 x$$

Replace $\sin^2 x$ using the basic trigonometric identity $\sin^2 x = 1 - \cos^2 x$ and simplify:

$$= 2 \cos^3 x - \cos x - 2 \cos x (1 - \cos^2 x)$$
$$= 2 \cos^3 x - \cos x - 2 \cos x + 2 \cos^3 x$$
$$= 4 \cos^3 x - 3 \cos x$$

try it! **Exercise 9.**   Using the idea of the previous example, derive a formula that expresses $\sin 3x$ in terms of $\sin x$.

try it! **Exercise 10.**   Show that $\sin(x + y) \sin(x - y) = \sin^2 x - \sin^2 y$.

Trigonometric Equations

To find a solution to a trigonometric equation, we find all solutions in the main period first, and then add the multiple of the period. To find the solution(s) in the main period, we relate them to the angles in the first quadrant. See examples below.

In this subsection, the symbol k denotes an integer.

Example 10. Solve the following equations.

(a) $\sin x = 1$ (b) $\tan x = 1$

Solution.

(a) Looking at the graph of $\sin x$ (see page 121), we see that $x = \frac{\pi}{2}$ is the only place in the main period where $\sin x = 1$. Since the period of $\sin x$ is 2π, it follows that all solutions to $\sin x = 1$ are given by $x = \frac{\pi}{2} + 2k\pi$.

(b) There is only one solution to $\tan x = 1$ in its main period (see the graph of $\tan x$ on page 125), $x = \frac{\pi}{4}$. Since the period of the tangent is π, all solutions are given by $x = \frac{\pi}{4} + k\pi$.

Exercise 11. Solve the following equations.

(a) $\cos x = -1$ (b) $\tan x = -1$

Example 11. Solve the following equations.

(a) $\cos x = 1/2$ (b) $\sin x = -1/2$

Solution.

(a) From the graph below, we see that there are two solutions of the given equation in the main period.

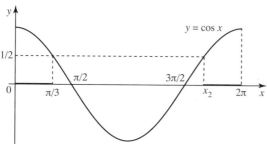

One of them is $x_1 = \frac{\pi}{3}$. Due to symmetry, the other solution is $\pi/3$ units to the left of 2π; thus, $x_2 = 2\pi - \pi/3 = 5\pi/3$. It follows that all solutions are given by $x = \frac{\pi}{3} + 2k\pi$ and $x = \frac{5\pi}{3} + 2k\pi$.

How do we know that $\cos(\pi/3) = 1/2$?

Earlier in this section, we discussed values of trig functions for some special angles, and $\pi/3$ was one of them. Suggestion: it is a good idea to memorize the values of sine, cosine and tangent for $\theta = \pi/6$, $\pi/4$ and $\pi/3$ (or, better yet, remember the triangles from which you can get these values); as well, memorize the graphs of sine, cosine and tangent, so that you will know the values of these functions at $\theta = 0$, $\pi/2$, π, etc.

(b) The graph below shows that there are two solutions of $\sin x = -1/2$ in the main period, labelled x_1 and x_2.

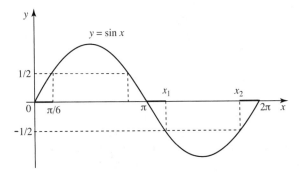

We know that $\sin \frac{\pi}{6} = \frac{1}{2}$. Since we are looking for the values where $\sin$ is equal to $-1/2$, we need to relate x_1 and x_2 to $\frac{\pi}{6}$. We see that x_1 is $\pi/6$ units to the right of π, so $x_1 = \pi + \pi/6 = 7\pi/6$. As well, x_2 is $\pi/6$ units to the left of 2π; thus, $x_2 = 2\pi - \pi/6 = 11\pi/6$.

So, the solutions are $x = \frac{7\pi}{6} + 2k\pi$ and $x = \frac{11\pi}{6} + 2k\pi$.

Exercise 12. Solve the following equations.
(a) $\cos x = -\sqrt{3}/2$ (b) $\tan x = \sqrt{3}$ (c) $\sin x = \sqrt{2}/2$

Example 12. Solve the equation $\sin 2x = \cos x$.

Solution. Using the double angle formula, and then factoring, we get

$$\sin 2x = \cos x$$
$$2\sin x \cos x = \cos x$$
$$\cos x(2\sin x - 1) = 0$$

Thus, $\cos x = 0$ or $2\sin x - 1 = 0$.

If $\cos x = 0$, then $x = \frac{\pi}{2} + k\pi$ (this equation was solved earlier).

If $\sin x = 1/2$, then $x = \frac{\pi}{6} + 2k\pi$ and $x = \frac{5\pi}{6} + 2k\pi$ (look at the graph of Example 11(b)).

Thus, the solution is $x = \frac{\pi}{2} + k\pi$, $x = \frac{\pi}{6} + 2k\pi$ and $x = \frac{5\pi}{6} + 2k\pi$.

Exercise 13. Solve the equation $\sin 2x = \sin x$.

Example 13. Solve the equation $2 + \cos 2x = 3\cos x$.

Solution. Using the double angle formula for $\cos x$, we write $2 + \cos 2x = 3\cos x$ as

$$2 + 2\cos^2 x - 1 = 3\cos x$$

Thus $2\cos^2 x - 3\cos x + 1 = 0$, and $(2\cos x - 1)(\cos x - 1) = 0$.

It follows that $2\cos x - 1 = 0$, and $\cos x = 1/2$ (in which case $x = \frac{\pi}{3} + 2k\pi$ and $x = \frac{5\pi}{3} + 2k\pi$, see Example 11(a)) and $\cos x - 1 = 0$, and $\cos x = 1$ (in which case $x = 2k\pi$). Thus, the solution is $x = 2k\pi$, $x = \frac{\pi}{3} + 2k\pi$ and $x = \frac{5\pi}{3} + 2k\pi$.

 Examples 12 and 13 suggest that, when an equation contains different arguments of trig functions (such as sin and/or cos of x and $2x$), it is a good idea to reduce the expressions to a single argument (which is usually x).

Example 14. Solve the equation $4\sin 2x \cos 2x = 1$.

Solution. If, in the double angle formula $2\sin x \cos x = \sin 2x$ we replace x by $2x$, we get $2\sin 2x \cos 2x = \sin 4x$. Thus, the given equation reduces to

$$4\sin 2x \cos 2x = 2(2\sin 2x \cos 2x) = 2\sin 4x = 1$$

i.e., $\sin 4x = 1/2$.

Recall that the solutions of $\sin A = 1/2$ in the main period (of the sine functions) are $A = \pi/6$ or $A = 5\pi/6$; see the figure below.

Thus, all solutions of $\sin A = 1/2$ are $A = \frac{\pi}{6} + 2k\pi$ and $A = \frac{5\pi}{6} + 2k\pi$.

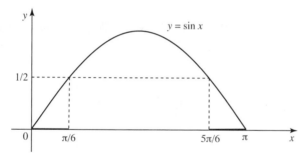

Thus (replacing A by $4x$), we get $4x = \frac{\pi}{6} + 2k\pi$ and $4x = \frac{5\pi}{6} + 2k\pi$; so the solutions to the given equation are $x = \frac{\pi}{24} + \frac{k\pi}{2}$ and $x = \frac{5\pi}{24} + \frac{k\pi}{2}$.

(try it!) **Exercise 14.** Solve the equation $2\cos 2x - 1 = 0$.

(?) How do we simplify trig answers?

Imagine that we are solving a problem involving trig functions and get $x = \pi + k\pi$ (k is an integer). However, the answer in the textbook says $x = k\pi$. Are we correct? Is $x = \pi + k\pi$ the same as $x = k\pi$? Likewise, is $x = \frac{5\pi}{6} + k\pi$ the same as $x = \frac{-\pi}{6} + k\pi$?

The answer in both cases is yes! Just because it looks different, it does not have to be!

If you are not sure whether or not the two answers are the same, expand them by taking a few values for k, say, $k = 0$, $k = 1$, $k = 2$, $k = 3$, $k = -1$, $k = -2$. So

$$\pi + k\pi = \pi, 2\pi, 3\pi, 4\pi, 0, -\pi, \ldots \quad \text{and} \quad k\pi = 0, \pi, 2\pi, 3\pi, -\pi, -2\pi, \ldots$$

and we see that $\pi + k\pi$ is equal to $k\pi$! Likewise,

$$\frac{5\pi}{6} + k\pi = \frac{5\pi}{6}, \frac{11\pi}{6}, \frac{17\pi}{6}, \frac{-\pi}{6}, \frac{-7\pi}{6}, \ldots \quad \text{and} \quad \frac{-\pi}{6} + k\pi = \frac{-\pi}{6}, \frac{5\pi}{6}, \frac{11\pi}{6}, \frac{-7\pi}{6}, \frac{-13\pi}{6}, \ldots$$

show that $\frac{5\pi}{6} + k\pi = \frac{-\pi}{6} + k\pi$.

 Exercise 15.   (a) Convince yourself that the solutions $x = \frac{\pi}{2} + 2k\pi$ and $x = \frac{3\pi}{2} + 2k\pi$ to the equation $\cos x = 0$ can be written in the form $x = \frac{\pi}{2} + k\pi$.

(b) Show that $(2k + 1)\pi = -\pi + 2k\pi$.

Inverse Trigonometric Functions

Even though inverse trig functions are not part of a high school curriculum, we discuss them here for two reasons: first, to apply the concepts we learned about inverse functions in Section 6, and second, to further our experience in working with trig functions.

Inverse trig functions are usually the topic where the university/college calculus course passes from a review of high school material to introducing new material — and to ease this passage a bit, we suggest that you read this and think about it. It is not difficult!

Although there are six trigonometric functions, we will construct inverses of only two, $\sin x$ and $\tan x$, since they appear most often in theory and applications. As well, after seeing how these two are constructed, if needed, you will have the knowledge and confidence to construct inverse functions of the remaining four functions.

 Recall that the domain of $\sin x$ consists of all real numbers, and its range is $[-1, 1]$. Looking at its graph (below, left), we see that it does not pass the horizontal line test (HLT for short): as a matter of fact, any horizontal line that crosses the graph crosses it infinitely many times. Thus, the function $y = \sin x$, *defined on* $\mathbb{R}$, does not have an inverse function!

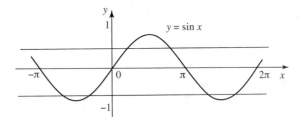 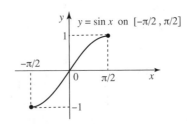

So, for the purpose of defining the inverse function, we restrict the domain of $\sin x$ to $[-\pi/2, \pi/2]$; see the figure above, right. Note that this graph does satisfy the HLT.

As well, extending the graph to the left of $-\pi/2$ or to the right of $\pi/2$ would violate the test. Thus, the interval $[-\pi/2, \pi/2]$ is the largest interval on which the graph of $\sin x$ satisfies the HLT.

Note that the length of the interval $[-\pi/2, \pi/2]$ is π. Of course, we can find other intervals for which $\sin x$ satisfies the HLT, but none is longer than π. That is what we meant by "the largest interval" in the sentence above.

So the function $f(x) = \sin x$, for x in $[-\pi/2, \pi/2]$ has the inverse function. In the arrow diagram (below, left), we show the domain and range of $\sin x$.

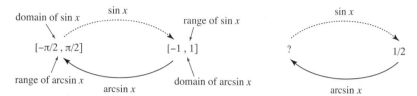

We define $y = \arcsin x$ to be the inverse function of $\sin x$. Quite often, the generic inverse function symbol $y = \sin^{-1} x$ is used. Since this might lead to confusion, we will use $y = \arcsin x$.

The meaning of $y = \sin^{-1} x$ depends on the context. If the context is inverse functions, then $y = \sin^{-1} x$ is the same as $y = \arcsin x$. But if it is not, $y = \sin^{-1} x$ could represent the reciprocal of $\sin x$, which is $y = \csc x$. It is very important to know the context, since $y = \arcsin x$ and $y = \csc x$ are *not* the same function!

Now that we clarified the notation, let us list the properties of $y = \arcsin x$.

First of all, from the diagram above (left) we see that the domain of $\arcsin x$ is $[-1, 1]$, and the range is $[-\pi/2, \pi/2]$.

One way to think about this is the following: function $\sin x$ takes an angle in $[-\pi/2, \pi/2]$ and assigns a number between -1 and 1 to it. So, arcsin will take a number between -1 and 1 and assign the angle in $[-\pi/2, \pi/2]$ to it.

How do we calculate $\arcsin(1/2)$? See diagram above, right.

To calculate $\arcsin(1/2)$, we need to find the angle in $[-\pi/2, \pi/2]$ whose sine is $1/2$; from memory, we know that $\sin(\pi/6) = 1/2$; thus, $\arcsin(1/2) = \pi/6$.

What is $\arcsin 0$?

To find $\arcsin 0$ means to find the angle whose sine is 0 *and* which lies in the interval $[-\pi/2, \pi/2]$. There are many angles whose sine is zero: $0, \pi, -\pi, 2\pi, -2\pi, \ldots$ but there is *only one*, namely 0, that lies in the range $[-\pi/2, \pi/2]$ of $\arcsin x$. Thus, $\arcsin 0 = 0$.

What is $\arcsin 2.3$?

To find $\arcsin 2.3$, we would have to identify the angle whose sine is 2.3. Since the sine of an angle is always between -1 and 1, we conclude that $\arcsin 2.3$ is not defined.

To review: remembering the definition of the inverse function (box on page 104), we write

$$\boxed{\text{if } \sin a = b, \text{ then } \arcsin b = a.}$$

(try it!)   **Exercise 16.** Find $\arcsin 1$, $\arcsin(-1/2)$, $\arcsin(1/\sqrt{2})$ and $\arcsin(-1/\sqrt{2})$.

Recall that the function and its inverse cancel each other. Thus,

$$\arcsin(\sin x) = x, \quad \text{if } x \in [-\pi/2, \pi/2] \qquad \sin(\arcsin x) = x, \quad \text{if } x \in [-1, 1]$$

We reflect the graph of $y = \sin x$ with respect to $y = x$ to obtain the graph of $y = \arcsin x$; see below.

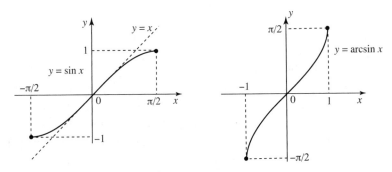

Now we retrace our steps to construct the inverse function to $\tan x$. Again, $\tan x$ in its domain does not satisfty the horizontal line test; see below, left.

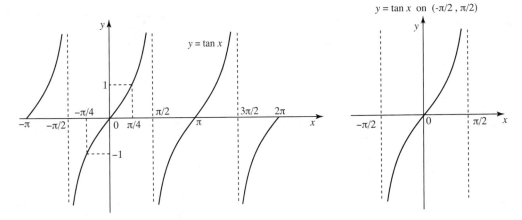

For the purpose of defining the inverse function, we restrict the domain of $\tan x$ to $(-\pi/2, \pi/2)$; see figure above, right. The range still consists of all real numbers.

Note that $(-\pi/2, \pi/2)$ is the largest interval on which the graph of $\tan x$ satisfies the horizontal line test ("largest" in the same sense as explained for $\sin x$).

In the arrow diagram (below) we show the domain and range of $\tan x$.

We define $y = \arctan x$ to be the inverse function of $\tan x$.

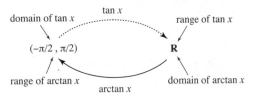

Quite often, the symbol $y = \tan^{-1} x$ is used; we will stick to $y = \arctan x$. The warning that we stated for $\sin x$ applies here as well: the meaning of $y = \tan^{-1} x$ depends on the context. If the context is inverse functions, then $y = \tan^{-1} x$ is the same as $y = \arctan x$. But if it is not, $y = \tan^{-1} x$ could represent the reciprocal of $\tan x$, which is $y = \cot x$. Keep in mind that $y = \arctan x$ and $y = \cot x$ are *not* the same function!

From the diagram (bottom of page 134) we see that the domain of $\arctan x$ is $\mathbb{R}$, and the range is $(-\pi/2, \pi/2)$. In words, the function $\tan x$ takes an angle in $(-\pi/2, \pi/2)$ and returns a real number. The function $\arctan x$ takes a real number and assigns the angle in $(-\pi/2, \pi/2)$ to it.

So how do we calculate $\arctan 1$? See the diagram below.

To calculate $\arctan 1$, we need to find the angle in $(-\pi/2, \pi/2)$ whose tangent is 1; from memory, we know that $\tan(\pi/4) = 1$; thus, $\arctan 1 = \pi/4$.

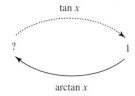

As another example, we calculate $\arctan 0$. This means that we need to find the angle whose tangent is 0 *and* which lies in the interval $(-\pi/2, \pi/2)$. There are many angles whose tangent is zero: 0, π, $-\pi$, 2π, $-2\pi, \ldots$ but there is *only one*, namely 0, that lies in the range $(-\pi/2, \pi/2)$ of $\arctan x$. Thus, $\arctan 0 = 0$.

Reasoning in the same way, we find that $\arctan(-1/\sqrt{3}) = -\pi/6$.

Using a calculator, we find that $\tan 0.57 \approx 0.640969$; thus, $\arctan 0.640969 \approx \tan 0.57$. (Keep in mind that angles are in radians! So 0.57 is 0.57 radians.) Likewise $\arctan 7.3 \approx 1.434658$ since $\tan 1.434658 \approx 7.3$.

We have seen many examples above, so let's remember that

$$\boxed{\text{if } \tan a = b, \text{ then } \arctan b = a.}$$

We reflect the graph of $y = \tan x$ with respect to the line $y = x$ to obtain the graph of $y = \arctan x$; see below.

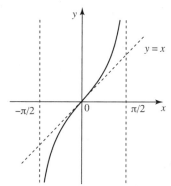

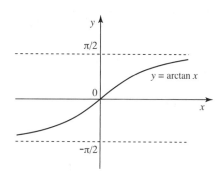

Cancellation formulas for tan and arctan are

$$\arctan(\tan x) = x, \quad \text{if } x \in (-\pi/2, \pi/2) \qquad \tan(\arctan x) = x, \quad \text{if } x \in \mathbb{R}$$

(try it!) **Exercise 17.** Find $\arctan(-1)$, $\arctan(1/\sqrt{3})$, $\arctan(\sqrt{3})$ and $\arctan(-1\sqrt{3})$.

Frequently Asked Question

Which trig formulas do I have to memorize?

There are many formulas in trigonometry, but the good news is that (not just in calculus) only a few of them are actually used. Those that are used appear in boxes in this section.

Suggestion: memorize the graphs of $\sin x$, $\cos x$ and $\tan x$! The graphs will help you remember what the ranges and the periods of these functions are, as well as the solutions of important equations, such as $\sin x = 0$, or $\cos x = 1$, or $\tan x = 1$.

As well, memorize the special triangles that were used to calculate the values of trig functions for $\pi/6$, $\pi/4$ and $\pi/3$.

Additional Exercises

Note: working on some questions, you will need to recall the convention about angles: if no unit is explicitly stated, then the unit is radians.

(extra) **Exercise 18.**

(a) Convert 315 degrees to radians.   (b) Express -240° in radians

(c)* Express $-5\pi/3$ radians in degrees   (d) Convert $11\pi/6$ radians to degrees

(e)* Convert π radians to degrees   (f)* Convert π degrees to radians

[Note: just because the measure of an angle has π in it, it does not mean that the units are radians!]

(g) Convert 4 radians to degrees   (h) Convert 4 degrees to radians

[Note: just because the measure of an angle has no π in it, it does not mean that the units are degrees!]

(try it!) **Exercise 19.** Let ABC be a right triangle, where $\angle C = 90^\circ$; see the figure below.

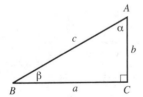

(a)* Given that $a = 21$ and $b = 20$, find $\sin\alpha$, $\cos\alpha$, $\sin\beta$, and $\cos\beta$.

(b)* Given that $\cos\beta = 12/13$ and $c = 13$, find a, b, $\sin\beta$, and $\tan\beta$.

(c)* Given that $c = 1$ and $b = 0.6$, find all six trigonometric ratios for angle α.

(extra)   **Exercise 20.**   Given is one trigonometric ratio; find the values of the remaining ratios. Assume that θ is in the first quadrant, i.e., $0 < \theta < \pi/2$.

(a) $\sin\theta = 1/5$ (b)* $\tan\theta = 3$ (c) $\sec\theta = 5/3$ (d) $\cot\theta = 1/6$

(extra)   **Exercise 21.**   In this exercise we practice common notation for angles. Assume that k is an integer.

(a) List the angles $\theta = \pi/3 + k\pi$ for $k = -3, -2, -1, 0, 1, 2, 3$.

(b) List the angles $\beta = \pi/4 + 2k\pi$ for $k = -3, -1, 0, 1, 4, 5$.

(c) List the angles $\alpha = \pi/2 + k\pi/2$ for $k = -4, -3, -2, -1, 0, 1, 2$.

(d) Express angles $\ldots, -\pi, -\pi/2, 0, \pi/2, \pi, 3\pi/2, 2\pi, \ldots$ in abbreviated notation (i.e., using a formula involving k)

(e)* Express angles $\ldots, -4\pi/3, -2\pi/3, 0, 2\pi/3, 4\pi/3, 2\pi, 8\pi/3, \ldots$ in abbreviated notation (i.e., using a formula involving k)

(f)* Express angles $\ldots, -5\pi/3, -\pi/3, \pi/3, \pi, 5\pi/3, 7\pi/3, 3\pi, \ldots$ in abbreviated notation (i.e., using a formula involving k)

(g) Show that the two formulas $k\pi$ and $2\pi + k\pi$ represent the same angles.

(h) Show that the two formulas $-\pi/2 + 2k\pi$ and $3\pi/2 + 2k\pi$ represent the same angles.

(i) Show that the two formulas $\pi/2 + 2k\pi$ and $3\pi/2 + 2k\pi$ can be summarized in the single formula $\pi/2 + k\pi$.

(extra)   **Exercise 22.**   What quadrant do the following angles belong to? (Keep in mind: no units mentioned means that units are radians.)

(a)* $36\pi/7$ (b)* 999° (c)* 989° (d)* $44\pi/5$ (e) -550°

(f) -530° (g) 10 (h) 11 (i) -4 (j) -13

(extra)   **Exercise 23.*** Assume that a straight line makes an angle θ with the positive x-axis. Which trig function of θ is equal to its slope?

(extra)   **Exercise 24.**   Without a calculator, determine the sign of the following expressions.

(a)* $\tan(13\pi/3)$ (b)* $\sin(500^{\circ})$ (c)* $\cos(37\pi)$ (d)* $\sin(\pi/12) + \cos(\pi/7)$

(e) $\sec 8$ (f) $\sin(-3)$ (g) $\cos 14$ (h) $\tan(-6)$

(extra)   **Exercise 25.**   Without a calculator, determine which of the following is larger.

(a)* $\sin 1^{\circ}$ or $\sin 1$ (b)* $\cos 2^{\circ}$ or $\cos 2$ (c) $\tan 1^{\circ}$ or $\tan 1$

(extra)   **Exercise 26.**   Identify the period of each function.

(a) $\cos 3x$ (b) $\sin 2.5x$ (c) $\tan(x/6)$ (d)* $\cos(2x/5)$

(e) $2\cos 4x$ (f) $4\sin 2x$ (g)* $\tan 0.4x + 6$ (h) $\cos 15x$

(extra) **Exercise 27.** Starting with a known graph, sketch, or describe in words the graph of each function. As well, determine its range.

(a)* $\cos(x + \pi/4)$ (b) $\cos 4x$ (c)* $\sin(x - \pi)$ (d) $\sin x - \pi/2$

(e) $2 - \cos x$ (f)* $\tan x + 1$ (g) $2 \cos 3x$ (h) $-3 \cos x/4$

(i) $2 \sin(x + \pi/4) + 1$ (j) $\sin(2x + \pi/4)$ (k)* $\cos(4x + \pi)$ (l) $-2 \cos(4x + \pi)$

(m)* $\sin(x/2 - \pi/3)$ (n) $\tan 3x + 10$ (o) $1 + 2 \cos(3x + 4)$ (p) $5 - 4 \sin(3x - 2)$

(extra) **Exercise 28.** By drawing graphs, convince yourself that the following identities are true.

(a)* $\sin(-x) = -\sin x$ (b) $\cos(-x) = \cos x$ (c) $\sin(x + \pi) = -\sin x$

(d) $\cos(x + \pi) = -\cos x$ (e)* $\sin\left(\frac{\pi}{2} - x\right) = \cos x$ (f) $\cos\left(\frac{\pi}{2} - x\right) = \sin x$

(extra) **Exercise 29.** Using $\cos 2x = 2\cos^2 x - 1$ express $\cos^2 x$ in terms of $\cos 2x$ and use it to graph the function $y = \cos^2 x$.

(extra) **Exercise 30.*** Using $\cos 2x = 1 - 2\sin^2 x$ express $\sin^2 x$ in terms of $\cos 2x$ and use it to graph the function $y = \sin^2 x$.

(extra) **Exercise 31.** Simplify the following expressions.

(a)* $\sec^2 x - \sin^2 x - \cos^2 x$ (b)* $\dfrac{\cos x}{1 + \sin x} + \tan x$

(c)* $\dfrac{\sin x}{1 + \cos x} + \dfrac{\sin x}{1 - \cos x}$ (d) $(\sin x + \cos x)^2 + (\sin x - \cos x)^2$

(extra) **Exercise 32.** Solve each equation. Express your answer in radians. For some equations, you will need a calculator.

(a) $\cos x = -1$ (b) $\cos 4x = -1$ (c)* $\cos(4x - \pi) = -1$

(d) $\sin x = -1/\sqrt{2}$ (e) $\sin(x/3) = -1/\sqrt{2}$ (f) $\sin(x/3 - 2) = -1/\sqrt{2}$

(g)* $\tan x = -\sqrt{3}/3$ (h)* $\cot x = -1$ (i)* $\cos x = \sqrt{3}/2$

(j) $\sin x = 0.4$ (k) $\cos x = -0.3$ (l)* $\tan x = 12$

(m)* $\sec x = -4$ (n) $\sec x = 2.5$ (o) $\tan x = -1.5$

(extra) **Exercise 33.** Solve each equation, or else say that there are no solutions.

(a) $\sin x + \cos x = 3$ (b)* $\tan x + \cot x = 0.5$ (c)* $\cos^2 x - \cos x - 2 = 0$

(extra) **Exercise 34.** Use appropriate addition or subtraction formula for sin or cos to prove each identity.

(a) $\cos(x + \pi) = -\cos x$ (b) $\cos(\pi/2 - x) = \sin x$ (c) $\sin(\pi/2 - x) = \cos x$

(d) $\sec(\pi/2 - x) = \csc x$ (e)* $\cot(\pi/2 - x) = \tan x$ (f) $\sec(x + \pi) = -\sec x$

extra **Exercise 35.** Prove the following identities.

(a)* $\dfrac{1 - \sin x}{\cos x} = \dfrac{\cos x}{1 + \sin x}$

(b)* $\dfrac{1}{1 + \tan^2 x} + \dfrac{1}{1 + \cot^2 x} = 1$

extra **Exercise 36.** Find the numeric value of each expression, or else say that it is not defined.

(a) $\arcsin(\sqrt{3}/2)$ (b) $\arcsin(-\sqrt{3}/2)$ (c)* $\arcsin(-1)$ (d)* $\arcsin \pi$

(e) $\arctan(-\sqrt{3})$ (f)* $\arctan(-1)$ (g) $\arctan(-2)$ (h) $\arctan 24$

extra **Exercise 37.** To define the inverse $y = \arccos x$, we declare the domain of $\cos x$ to be the interval $[0, \pi]$. Find the numeric value of each expression (or else say that it is not defined).

(a) $\arccos 0$ (b)* $\arccos(-1)$ (c)* $\arccos \sqrt{2}$ (d) $\arccos(1/\sqrt{2})$

8. Exponential and Logarithmic Functions

What is in this section?

Laws of exponents and logarithms; exponents and logarithms as inverses; exponential and logarithmic functions, graphs and properties; solving equations involving exponential and logarithmic functions.

You will find a large selection of extra practice problems at the end of the section.

Exponential Functions

An *exponential function* is a function of the form $y = a^x$, where the basis a is positive and the exponent x is any real number. Although we can sometimes compute a power of a negative number, such as $(-4)^3$, the exponential function is defined only for positive bases. The domain of $y = a^x$ consists of all real numbers.

Since $a^x > 0$ for all x (remember that $a > 0$!), it follows that the range of the exponential function $y = a^x$ consists of positive numbers only. By plotting points, we obtain the graph of $y = a^x$.

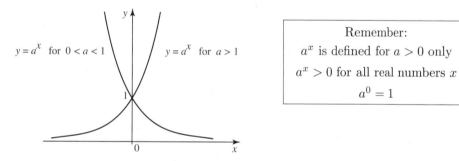

$y = a^x$ for $0 < a < 1$ $y = a^x$ for $a > 1$

Remember:

a^x is defined for $a > 0$ only

$a^x > 0$ for all real numbers x

$a^0 = 1$

Since $a^0 = 1$, the graph of $y = a^x$ goes through the point $(0, 1)$ on the y-axis. If $a > 1$, the graph of $y = a^x$ is increasing; for $0 < a < 1$, it is decreasing; see Example 1 below, where we graph 2^x and $(1/2)^x$. In either case, the x-axis is its horizontal asymptote.

What about a^x for negative values of a?

For $x = 1/2$, we get $a^x = a^{1/2} = \sqrt{a}$, which is not a real number; so $1/2$ is not in the domain of a^x. Likewise, for $x = 1/4$ we get $a^x = a^{1/4} = \sqrt[4]{a}$, which is again not real. Similarly, we can check that $x = 3/8$, $x = -1/2$, or $x = 7/100$ do not belong to the domain of a^x either (as a matter of fact, there are infinitely many numbers x for which a^x is not defined if a is negative).

This fact about the domain makes the function a^x for negative values of a quite complicated (and in a way useless), and thus we do not study it in calculus (however, such functions make lots of sense for complex numbers.)

Example 1. Sketch the graphs of $y = 2^x$ and $y = 2^{-x}$ in the same coordinate system.

Solution. Since $2^{-x} = (2^{-1})^x = (1/2)^x$, we need to graph the functions $y = 2^x$ and $y = (1/2)^x$.

We plot points: when $x = 0$, we get $2^0 = 1$ and $(1/2)^0 = 1$. For $x = 3$, we compute $2^3 = 8$ and $(1/2)^3 = 1/2^3 = 1/8$. Likewise, when $x = -2$ we get $2^{-2} = 1/2^2 = 1/4$ and

$$\left(\frac{1}{2}\right)^{-2} = \frac{1}{(1/2)^2} = \frac{1}{1/4} = 4$$

Taking a few more values of x (see the table below), we obtain the following graphs.

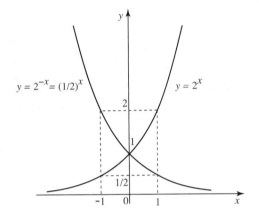

x	2^x	$(1/2)^x$
0	1	1
1	2	1/2
2	4	1/4
3	8	1/8
-1	1/2	2
-2	1/4	4
...	...	...

As a matter of fact, we did not have to plot points — the graph of $y = 2^{-x}$ is the symmetric image of the graph of $y = 2^x$ with respect to the y-axis (remember the general rule from Section 6: to obtain the graph of $f(-x)$ we take the graph of $f(x)$ and mirror it with respect to the y-axis).

Example 2. Sketch the graphs of $y = 2^x$, $y = 3^x$ and $y = 5^x$ in the same coordinate system.

Solution. By computing the values of the given functions for different values of x and plotting points, we obtain the following graphs.

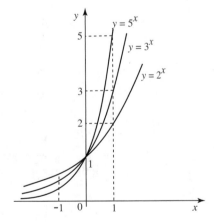

x	2^x	3^x	5^x
0	1	1	1
1	2	3	5
2	4	9	25
-1	1/2	1/3	1/5
-2	1/4	1/9	1/25
...	...	...	...

We see from the graphs that, as x approaches ∞, a^x approaches ∞ more quickly as a increases. Likewise, as x approaches $-\infty$, a^x approaches zero more quickly as a increases.

Example 3. Starting with the graph of $y = 3^x$, sketch the graphs of the functions $f(x) = 3^x - 1$, $g(x) = 3^{x-1}$ and $h(x) = -3^{-x}$.

Solution. The function $f(x)$ is obtained by subtracting 1 from 3^x; thus, to graph $f(x)$ we shift the graph of 3^x one unit down (below, left).

Replacing x in 3^x by $x - 1$, we obtain $g(x)$; thus, by moving the graph of 3^x one unit to the right we obtain the graph of $g(x) = 3^{x-1}$ (below, centre).

The fact that $g(x) = 3^{x-1} = 3^x 3^{-1} = \frac{1}{3} 3^x$ gives an alternative way to graph $g(x)$: start with 3^x and compress it vertically by the factor of 3.

Recall that replacing x by $-x$ produces a graph that is symmetric to the given graph with respect to the y-axis. So to graph $h(x) = -3^{-x}$ we take 3^x, mirror it with respect to the y-axis (thus getting 3^{-x}) and then mirror that graph with respect to the x-axis (below, right).

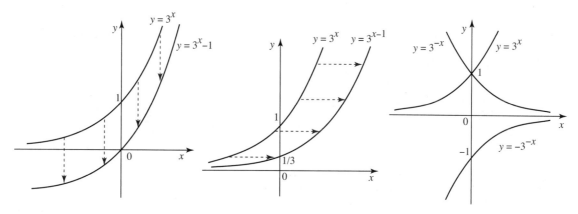

try it!   **Exercise 1.** State the transformations necessary to sketch the graphs of the following functions, starting with the graph of $y = 2^x$.
  (a) $y = 2^x + 4$ (b) $y = 2^{x-4}$ (c) $y = -2^x$ (d) $y = -2^{-x}$

try it!   **Exercise 2.** Sketch the graphs of $y = 2^{-x}$, $y = 3^{-x}$ and $y = 4^{-x}$ in the same coordinate system. Compare the three graphs in terms of their behaviour as x approaches ∞ and $-\infty$.

Although algebraic rules for working with exponents have been given already, we repeat them here for convenience.

$$a^0 = 1 \qquad a^1 = a \qquad a^x a^y = a^{x+y} \qquad (a^x)^y = a^{xy}$$
$$\frac{a^x}{a^y} = a^{x-y} \qquad \frac{1}{a^x} = a^{-x} \qquad \frac{1}{a^{-x}} = a^x$$

Example 4. Simplify the following expressions (i.e., reduce to a single exponential function).

  (a) $4^{x+6} \cdot 8^{2-x}$ (b) $\dfrac{27^{2x-3}}{9^{x-4}}$ (c) $(2^x)^3 \cdot (4^{2-x})^4$

Solution.

(a) Using the above formulas, we get

$$4^{x+6} \cdot 8^{2-x} = (2^2)^{x+6} \cdot (2^3)^{2-x} = 2^{2(x+6)} \cdot 2^{3(2-x)}$$
$$= 2^{2x+12} \cdot 2^{6-3x} = 2^{(2x+12)+(6-3x)} = 2^{-x+18}$$

(b) Similarly,

$$\frac{27^{2x-3}}{9^{x-4}} = \frac{(3^3)^{2x-3}}{(3^2)^{x-4}} = \frac{3^{6x-9}}{3^{2x-8}} = 3^{(6x-9)-(2x-8)} = 3^{4x-1}$$

(c) Start by exponentiating the exponents:

$$(2^x)^3 \cdot (4^{2-x})^4 = 2^{3x} \cdot 4^{8-4x} = 2^{3x} \cdot (2^2)^{8-4x} = 2^{3x} \cdot 2^{16-8x} = 2^{-5x+16}$$

(try it!) **Exercise 3.** Simplify the following expressions (i.e., reduce to a single exponential function).

(a) $5^{x-2} \cdot 25^{3-x}$ 　　　　　　(b) $3^{x-1} \cdot 9^{x-2} \cdot 27^{x-3}$ 　　　　　　(c) $\dfrac{8^{x+4}}{16^{x-2}}$

> When solving equations with exponential functions, we often use the following fact:
>
> if $a^m = a^n$ for real numbers m and n, then $m = n$

Example 5. Solve each of the following equations for x.

(a) $4^x = 16^{2x-2}$ 　　　　　　(b) $2^{x^3} = 0.25$ 　　　　　　(c) $3^{2x} - 6 \cdot 3^x - 27 = 0$

Solution. (a) Simplify so that both sides have the same base:

$$4^x = 16^{2x-2}$$
$$4^x = (4^2)^{2x-2}$$
$$4^x = 4^{4x-4}$$

It follows that $4x - 4 = x$ and so $x = 4/3$.

(b) We need to write 0.25 as a power of 2:

$$0.25 = \frac{1}{4} = \frac{1}{2^2} = 2^{-2}$$

Thus, $2^{x^3} = 2^{-2}$, which implies that $x^3 = -2$ and so $x = \sqrt[3]{-2}$.

(c) This is a bit more challenging. The idea lies in the fact that $3^{2x} = (3^x)^2$; this implies that the given equation is a quadratic equation in 3^x. To see that, we let $y = 3^x$; then $3^{2x} - 6 \cdot 3^x - 27 = 0$ reads $y^2 - 6y - 27 = 0$. From

$$y^2 - 6y - 27 = (y+3)(y-9) = 0$$

we conclude that $y = 3^x = -3$ or $y = 3^x = 9$.

The equation $3^x = -3$ has no solutions, since $3^x > 0$ no matter what x is. From $3^x = 9$, we get $x = 2$. Thus, the only solution is $x = 2$.

> Remember: since $a^x > 0$ for all $a > 0$ and any real number x, the equations
> $$a^x = 0 \text{ and } a^x = \text{negative number}$$
> do not have solutions.

 Exercise 4. Solve each of the following equations for x.

(a) $0.5^{x^2} = 0.125$ (b) $3^x(3^x - 3) = 0$ (c) $2^{2x} - 5 \cdot 2^x + 4 = 0$

In the case where $a = e \approx 2.71828$, we obtain the *natural exponential function* $y = e^x$. This function is used in a number of applications, from population problems to compound interest and radioactive decay.

The graphs of $y = e^x$ and $y = e^{-x} = 1/e^x$ are shown below. (Recall that replacing x by $-x$ results in the symmetry across the y-axis.)

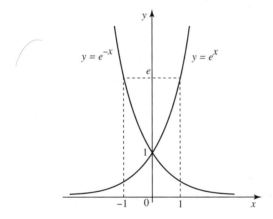

As any exponential function, the natural exponential function satisfies $e^0 = 1$ and $e^x > 0$ for all x (i.e., the range of $y = e^x$ consists of all positive real numbers). The domain of $y = e^x$ consists of all real numbers.

Graphs of functions of the form e^{ax} look like e^x if $a > 0$ and like e^{-x} if $a < 0$. The pictures below show several functions of the form e^{ax}. Note that each graph has its symmetric counterpart (across the y-axis).

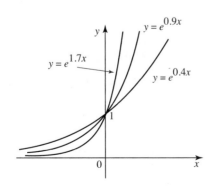 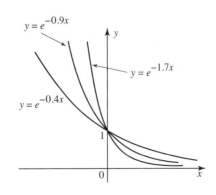

Logarithms

We recall the definition first.

> *Logarithm* to the base $a > 0$: $\log_a n = m$ if and only if $a^m = n$

In words: $\log_a n$ is equal to the number to which we have to raise a to get n.

So what is $\log_{10} 100$, i.e., 10 to which exponent gives 100?

Clearly, $10^2 = 100$, and so $\log_{10} 100 = 2$.

Likewise, $\log_{10} 10,000 = 4$, since $10^4 = 10,000$, and $\log_{10} 0.1 = -1$, since $10^{-1} = 1/10 = 0.1$.

One more: what is $\log_2 16$? In other words, we are looking for the number such that 2 raised to it gives 16.

Since $2^4 = 16$, we have our answer: $\log_2 16 = 4$.

Similarly, from $7^{-2} = 1/49$ we conclude that $\log_7(1/49) = -2$.

Example 6. In the table below (left) we wrote the same statements in exponential and logarithmic forms.

For instance, $5^4 = 625$ can be restated as $\log_5 625 = 4$. Similarly, the statement $\log_2 32 = 5$ is another way of saying that $2^5 = 32$.

Exponential	Logarithm
$5^4 = 625$	$\log_5 625 = 4$
$2^5 = 32$	$\log_2 32 = 5$
$3^0 = 1$	$\log_3 1 = 0$
$4^{-3} = 1/64$	$\log_4(1/64) = -3$
$10^{-4} = 0.0001$	$\log_{10} 0.0001 = -4$

Exponential	Logarithm
	$\log_{10} 10 = 1$
$3^{-2} = 1/9$	
	$\log_5 0.04 = -2$
$10^{-3} = 0.001$	
$10^0 = 1$	
	$\log_{10} 1,000,000 = 6$

Exercise 5. Fill in the blank entries in the table above (right).

Recall the definition: $\log_a n = m$ (base a must be positive) if and only if $a^m = n$. Thus, because a^m is always positive, we conclude that $n = a^m > 0$ must be positive as well. But n is the number for which we are computing the logarithm; so

> $\log_a n$ is defined only for positive numbers n

Substituting $m = \log_a n$ into $a^m = n$, we get $a^{\log_a n} = n$.

In words, if we take a number (call in n), apply $\log_a$ to it and then exponentiate it (with the base a) we get our number back.

Similarly, substituting $n = a^m$ into $m = \log_a n$, gives $\log_a a^m = m$. Thus, taking a number m, exponentiating it (with the base a) and then taking $\log_a$ of that will return m.

> Exponentiating and taking a logarithm are inverses of each other: $a^{\log_a n} = n$ and $\log_a a^m = m$.

Logarithmic Functions

The *logarithmic function* $y = \log_a x$ is defined as the inverse function of the exponential function $y = a^x$. Consequently, when we apply the composition of the two functions (in any order) to a number x, we get it back:

> $a^{\log_a x} = x$ for $x > 0$ and $\log_a a^x = x$ for all $x \in \mathbb{R}$

As we said a bit earlier, the domain of $\log_a x$ consists of positive numbers only. Its range is all of $\mathbb{R}$; see the graphs below.

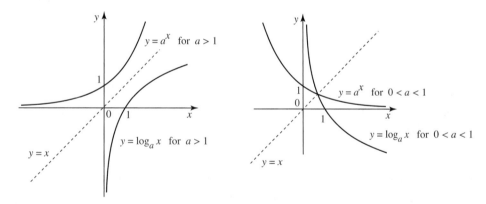

The graph of $\log_a x$ is the symmetric image of the graph of $y = a^x$ with respect to the line $y = x$. (Recall that this is the general relationship between the graph of a function and the graph of its inverse function.)

Since $a^0 = 1$, it follows that $\log_a 1 = 0$ (i.e., the value of $\log_a$ at 1 is 0). Thus, $\log_a x$ goes through the point $(1, 0)$ on the x-axis.

If $a > 1$, $\log_a x$ is an increasing function; if $0 < a < 1$, it is a decreasing function. In either case, the y-axis is the vertical asymptote.

The graph on page 148 shows of $y = \log_a x$ for several values of a (obtained by plotting points).

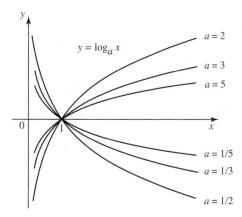

Next, we state properties of logarithms.

Laws of Logarithms

(Assume that expressions A, B and the base a satisfy A, B, $a > 0$.)

$$\log_a 1 = 0 \qquad \log_a a = 1$$

$$\log_a(AB) = \log_a A + \log_a B \qquad \log_a \frac{A}{B} = \log_a A - \log_a B \qquad \log_a(A^n) = n \log_a A$$

For obvious reasons, the three formulas in the bottom line are referred to as the product, quotient and power laws of logarithms.

Remember that $\log_a(A + B)$ and $\log_a(A - B)$ do not simplify!

Example 7. We show that the formula $\log_{10}(x + y) = \log_{10} x + \log_{10} y$ does not hold.

Take, for instance $x = y = 1$. The left side is $\log_{10}(1 + 1) = \log_{10} 2 \approx 0.30103$, whereas the right side is $\log_{10} 1 + \log_{10} 1 = 0 + 0 = 0$.

Exercise 6. Using the approach from the previous example, show that the formula $\log_a(x + y) = \log_a x + \log_a y$ does not hold for any $a > 0$. Also show that $\log_{10}(x - y) = \log_{10} x - \log_{10} y$ is not correct.

Example 8. Simplify the following expressions using laws of logarithms:

(a) $\log_6(x^2 - 4)$ (b) $\log_{10} \dfrac{x^2 y}{10(y^2 + 1)}$ (c) $\log_{0.5} \sqrt{\dfrac{a^3 b}{c^2 d}}$

Solution.

(a) We factor using the difference of squares formula, and then decompose the logarithm of the product:

$$\log_6(x^2 - 4) = \log_6[(x - 2)(x + 2)] = \log_6(x - 2) + \log_6(x + 2)$$

Note that $\log_6(x - 2)$ and $\log_6(x + 2)$ cannot be broken down any further.

(b) We start by rewriting the logarithm of the quotient as the difference of logarithms

$$\log_{10} \frac{x^2 y}{10(y^2+1)} = \log_{10}(x^2 y) - \log_{10}[10(y^2+1)]$$

then decompose the products

$$= \log_{10} x^2 + \log_{10} y - (\log_{10} 10 + \log_{10}(y^2+1))$$

and simplify using the formula $\log_{10} x^2 = 2 \log_{10} x$ and the fact that $\log_{10} 10 = 1$

$$= 2 \log_{10} x + \log_{10} y - 1 - \log_{10}(y^2+1)$$

The term $\log_{10}(y^2+1)$ cannot be decomposed any further.

(c) Rewrite the square root as the exponent of $1/2$ and simplify

$$\log_{0.5} \sqrt{\frac{a^3 b}{c^2 d}} = \log_{0.5} \left(\frac{a^3 b}{c^2 d}\right)^{1/2}$$

$$= \frac{1}{2} \log_{0.5} \frac{a^3 b}{c^2 d}$$

then decompose the quotient and the products

$$= \frac{1}{2} \left(\log_{0.5}(a^3 b) - \log_{0.5}(c^2 d)\right)$$

$$= \frac{1}{2} \left(\log_{0.5} a^3 + \log_{0.5} b - (\log_{0.5} c^2 + \log_{0.5} d)\right)$$

and finally simplify the exponents

$$= \frac{1}{2} \left(3 \log_{0.5} a + \log_{0.5} b - 2 \log_{0.5} c - \log_{0.5} d\right)$$

 Exercise 7. Simplify the following expressions, if possible:

(a) $\log_{12}(y^3 + 8)$ (b) $\log_{10} \dfrac{100 a^4 c^{-1}}{a+b}$ (c) $\log_2 \sqrt{\dfrac{1}{2}}$

Sometimes it might be necessary to convert logarithms from one base to another.

$$\boxed{\text{conversion formula: } \log_a x = \frac{\log_b x}{\log_b a}}$$

Example 9. To express $\log_{12}$ in terms of $\log_5$, we use the formula $\log_{12} x = \dfrac{\log_5 x}{\log_5 12}$.

Suppose we need to calculate $\log_4 7$; there is no $\log_4$ key on a calculator, so we convert to $\log_{10}$ and then use the calculator:

$$\log_4 7 = \frac{\log_{10} 7}{\log_{10} 4} \approx \frac{0.84510}{0.60206} \approx 1.40368$$

 Exercise 8. Express $\log_4 x$ in terms of $\log_{16} x$ and $\log_{0.5} x$ in terms of $\log_2 x$. Calculate (i.e., find the numeric value) of $\log_{11} 1.45$ and $\log_{0.4} 44$.

The inverse function of the natural exponential function $y = e^x$ is called the *natural logarithm function* and is usually denoted by $\ln x$ (instead of $\log_e x$).

Although we have already stated the properties of $y = \ln x$ when we talked about a general logarithmic function, we repeat them here.

The domain of $\ln x$ is $(0, \infty)$. Its range consists of all real numbers.

As we just said, e^x and $\ln x$ are inverse functions, and so

$$e^{\ln x} = x \ \text{(for all } x > 0) \quad \text{and} \quad \ln e^x = x \ \text{(for all } x \in \mathbb{R})$$

Moreover, $\ln 1 = 0$ and $\ln e = 1$ (the latter is true since $\ln e = \ln e^1 = 1$). The natural logarithm can be used to simplify products, quotients and powers (assume that $A, B > 0$):

$$\ln(AB) = \ln A + \ln B \qquad \ln \frac{A}{B} = \ln A - \ln B \qquad \ln(A^n) = n \ln A$$

Since we stated these formulas for a general logarithm, why did we repeat them here? It helps us memorize them easier!

The graph of $\ln x$ is given below (it is the symmetric image of $y = e^x$ with respect to the line $y = x$).

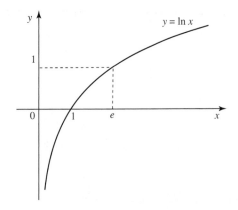

> Remember:
> $\ln 1 = 0$
> if $x > 1$ then $\ln x > 0$
> if $0 < x < 1$ then $\ln x < 0$

Sometimes, we need to use conversion formulas.

$$\ln x = \frac{\log_a x}{\log_a e} \qquad \log_a x = \frac{\ln x}{\ln a}$$

The conversion formula

$$\log_a x = \frac{\ln x}{\ln a} = \frac{1}{\ln a} \ln x$$

states that $\log_a x$ is a multiple of $\ln x$.

We can say more: if $a > 1$, then $\ln a > 0$, and so $\log_a x$ is a positive multiple of $\ln x$. If $0 < a < 1$, then $\ln a < 0$, and $\log_a x$ is a negative multiple of $\ln x$.

For instance, $\log_2 x = \ln x / \ln 2 = (1/\ln 2)\ln x = 1.44270 \ln x$, $\log_{10} x = \ln x / \ln 10 = 0.43429 \ln x$, and $\log_{0.4} x = \ln x / \ln 0.4 = -1.09136 \ln x$.

What we just said means that the graph of $\log_a x$ is: vertical compression or expansion of the graph of $\ln x$ if $a > 1$, or vertical compression or expansion of the graph of $\ln x$ followed by reflection with respect to the x-axis if $0 < a < 1$. See the figure below.

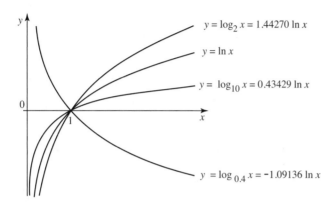

Example 10. Simplify the following expressions:

(a) $\ln(x \sin x)^x$ (b) $\ln(\ln a)^{1/x}$ (c) $\ln(\ln y^3)$ (d) $\ln \sqrt{ex^3}$

Solution. We make use of laws of logarithms (see the box on page 148, where $\log_a x$ needs to be replaced by $\log_e x = \ln x$; or, see the top two boxes on page 150).

(a) Using the power law with $A = x \sin x$ and $n = x$, we get $\ln(x \sin x)^x = x \ln(x \sin x)$. Now, we use the product law to finish simplifying:

$$\ln(x \sin x)^x = x \ln(x \sin x) = x(\ln x + \ln(\sin x))$$

(b) Using the power law with $A = \ln a$ and $n = 1/x$, we get $\ln(\ln a)^{1/x} = \frac{1}{x} \ln(\ln a)$.

(c) Simplify the term in the brackets, and then use the product law:

$$\ln(\ln y^3) = \ln(3 \ln y) = \ln 3 + \ln(\ln y)$$

(d) Write the root as the power of $1/2$, and use the power law; continue by using the product law:

$$\ln \sqrt{ex^3} = \ln(ex^3)^{1/2} = \frac{1}{2} \ln(ex^3) = \frac{1}{2}(\ln e + \ln x^3) = \frac{1}{2}(1 + 3 \ln x)$$

In the last step, we used the fact that $\ln e = \ln e^1 = 1$.

Example 11. The formula $e^{\ln x} = x$ becomes quite useful when we need to convert a general exponential function to the natural exponential function.

(a) Express 5^x in the form e^{ax} (i.e., find a).   (b) Write 0.69^x in the form e^{ax}.

Solution.

(a) Since $5 = e^{\ln 5}$, we get $5^x = \left(e^{\ln 5}\right)^x = e^{(\ln 5)x}$ (in the last step, we used the law of exponents formula $\left(e^A\right)^B = e^{AB}$).

Using a calculator, we find that $\ln 5 = 1.60944$, and so $5^x = e^{1.60944x}$.

(b) As in (a), we get $0.69^x = \left(e^{\ln 0.69}\right)^x = e^{(\ln 0.69)x} = e^{-0.37106x}$.

Let us repeat in general the calculations we did in the previous example. Assume that $a > 0$. Then
$$a^x = \left(e^{\ln a}\right)^x = e^{(\ln a)x}$$
Thus, the graphs of exponential functions a^x look like scaled graphs of the natural exponential function.

Example 12. Solve each of the following equations for x.

(a) $\log_2 x = 7$ (b) $\log_x 8 = 3$ (c) $\log_{16} 8 = x$ (d) $\log_2(\log_5 x) = 2$

Solution. Keep in mind the general principle: $\log_a B = C$ is equivalent to $B = a^C$.

(a) Rewriting $\log_2 x = 7$ in the exponential form, we get $x = 2^7$; thus, $x = 128$.

Alternatively, we start from the equation $\log_2 x = 7$ and realize that, in order to isolate x, we need to remove $\log_2$; so, we apply its inverse function 2^x to both sides of the equation, getting
$$2^{\log_2 x} = 2^7$$

Since $2^{\log_2 x} = x$ (see boxes on page 147; function and its inverse function cancel each other out!), we get $x = 2^7 = 128$.

(b) Rewriting $\log_x 8 = 3$ in the exponential form, we get $x^3 = 8$; thus, $x = 2$.

(c) Transforming to the exponential form, as we did in (a) or (b), we get $16^x = 8$. We recognize 8 and 16 as powers of 2, and write
$$(2^4)^x = 2^3$$
and $2^{4x} = 2^3$; it follows that $4x = 3$ and $x = 3/4$.

What's another way to solve $16^x = 8$?

Apply the logarithm (we will use ln, but a logarithm with any base can be used). Starting from $16^x = 8$, we get $\ln 16^x = \ln 8$, and
$$x \ln 16 = \ln 8$$

Thus, $x = \ln 8 / \ln 16$. To simplify, we write
$$\frac{\ln 8}{\ln 16} = \frac{\ln 2^3}{\ln 2^4} = \frac{3 \ln 2}{4 \ln 2} = \frac{3}{4}$$

(d) Applying the general principle ($\log_a B = C$ is equivalent to $B = a^C$) with $a = 2$, $B = \log_5 x$ and $C = 2$, we get $\log_5 x = 2^2 = 4$. Applying it once again, we get $x = 5^4 = 625$.

Exercise 9. Solve each of the following equations for x.
(a) $\log_x 4 = 1/2$ (b) $\log_3 x = 5$ (c) $\log_2 x^3 = \log_2(4x)$ (d) $16^{\log_4 x} = 4$

Example 13.

(a) Evaluate $e^{3 \ln 2} \cdot e^{2 \ln 3}$.

(b) Express $2 \ln 4 - \ln 8 - \ln 5$ as a single logarithm.

(c) Solve $\ln(4x - 3) = 7$ for x.

(d) Solve $\ln(\ln x) = 1$ for x.

(e) Solve $\ln x + \ln(x + 7) = \ln 4 + \ln 2$ for x.

Solution.

(a) We simplify exponents (using the power rule for logarithms):
$$e^{3\ln 2} \cdot e^{2\ln 3} = e^{\ln 2^3} \cdot e^{\ln 3^2} = e^{\ln 8} \cdot e^{\ln 9} = 8 \cdot 9 = 72$$

In the next-to-last step, we used the fact that $e^{\ln x} = x$.

(b) Using laws of logarithms $n \ln A = \ln A^n$ and $\ln A - \ln B = \ln(A/B)$, we get
$$2\ln 4 - \ln 8 - \ln 5 = \ln 4^2 - \ln 8 - \ln 5 = (\ln 16 - \ln 8) - \ln 5$$
$$= \ln(16/8) - \ln 5 = \ln 2 - \ln 5 = \ln(2/5)$$

(c) Applying e^x (the inverse function to $\ln x$!) to both sides, we get
$$\ln(4x - 3) = 7$$
$$e^{\ln(4x-3)} = e^7$$
$$4x - 3 = e^7$$
$$x = \frac{e^7 + 3}{4}$$

(d) We repeat twice the strategy we employed in (c):
$$\ln(\ln x) = 1$$
$$e^{\ln(\ln x)} = e^1$$
$$\ln x = e$$
$$e^{\ln x} = e^e$$

and thus $x = e^e$.

(e) Combining the terms on both sides (using the product law for logarithms), we get
$$\ln x + \ln(x + 7) = \ln 4 + \ln 2$$
$$\ln x(x + 7) = \ln 8$$
$$x(x + 7) = 8$$
$$x^2 + 7x - 8 = 0$$
$$(x + 8)(x - 1) = 0$$

Thus, $x = -8$ and $x = 1$. The value $x = 1$ is a solution, since both terms $\ln x$ and $\ln(x + 7)$ on the right side of the given equation are defined. However, the same is not true for $x = -8$, and so $x = 1$ is the only solution.

(try it!) **Exercise 10.**

(a) Evaluate $e^{\ln 4 + \ln 5}$.

(b) Express $4\ln 2 + \ln 3 + 2$ as a single logarithm.

(c) Solve $e^{3x-2} = 4$ for x.

(d) Solve $\ln(x^2 + x - 1) = 0$ for x.

What is the meaning of $\sin^3 x$ and $\sin x^3$? Or $\ln^3 x$ and $\ln x^3$?

This is an issue of notation; here is the rule: when the power appears between the name of a function and the variable, then it refers to the entire function, i.e., $\sin^3 x = (\sin x)^3$ and $\ln^3 x = (\ln x)^3$.

As well,

$$\tan^{1/2} 3x = (\tan 3x)^{1/2} = \sqrt{\tan 3x}$$

and

$$\ln^{5.1}(2x^3 - 7) = (\ln(2x^3 - 7))^{5.1}$$

If the power appears at the end, then it refers to the variable only, i.e., $\sin x^3 = \sin(x^3)$ and $\ln x^3 = \ln(x^3)$. Likewise,

$$\cos x^{-1} = \cos(x^{-1}) = \cos(1/x)$$

In a combination of the two cases, inserting brackets, we write $\tan^3 x^4 = (\tan(x^4))^3$.

One more: how do we simplify $\ln^2 x^7$?

First, we insert the brackets, then use the power law for logarithms and simplify:

$$\ln^2 x^7 = (\ln(x^7))^2 = (7 \ln x)^2 = 49(\ln x)^2 = 49 \ln^2 x$$

Go back to the graph on page 148. It looks like $\log_2 x$ and $\log_{1/2} x$ are symmetric with respect to the x-axis; same seems to be true for the pairs of graphs $\log_3 x$, $\log_{1/3} x$ and $\log_5 x$, $\log_{1/5} x$. So, is it true or not?

Yes, it's true; we give two different explanations.

Geometric: $\log_2 x$ is the inverse of 2^x, and $\log_{1/2} x$ is the inverse of $(1/2)^x = 2^{-x}$. The graphs of 2^x and 2^{-x} are symmetric with respect to the y-axis (we mentioned that before). Thus their inverses, i.e., their reflections with respect to $y = x$, must be symmetric with respect to the reflection of the y-axis (axis of symmetry of the original functions!) with respect to the same line. Clearly, the reflection of the y-axis with respect to $y = x$ is the x-axis.

Now, using algebraic reasoning, we find the relationship between $\log_2 x$ and $\log_{1/2} x$.

Let $\log_2 x = m$. By definition, this means that $2^m = x$. We need to rewrite this identity as an exponential function whose base is $1/2$. Using laws of exponents, we get

$$x = 2^m = (2^{-1})^{-m} = \left(\frac{1}{2}\right)^{-m}$$

From $\left(\frac{1}{2}\right)^{-m} = x$, we conclude that $\log_{1/2} x = -m$. Thus,

$$\log_{1/2} x = -m = -\log_2 x,$$

so the two graphs are symmetric with respect to the x-axis. Replacing 2 by any $a > 0$, we get

$$\boxed{\text{the graphs of } \log_a x \text{ and } \log_{1/a} x \text{ are symmetric with respect to the } x\text{-axis}}$$

Additional Exercises

For extra practice, work on the following questions.

(extra) **Exercise 11.** Finish each sentence by providing either the exponential or the logarithmic form, as in Example 6.

(a) If $x^5 = 243$, then

(b) If $\ln A = 13$, then

(c) If $A^n = B$, then

(d)* If $10^x = 0.001$, then

(e)* If $\ln y = x$, then

(f)* If $6^C = D$, then

(extra) **Exercise 12.**

(a)* Simplify $10 \cdot 100^2 \cdot 1000^4$ by reducing it to a single exponential function.

(b)* Reduce $3^7 + 6 \cdot 3^6$ to a single term.

(c)* Reduce $9 \cdot 27^3 + 2 \cdot 3^{11}$ to a single term.

(d)* Simplify $\dfrac{36^{n+3}}{6^{2n+5}}$ by reducing it to a single exponential function.

(e) Compute the product $\dfrac{5^{x+3}}{3^{2x}} \cdot \dfrac{6^{3x}}{10^x}$ and simplify as much as possible.

(f) Factor $5^{x+4}7^x - 2 \cdot 5^{x+2}7^{x+1} + 5^{x+3}7^{x+2}$ and simplify.

(g) Factor $4^x - 9^x$ as the difference of squares.

(h) Compute $\left(\dfrac{e^x + e^{-x}}{2} \right)^2 - \left(\dfrac{e^x - e^{-x}}{2} \right)^2$ and simplify

(i) Cancel the fraction $\dfrac{e^x + e^{-2x}}{2e^x - e^{-3x}}$ by e^x (i.e., divide the numerator and the denominator by e^x).

(j)* Cancel the fraction $\dfrac{e^{4x} - 3e^{-x}}{e^x + e^{-7x}}$ by e^{-x} (i.e., divide the numerator and the denominator by e^{-x}).

(extra) **Exercise 13.** Without a calculator, evaluate each expression.

(a) $\dfrac{11^{-2}}{11^2}$

(b) $\dfrac{2 \cdot 7^4}{49}$

(c) $\dfrac{2^5 + 2^6 + 2^7}{2^5}$

(d) $4^{-1} \cdot 16^{-2} \cdot 2^8$

(e)* $\dfrac{(0.5 \cdot 10)^{-3}}{16 \cdot 0.1^4}$

(f)* $0.2^{-4} \cdot 16$

(g)* $-32 \cdot \left(\dfrac{1}{2} \right)^4$

(h)* $\log_{10} 0.0001$

(i)* $\log_{10} \dfrac{1}{100}$

(j) $\log_{10} 100^{-3}$

(k) $\log_5 25$

(l) $\log_5 25^2$

(m) $\log_5 \dfrac{1}{5}$

(n) $\log_4 2$

(o)* $\log_4 2^5$

(p)* $(\log_4 2)^5$

(extra) **Exercise 14.** Without a calculator, find a numeric value of each expression.

(a)* $e^{(1/2)\ln 16}$

(b)* $10^{\log_{10} 5}$

(c)* $\log_{10} 100000$

(d)* $10^{3\log_{10} 4}$

(e) $\log_{1000} 10$

(f) $6^{\log_6 7}$

(g) $\ln(e^4)$

(h) $\ln(5e^4) - \ln 5$

(i) $\ln \frac{1}{2e^6} + \ln 2$

(j) $e^{-4\ln 3}$

(k) $12^{2\log_{12} 11}$

(l) $\log_{10} 1 - \log_6 1 + \ln 1$

(m)* $\log_3(1/9)$

(n)* $\ln \left(e^{\ln(e^2)} \right)$

(o)* $e^{-\ln 23}$

(p) $\log_{1/9} 3$

(extra) **Exercise 15.**   Simplify each expression.

(a)* $6^{\log_6 x^3}$ (b)* $2^{\log_2 e^x}$ (c) $10^{\log_{10}(x^2+1)}$ (d)* $e^{\ln x^2}$

(e) $e^{\ln(\ln x)}$ (f) $\ln(e^{x^2})$ (g)* $\ln(5e^{x^2})$ (h)* $e^{2\ln x^2}$

(extra) **Exercise 16.**   (a)* Convert $\log_5 x$ to log base 10, log base 12 and the natural logarithm.

(b)* Convert $\ln x$ to log base 10 and log base 12.

(c) Convert $\log_{14} x$ to the natural logarithm. Use your answer to sketch the graph of $y = \log_{14} x$.

(d) Convert $\log_{1/5} x$ to the natural logarithm. Use your answer to sketch the graph of $y = \log_{1/5} x$.

(extra) **Exercise 17.**   Starting with a known graph, sketch, or describe in words, the graph of each function.

(a) $y = 5e^x$ (b)* $f(x) = e^{-5x}$ (c)* $g(x) = 1 - e^{-5x}$ (d) $f(x) = 1 - 4e^{-5x}$

(e) $f(x) = 6^{-x}$ (f) $y = 6^{-x-1} - 1$ (g) $y = 6^{-4x}$ (h) $f(x) = 6^{-4x+2}$

(i) $f(x) = \ln(x + 5)$ (j)* $g(x) = -\ln(x - 5)$ (k) $y = 1 - \ln x$ (l) $f(x) = 1 + 2\ln(x - 3)$

(m)* $y = \log_{10}(2x)$ (n) $f(x) = \log_{10} x + 2$ (o) $y = 3\log_{10}(x + 1)$ (p) $g(x) = \log_{10}(2x + 1)$

(extra) **Exercise 18.**   Identify each formula as correct or incorrect.

(a) $\ln(x + y) = \ln x + \ln y$ (b)* $\ln(x + y) = \ln x \cdot \ln y$ (c) $\ln(xy) = \ln x + \ln y$

(d) $\ln(3x) = 3\ln x$ (e) $e^x e^y = e^{x+y}$ (f)* $(e^x)^y = e^{xy}$

(g) $e^{-4x} = -4e^x$ (h)* $\ln(x/2) = \ln\sqrt{x}$ (i) $\frac{1}{2}\ln x = \ln\sqrt{x}$

(extra) **Exercise 19.**   Expand each expression using laws of logarithms, or else say that it cannot be done.

(a) $\ln(3e^x \sin x)$ (b) $\ln(4 + 3x^2)$ (c) $\log_{10} \dfrac{3x^2}{100}$

(d)* $\log_{10} x^{-3}\sqrt{yz^4}$ (e) $\ln\sqrt{\dfrac{e^{2x}x^3}{x+1}}$ (f)* $\ln\dfrac{\sqrt[3]{x}}{x^2(e^x + 1)}$

(extra) **Exercise 20.**   Write each expression using a single logarithm and simplify if possible.

(a) $\ln x - \ln y + 4$ (b)* $\ln(x^2 - y^2) - \ln(x - y)$ (c) $\ln x - 3\ln(x - 4) + \dfrac{1}{2}\ln x$

(d)* $\log_{10} x - 3\log_{10} y^2 + 4\log_{10}(xy^3)$ (e) $\dfrac{1}{3}\log_{10} x + \dfrac{1}{5}\log_{10} x^2 - \dfrac{2}{3}\log_{10} 8$

(extra) **Exercise 21.**   Solve each equation.

(a)* $0.1^x = 100$ (b)* $(1/4)^x = 2$ (c)* $0.25^x = 16$

(d) $7e^{5x} = 21$ (e) $4e^{2x-1} = 27$ (f) $4e^{-3x+1} = 6e^{7x}$

(g) $5 \cdot 6^x = 8$ (h) $5 \cdot 6^x = 8^{3x-1}$ (i) $3e^{-3x+1} = 4^{-x}$

(j)* $0.1^{x+2} = 100^{1/3}$ (k)* $e^{2x} + 2e^x - 8 = 0$ (l)* $100^{\cos x} = 10$

(m) $\ln(4x - 2) = 17$ (n) $\log_{10}(x^2 - 1) = 5$ (o) $\ln x + \ln(x + 1) = \ln 2$

(p)* $\log_{10}(x - 98) = 4$ (q)* $\ln(\ln x) = 1$ (r) $\log_{10}(\log_{10} x) = 0$

 Exercise 22. * In Example 9, we used the $\log_{10}$ key on a calculator to find the numeric value of $\log_4 7$. Explain how you would calculate $\log_4 7$ if your calculator only has an ln key instead of a $\log_{10}$ key.

9. Mathematical Language; Mathematical Thinking and Logic

What is in this section?

Elements of the language of mathematics; the concepts of definition, theorem, proof; "if-then" and "if-and-only-if" statements; universal ("for all") and existential ("there exists") quantifiers.

Math Language

Mathematics language and its important features are usually not covered in high school; however, college/university math instructors assume that their students are familiar with it and know how to use it. Surprisingly, standard calculus textbooks that review high school material do not even have hints or guidelines on proper use of the mathematics language.

> Understanding math language and using it correctly to communicate math ideas and thoughts are key ingredients in learning mathematics.

In this section, we need to distinguish the language used in mathematics (we will refer to it as "math language") and the language that we use in everyday situations ("English language"; sometimes, we will say "language in general usage" or "everyday language"). As we will see, the two languages are quite different.

> Since we want everyone who reads or listens to the same piece of math to receive the same message, we have to make sure that math language is clear, precise and unambiguous. As well, the context — which could be explicitly stated, or suggested but not spelled out — must be clear.

The sentence

The sum of two odd numbers is an even number.

is an example of a math statement. In building mathematics, previous to this statement, concepts of the sum, as well as even and odd numbers were defined. So, the statement above establishes one possible relationship between known concepts and/or known objects. From the development of the material, it is clear (but not specified in the sentence above) that we are talking about integers.

As another example, consider the statement we find in calculus textbooks:

If f is differentiable at a, then f is continuous at a.

How do we read it and understand its meaning?

First, we need to identify the context (in this case, it is calculus, so we are talking about real numbers and functions; thus, a is a real number); next, we make sure that we know what "f is differentiable at a" and "f is continuous at a" mean. As well, we have to know how to interpret the construct "if ... then". In a moment, we'll say more about this statement, as it is an example of a theorem.

In everyday language, we use words whose meaning is often vague, unclear or depends on our experience. For instance, the word "warm" in "It is warm outside" does not have the same meaning for everyone. Thus, "It is warm outside" is not a math statement. A few more examples contrast the two languages:

Math Language Statement	English Language Statement
−1 is larger than 2.	The roof on that building is red.
The product of two positive numbers is positive.	This chair is uncomfortable.
The function $y = x^2$ is increasing when $x \geq 0$.	I like working on math problems.

In certain situations, we use math terms but not in their precise mathematical sense. For instance, "a square of chocolate" is not a square! To say "Earth is a sphere" is not correct: Earth is a three-dimensional solid, whereas a sphere is a two-dimensional surface. When we say "area of a circle" (many books use this phrase) we mean the area of the region (i.e., the disk) enclosed by the circle. The circle is a curve and so has length, but not area.

The most important examples of math statements are definitions and theorems.

Definition

A *definition* is a statement that introduces something new — math object(s), or a property of math object(s) — based on objects and/or properties that have been previously defined and established.

For example, consider the following definition:

> A prime number is a natural number that has exactly two distinct divisors: number 1 and itself.

So the new object being introduced is a prime number. Previously defined objects and/or properties (assumed to be known) are "natural number" (natural numbers are positive integers: 1, 2, 3, etc.) and "divisors" (for instance, divisors of 15 are 1, 3, 5 and 15).

Note that there is no ambiguity here: since the only divisors of 17 are 1 and 17, we conclude that 17 is a prime number. The fact that numbers 3 and 5 (as well as 1 and 15) divide 15 means that 15 is not a prime number.

Is 1 a prime number?

No, because the definition requires that a prime number has *exactly two distinct* divisors (the only divisor of 1 is 1). Thus, the prime numbers are 2, 3, 5, 7, 11, 13, 17, etc.

Definitions can be expressed in different ways without changing the meaning. For instance, we could have said this:

> A prime number is a positive integer greater than 1 that has no positive integer divisors other than 1 and itself.

Sometimes we use definitions to make a choice when other means (such as logical deduction) fail. These definitions are sometimes referred to as *conventions*. So a convention cannot be logically deduced nor calculated from the given context. Let us mention two examples.

Recall that a function $y = f(x)$ must return a unique value for each x in its domain.

So what is $\sqrt{16}$?

There are two numbers whose square is 16, namely 4 and −4. To ensure uniqueness, we *agree* to take the positive value, and thus $f(16) = \sqrt{16} = 4$. In other words, by *convention*, or by *definition*, we have $f(x) = \sqrt{x} > 0$ (and, of course, $\sqrt{0} = 0$).

In Section 7, we constructed the function inverse to $\sin x$. Of infinitely many choices, we *declared* that the interval $[-\pi/2, \pi/2]$ be the domain of $\sin x$. We could have taken $[\pi/2, 3\pi/2]$, $[3\pi/2, 5\pi/2]$ or $[-3\pi/2, -\pi/2]$, etc. But to ensure that we all obtain the same value for, say, $\arcsin(1/2)$, we had to agree on what the range of $\arcsin x$ (= domain of $\sin x$) was going to be.

Theorem

A *theorem* is a statement that establishes a relationship between previously defined mathematical objects and/or their properties. Every theorem consists of two parts: assumption(s) and conclusion(s).

Here is an example (context is natural numbers, i.e., positive integers).

If m divides a, and m divides b, then m divides $a + b$.

There are two assumptions: "m divides a" and "m divides b". The conclusion is "m divides $a + b$".

How do we use a theorem?

First, we need to check that *all* assumptions are satisfied. If so, then the conclusion(s) is/are true.

For instance, take $m = 14$, $a = 28$ and $b = 140$; since $m = 14$ divides $a = 28$, and $m = 14$ divides $b = 140$, we see that both assumptions are satisfied. Thus, the theorem tells us that $m = 14$ divides $a + b = 168$.

> In order to use a theorem, we must check that *all* assumptions are satisfied. If just one of the assumptions does not hold, the theorem cannot be used — even though its conclusion(s) might still hold.

We need to make sure we understand this: if one or more assumptions in a theorem do not hold, the theorem does not say anything! Its conclusion(s) might still be true or might be false, but we cannot conclude that from the theorem. Consider the following two examples.

If we choose $m = 14$, $a = 28$ and $b = 15$, then we cannot use the theorem since the assumption "$m = 14$ divides $b = 15$" does not hold ("$m = 14$ divides $a = 28$" holds). In this case, the conclusion does not hold either: $m = 14$ does not divide $a + b = 43$.

If we choose $m = 14$, $a = 20$ and $b = 8$, then we cannot use the theorem since neither of the two assumptions "$m = 14$ divides $a = 20$" and "$m = 14$ divides $b = 8$" holds. However, the conclusion of the theorem is true, since $m = 14$ divides $a + b = 28$.

Here is another example. Assume that the context is the set of all animals of Earth, and that all cats on Earth have four legs. In that case, the theorem

If an animal X is a cat, then X has four legs.

is true.

This theorem has one assumption "an animal X is a cat" and one conclusion "X has four legs."

How do we use this theorem?

We pick an animal and check: if it is a cat, then the theorem says that it has 4 legs. But if it is not a cat, the theorem does not apply! The animal could still have four legs (could be an elephant) but does not have to (could be a spider).

It is important to clearly distinguish assumption(s) from conclusion(s). In the standard form of a theorem

If <assumption(s)> then <conclusion(s)> .

we use the words "if" and "then" to separate assumption(s) from conclusion(s). In our previously mentioned theorem

If f is differentiable at a, then f is continuous at a.

the assumption is "f is differentiable at a" and the conclusion is "f is continuous at a."

Even though we might not understand what *continuous* and *differentiable* mean (that will be discussed in calculus), we understand how to use this theorem: we take a function f and check whether or not it is differentiable at a. If it is differentiable, then we conclude that f is also continuous at a. However, if f is not differentiable at a, then the theorem does not tell us anything about it being (or not being) continuous at a.

Sometimes, a theorem is written in the following form:

Assume that <assumption(s)>. Then <conclusion(s)>.

So we can reformulate theorems we discussed as: "Assume that f is differentiable at a. Then f is continuous at a." and "Assume that X is a cat. Then X has four legs." Rarely in first year calculus, but more often in upper year math courses, we meet theorems written in the form

<Assumption(s)> is/are <conclusion(s)>.

So we say "A function differentiable at a is continuous at a as well." and "An animal that is a cat has four legs."

Every theorem requires *proof.* Starting with assumption(s), we must go through a sequence of steps (sometimes one or two, sometimes hundreds) until we reach the conclusion(s). In calculus, we see very few proofs.

Other Mathematical Statements

There are other statements (corollary, lemma, proposition) that are exactly the same in structure as a theorem (and we treat them as such, so everything we said above applies). The distinction is made because we want to emphasize their role within math theory.

A *corollary* is a straightforward consequence of a theorem (which could refer to some special case, for instance). A *lemma* usually contains a technical result that is needed to prove a theorem. This way, a long proof of some theorem can be broken into a sequence of smaller steps, each proven within a separate lemma. A *proposition* is a "smaller" theorem, i.e., its statement is not as important as the statement of a theorem.

If all statements (definitions, theorems, propositions, etc.) are built on something that has been previously done, where does it all start?

It starts with axioms. An *axiom* is a statement whose validity is taken for granted, i.e., cannot be proven — because a proof would have to rely on something previous to the axiom(s), but there is nothing there!

In calculus, axioms establish existence of real numbers and their properties. For instance, the fact that zero times any number is zero is an axiom. (Axioms are not discussed in elementary calculus courses, so we will not discuss them further.)

Context

Mathematics requires that we are always certain and clear about the context within which we write definitions, make calculations, state theorems, etc. As well, without it, we might not be able to establish whether a given statement is true or false.

The context is not always spelled out: it might be mentioned once or a few times, and then dropped.

Early in a calculus course, we mention that calculus deals with real numbers and their properties, but we don't repeat this every time we do something with calculus. For instance, in the statement we used before "f is differentiable at a" we did not say "at a real number a" but just "at a."

Or, initially, we define a function by specifying both the formula (rule of assignment) and its domain — and say, for example, "consider the function $f(x) = 1/x$, where $x \neq 0$"; later we just say "consider the function $y = 1/x$" assuming (but not communicating it explicitly) that $x \neq 0$.

Example 1. Determine whether the statement "$x^2 = -1$ has no solutions" is true or false.

Solution. As stated, we are not given enough information to answer the question. What is x? Real number? Integer? Something else?

We need to provide a context. Suppose that the statement "$x^2 = -1$ has no solutions" appeared in something we did in calculus; in that case, x is a real number. Then the statement is true, and we can justify it this way: if we multiply any real number x by itself, we get either a positive number or zero (it is zero if x is zero). Thus, there is no real number whose square is negative, or in particular equal to -1.

However, in the context of complex numbers the above statement is false. As a matter of fact, the equation $x^2 = -1$ has two solutions, $x = \sqrt{-1} = i$ and $x = -\sqrt{-1} = -i$.

Implication and Equivalence: "If-Then" and "If-and-Only-If"

> An *implication* is a sentence of the form "if A, then B," where A and B are mathematics statements.

Using the symbol $\Rightarrow$ we write the implication "if A, then B" as "$A \Rightarrow B$". In the English language, there are several ways to express an implication, such as "A implies B," or "A then B," or "B is a consequence of A," or "in case A, then B," etc.

We have already met implications when we were discussing theorems. Now we want to further understand how to work with them.

There are situations when it is useful to interpret an implication visually. To do that, we think of "$A \Rightarrow B$" as "A is a subset of B"; see below, left.

Throughout this section we assume that all cats in Universe have four legs.

For example, the implication

If an animal X is a cat, then X has four legs.

is visualized as shown below (right): the set of cats (represented by the smaller box) is a subset of the set of all animals that have four legs (larger box, which contains the smaller box).

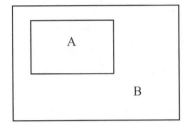
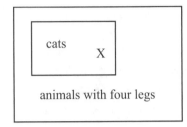

visualizing implication A⇒B

How do we use these diagrams?

Look at the letter X in the diagram above, right: it belongs to the smaller box, so it represents a cat. Since X also belongs to the larger box, it means that X has four legs. So, cat implies four legs.

Quite often, we interpret the implication A $\Rightarrow$ B by saying that "A is a *sufficient condition* for B" or "B is a *necessary condition* for A"

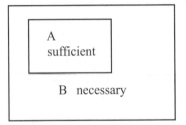

interpreting implication A⇒B

Thus, being a cat is a *sufficient* condition for four legs. Four legs is a *necessary* condition to be a cat. *Necessary* means that, if we are looking for a cat, we need to look no farther than for beings with four legs. (But that does not suffice–once we have a being with four legs, we need to determine whether or not it is a cat, by performing an appropriate test. So, that being might, or might not be a cat in the end.)

Let's translate this observation into an abstract situation in calculus (which you will inevitably encounter). Fermat's Theorem says: "If a function $f(x)$ has a relative extreme value at $x = a$, then $x = a$ is a critical point of $f(x)$."

Thus, to identify a relative extreme value of a function, we need to look no farther than its critical points. Consequently, if a function has no critical points, then it cannot have relative extreme values.

As well–findning critical points does not suffice. We need to test each critical point to figure out whether or not it yields a relative extreme value.

Keep in mind that implication has direction (that's why an arrow is used); i.e., if "A $\Rightarrow$ B" is true, then we cannot conclude that "B $\Rightarrow$ A" is true as well (and, in general, it will not be true!).

Consider the cat example: while "If an animal X is a cat, then X has four legs" is true, reversing the order produces the statement "If an animal X has four legs, then X is a cat," which is clearly false (an elephant has four legs, but is not a cat).

> The direction of implication matters!
> If "if A, then B" is true, that does NOT mean that "if B, then A" is true.

The statement "if B, then A" is called the *converse* of the statement "if A, then B".

Another example: the statement "If an integer ends with 4, then it is even" is true but its converse "If an integer is even, then it ends with 4" is false (an even number could end with, say, 2, or 8).

As we just saw, the converse of an implication does not work (i.e., might not produce a true statement from a true statement). But, there is a way to correctly reverse the implication. Back to our example with cats:

If an animal X is a cat, then X has four legs.

Consider an animal labeled X in the diagram below.

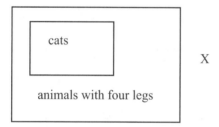

X is outside the larger box, so it represents an animal that does not have 4 legs. Since X is not in the smaller box, X cannot be a cat. Thus, the statement

If an animal X does *not* have four legs, then X is *not* a cat.

is true.

In other words:

> Correct Reversal of Direction of Implication
> Assume "if A, then B" is true. Then "if *not* B, then *not* A" is true as well.

The statement "if *not* B, then *not* A" is called the *contrapositive* of the statement "if A, then B."

Thus, the true statement "If an integer ends with 4, then it is even" is correctly reversed as "If an integer is *not* even, then it does *not* end with 4."

 It is really important that we understand implications and how they work; what we said above might feel straightforward, because the statements involved were easy to understand. However, in calculus and elsewhere in math, the statements will involve objects that are a lot more abstract than cats and even numbers.

As mentioned earlier, one calculus theorem states:

If f is differentiable at a, then f is continuous at a.

We recognize its structure as the implication A $\Rightarrow$ B, where A = "f is differentiable at a" and B = "f is continuous at a." As suggested, we can represent it in a diagram:

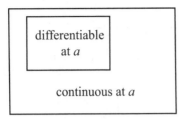

The diagram suggests (and it will be shown to be true in calculus) that there are functions that are in the larger box, but not in the smaller box — so, there are functions that are continuous, but not differentiable. In other words, the converse (i.e., the reversal of the implication A ⇒ B so that it reads B ⇒ A):

If f is continuous at a, then f is differentiable at a.

is false!

As well: if a function is outside the larger box (i.e., not continuous), then it cannot be in the smaller box either (i.e., not differentiable). So, the contrapositive (i.e., the reversal of A ⇒ B so that it reads *not* B ⇒ *not* A):

If f is not continuous at a, then f is not differentiable at a.

is true.

To practice writing converse and contrapositive statements, we look at few more examples:

Implication	Converse	Contrapositive
if A, then B	if B, then A	if *not* B, then *not* A
(A ⇒ B)	(B ⇒ A)	(*not* B ⇒ *not* A)
if an animal X is a cat, then X has four legs	if an animal X has four legs, then X is a cat	if an animal X does not have four legs, then X is not a cat
if $x > 1$, then $x^2 > 1$	if $x^2 > 1$, then $x > 1$	if $x^2 \le 1$, then $x \le 1$
if $y = x + 2\pi$, then $\sin x = \sin y$	if $\sin x = \sin y$, then $y = x + 2\pi$	if $\sin x \ne \sin y$, then $y \ne x + 2\pi$
if $x > 1$, then $\ln x > 0$	if $\ln x > 0$, then $x > 1$	if $\ln x \le 0$, then $x \le 1$

Keep in mind that, if implication is true, then its contrapositive must be true as well. But the converse might or might not be true.

All statements (leftmost column) in the table above are true. The converse to the next-to-last statement (if $y = x + 2\pi$ then $\sin x = \sin y$) is not true (if $\sin x = \sin y$, then y could be equal to x, or to $x + 4\pi$ or to $x + 6\pi$, etc.; it does not have to be that $y = x + 2\pi$). The converse to the last statement (if $x > 1$, then $\ln x > 0$) is true.

 Exercise 1. Rewrite each statement as an implication in the form "if A, then B."

(a) The square of an even number is even.

(b) Any increasing function has an inverse function.

(c) For every real number x, $|x| \geq 0$.

(d) The equation $x^2/a^2 + y^2/b^2 = 1$ represents a circle whenever $a = b$.

 Exercise 2. Each statement is an implication of the form "if A, then B". Identify A and B and determine whether the implication is a true statement. Determine whether the converse "if B, then A" is true or false.

(a) If x is positive, then e^x is positive.

(b) If $a = b$, then $a^2 = b^2$.

(c) If $m_1 m_2 = -1$, then the lines $y = m_1 x$ and $y = m_2 x$ are perpendicular.

 Exercise 3. Find the contrapositive of each implication.

(a) If $\sin x \neq 0$, then $\csc x$ is defined.

(b) If $x_1 \neq x_2$, then $f(x_1) \neq f(x_2)$.

(c) If a curve is a straight line, then it has the same slope at all points.

We define "A is *equivalent* to B" as "A implies B" and "B implies A." Using the symbol $\Leftrightarrow$ for equivalence, we write

$$\boxed{\text{A} \Leftrightarrow \text{B means A} \Rightarrow \text{B and B} \Rightarrow \text{A.}}$$

Unlike implication, equivalence is symmetric: if one direction is a true statement, so is the other. Instead of saying "A is equivalent to B" we often say "A if and only if B" and abbreviate as "A iff B." An example of equivalence is:

An integer is divisible by 5 iff it ends with 0 or 5.

The structure is A $\Leftrightarrow$ B, where A = "integer is divisible by 5" and B = "it/integer ends with 0 or 5." In terms of our diagrams representing equivalence as the relationship of being a subset, equivalence means that both A and B are represented by the same box.

Universal and Existential Quantifyers: "For All" and "There Exists"

Universal quantifier is used to describe a situation where *all* elements in some set possess a certain property. In English, the words/phrases such as "for all," or "all," or "any" or "(for) every," etc. determine a universal quantifier.

Examples include: "the sum of angles in any triangle is 180 degrees," or "every function that is differentiable at a is also continuous at a," or "every even number is divisible by 2."

On the other hand, *existential quantifier* is used to describe a situation where *some* elements in some set possess a certain property. In English, the words/phrases such as "there exist(s)," or "(for) some" or "there is (are)," etc. determine an existential quantifier.

For example: "there exists a real number x such that $x^2 - 4 = 0$," or "some animals are cats," or "there is a function that is continuous at a but not differentiable at a."

How do we deal with statements that involve universal and existential quantifiers?

Consider the statement involving the universal quantifier "All cats on Earth are black."

If we wish to prove that this statement is true, then finding one cat, or two or more cats, and verifying they are all black will not do. We have to find *every single cat* on Earth and verify that they are black.

However, if we wish to prove that the claim "all cats on Earth are black" is false, then all we need is to find *one cat that is not black* (it does not matter what colour, as long as it is not black). That cat is called a *counterexample*.

Thus, we reached an important conclusion:

> In order to prove that a statement involving a universal quantifier is true, we have to prove that it holds for each and every object that is implicated. To show that a statement involving a universal quantifier is false, we must find a counterexample, i.e., one case for which it does not hold.

We cannot use an example to prove that a statement involving a universal quantifier is true. However, to *disprove* such statement, we *can* use an example (that's what we call a counterexample).

Example 2. Prove that the following statement is true:

For every real number x, the expression $x^2 + 1$ is positive.

Solution. An argument of the form: "if $x = -2$, then $x^2 + 1 = (-2)^2 + 1 = 5 > 0$; if $x = 0$, then $x^2 + 1 = (0)^2 + 1 = 1 > 0$; if $x = 4$, then $x^2 + 1 = (4)^2 + 1 = 17 > 0$; etc.," does not constitute a proof. We checked three of infinitely many cases! Obviously, checking the statement number by number will not work — we need a general argument.

We could argue as follows: the square of any real number x satisfies $x^2 \geq 0$. Adding 1 to both sides gives $x^2 + 1 \geq 0 + 1 = 1$. Since $x^2 + 1$ is greater than or equal to 1, it must be positive. Done.

Example 3. Prove that the following statement is false:

Every polynomial of degree 2 has two distinct real roots.

Solution. All we need is one counterexample, i.e., we need to find one polynomial of degree 2 that does not have two distinct real roots. For instance, $x^2 + 1$ (has no real roots) or $x^2 - 2x + 1$ (has a repeated root $x = 1$) are counterexamples.

Now, consider the statement involving the existential quantifier "There is a black cat on Earth."

Finding one black cat on Earth will prove this statement true. However, if we wish to prove that the statement is false, we have to show that *not a single cat* on Earth is black. So, we have to find all cats, and check that none is black.

We conclude the following:

> In order to prove that a statement involving an existential quantifier is true, we have to show that it holds for at least one object that is implicated. To disprove a statement involving a universal quantifier (i.e., to show it is false), we must show that it does not hold for *any one* of the objects implicated.

Let us show that the statement

There is a real number x such that $x^5 + 4x - 3 = 2$.

is true. Keep in mind that we are not asked to solve this equation — all we need is to find *one* x for which $x^5 + 4x - 3$ is equal to 2. By guess-and-check, we discover that, when $x = 1$, $x^5 + 4x - 3 = (1)^5 + 4(1) - 3 = 2$. Done.

We would like to prove that the statement

There is a real number x such that $x^4 = -2$.

is false. To do this, we have to show that $x^4 = -2$ does not hold for any real number x. In other words, by checking examples (such as if $x = 2$, then $(2)^4 = 16 \neq -2$; if $x = 0$, then $(0)^4 = 0 \neq -2$; if $x = -3$, then $(-3)^4 = 81 \neq -2$; etc.) we will not be able to prove this.

So, we need to use a general argument, something like this: the fourth power of any real number is positive, or zero. So, it can never be equal to -2.

 Exercise 4. Determine whether each statement is true or false, and justify your answer.

(a) For any prime number p, the number $p + 2$ is prime.

(b) There exists a prime number p such that the number $p + 2$ is also prime.

(c) For all real numbers $x \geq 0$, $\sqrt{x} \geq 0$.

(d) There is a real number x such that $x^2 + 3x + 7 = 0$.

 Mathematics texts tend to be quite careful about the language they use to describe universal and existential quantifiers. However there is one situation that could cause confusion; it is related to the use of the indefinite article "a."

In some cases, such as "a differentiable function is continuous," the article "a" means "any" or "all" — so it represents a universal quantifier. Likewise, "a" in "for a real number x, the graph of e^x is above the x-axis" means "for all."

In some cases, though, "a" refers to an existential quantifier. For instance, "a" in "find a prime number between 10 and 1000" means we need to find *one* (*any*) prime number between 10 and 1000, but not all of them.

Additional Exercises

For extra practice, work on the following questions.

 Exercise 5. Rewrite each statement in the form "if A, then B" (do not worry about the meaning of math terms in (c), (e) and (i); they will be explained in your calculus course).

(a) For two positive numbers a and b, $\sqrt{ab} = \sqrt{a}\sqrt{b}$.

(b) Exponential function $y = a^x$ is increasing when $a > 1$.

(c) A bounded and increasing sequence is convergent.

(d)* The square of a number is divisible by 4, as long as the number is even.

(e) Assume that $f(x)$ is differentiable and has a relative maximum at $x = a$. Then we conclude that $f'(a) = 0$.

(f) The reciprocals of positive numbers m and n for which $m > n$ satisfy $\dfrac{1}{m} < \dfrac{1}{n}$.

(g)* Parallel lines have equal slopes.

(h) For all non-zero real numbers x, $|x| > 0$.

(i) The composition $\sin f(x)$ is continuous as long as $f(x)$ is continuous.

(j) Assuming that $m_1 \neq m_2$, the lines $y = m_1x + b_1$ and $y = m_2x + b_2$ intersect at a point.

(extra) **Exercise 6.** Write the converse and the contrapositive statements derived from each implication. (do not worry about the meaning of math terms in (f) and (g); they will be explained in your calculus course). (We do not claim that all implications are true.)

(a) If $x \neq 0$ then $1/x$ is a real number.

(b) If $f(x)$ is an increasing function, then $f(x)$ satisfies the horizontal line test.

(c) If it rains, then the roads are wet.

(d) If $\ln x = \ln y + \ln z$ then $x = yz$.

(e)* If $f(g(x)) = x$, then $f(x)$ is an inverse function of $g(x)$.

(f) If $f(x)$ has a relative extreme value at $x = a$, then $x = a$ is a critical point.

(g) If a sequence a_n is convergent, then it is bounded.

(h) If $m_1 = m_2$, then the lines $y = m_1x + b_1$ and $y = m_2x + b_2$ are parallel.

(i)* If $m_1 \neq m_2$, then the lines $y = m_1x + b_1$ and $y = m_2x + b_2$ are not parallel.

(j) If $x_1 \neq x_2$, then $f(x_1) = f(x_2)$.

(extra) **Exercise 7.** Each statement is an implication of the form "if A, then B". Identify A and B and determine whether the implication is a true statement. Determine whether the converse "if B, then A" is true or false.

(a) If $\ln x = \ln y$ then $x = y$.

(b) If $x > 4$, then $|x| > 4$.

(c) If $\cos x = 0$, then $x = 0$.

(d)* If $x = 7$, then $x^2 = 49$.

(e)* If $f(g(x)) = g(f(x))$, then $f(x)$ and $g(x)$ are inverse of each other.

(f) If x is a real number, then $1/x$ is a real number.

(g) If a real number satisfies $x > 1$, then its square satisfies $x^2 > 1$.

(h) If a line is horizontal, then its slope is zero.

(extra) **Exercise 8.** State what you would need to do to:

(a)* Disprove the statement "There is a landlocked country in South America."

(b)* Prove that the statement "There is a landlocked country in South America" is true.

(c) Disprove the statement "All cars in Canada have four wheels."

(d) Prove that the statement "All cars in Canada have four wheels" is true.

(e) Disprove the statement "There is a living dinosaur on Earth."

(f) Prove that the statement "There is a living dinosaur on Earth" is true.

(g)* Prove that the statement "All dogs in Ontario bark" is true.

(h)* Disprove the statement "All dogs in Ontario bark."

(i) Disprove the statement "For all non-zero real numbers x, $\ln x^2 = 2\ln x$."

(j) Prove the statement "There is a line which does not satisfy the horizontal line test."

 Exercise 9.   Determine whether each statement is true or false, and justify your answer.

(a)* There exist real numbers a and b such that $\sqrt{a+b} = \sqrt{a} + \sqrt{b}$.

(b)* For all real numbers a and b, $\sqrt{a+b} = \sqrt{a} + \sqrt{b}$.

(c) There exists a real number $x > 0$ for which the expression $1 + \dfrac{1}{x}$ is positive.

(d) For all real numbers $x > 0$ the expression $1 + \dfrac{1}{x}$ is positive.

(e) All functions of the form $y = \cos(ax)$ where $a > 1$, have the same range.

(f)* There is a number $b > 0$ so that the range of the function $y = b\sin x$ is $[0, 2]$.

(g)* There is a real number c so that the range of the function $y = c + \sin x$ is $[0, 2]$.

(h) There is a real number $a > 0$ so that the function $y = a^x$ is decreasing.

(i) For all real numbers $a > 0$ the function $y = a^x$ is decreasing.

(j) For all real numbers x, $f(x) = xe^{-x+4} \geq 0$.

(k) There is a real number x such that x, $f(x) = e^{-x+4} < 0$.

Answers to Exercises

In this section, answers are provided for all (try it!) exercises as well as (extra) exercises marked with a symbol $*$.

Section 1. Numbers and Operations

1. (c) $11/13$ (f) $3x/2$

2. (a), (c), (e), (g)

4. (e) $\dfrac{13x - 4y}{3}$ (g) $\dfrac{3a^2 - 24ab + 4b^2}{6ab}$ (h) $\dfrac{15x^2y - 15xy^2 - 6xy - 10x - 6y^2 + 8y}{30xy}$

5. (c) $m^2/3$ (g) $147/2$

6. (c) $12/13$ (d) $29/14$ (i) $\dfrac{1}{ab}$

7.

8. $(-\infty, -2], (-1, 2], (3, 4)$

9. (c) $(-\infty, -8)$ or $(-2, \infty)$ (f) $(-\infty, -4)$ and $(-4, 0)$

11. (c) Correct   (d) incorrect   (e) incorrect

12. (d) $10 - 0.2x$ if $x \le 50$ and $-10 + 0.2x$ if $x > 50$

13. (a) $\pi, -1/2, 0.33$ (b) 1 (c) -1 (d) $9/7$

14. (d) 9 and -13 (e) By the property of the absolute value, $|5x| = |5| \cdot |x| = 5 \cdot |x|$

15. (a) 81 (b) $1/64$ (c) not defined   (d) 8

16. (d) $10^4 = 10,000$ (f) $1/25$ (g) $-1/25$ (j) -8

17. (e) x^{23} (h) c^{25} (l) $a^4 b^4$ (n) $x^5 y^7 (x + y)^{-7}$

18. (c) -2 (g) 0 (h) 2 (m) not defined

19. (b) $3\sqrt{5}$ (c) $10\sqrt{10}$ (g) $3\sqrt[3]{3}$ (i) $2\sqrt[4]{2}$

20. (b) 2 (e) $\sqrt{14}$ (l) $2a - 5b + 9\sqrt{ab}$ (n) $a + b$

21. (b) Incorrect   (e) correct   (f) incorrect   (i) incorrect

22. (a) $-5/4$ (b) $1/\sqrt{2}$ (c) $27/8$ (d) $27/64$

23. (d) 14 (f) $15\sqrt{3}$ (g) $-5\sqrt{5}$

24. (c) $(x^{5/2})^2$ (d) $(x^{1/2} y^{1/2} z^{3/2})^2$ (e) $(x^{1/6})^2 = (\sqrt[6]{x})^2$

25. (c) $(x^{2/3})^3$ (e) $(x^{1/6})^3 = (\sqrt[6]{x})^3$ (f) $(x^{-1/3})^3 = (1/\sqrt[3]{x})^3$

26. (a) $x^{5.58}$ (b) $x^{-3/2} y^{15/4}$ (c) $(x - a)^1 = x - a$

27. (c) $y^{-3.52}$ (d) $a^6 b^{6\sqrt{2}}$ (f) $x^{10.2}(x + y)^{-8.5}$

28. (c) Incorrect   (g) incorrect   (i) incorrect   (k) correct

Section 2. Basic Algebra

1. (e) $m = 0$, $b = -3$ (f) $m = 1$, $b = 0$ (g) $m = 0$, $b = 0$

2. (d) $a = -1$, $b = 0$, $c = 0$ (e) $a = 0$, $b = -1$, $c = 1$ (f) $a = 0$, $b = 0$, $c = 0$

3. (c) $m = -3/2$, $n = 1/2$, $p = 0$

4. (a) $3x^3 - 7x^2 + 7x - 4$ (b) $x^4 - 0.4x^2 + 0.04$ (c) $x^7 - x$ (d) $8x^3 - 12x^2 + 6x - 1$

5. (d) $a = -0.25$, $b = 0.85$, $c = 0.6$ (e) $a = -2/3$, $b = 2/3$, $c = -1/8$

6. (c) $-\frac{6}{5x^2} + \frac{43}{5x} - 4$ (g) $9x - 30\sqrt{x} + 25$ (k) $x^2 - 6$

7. (c) $(a + 2b)^2$ (h) $(x + 1/2)^2$ (j) $(2x/3 - 1/4)^2$

8. (a) $(x + 8)^2 - 64$ (d) $(x + 7/2)^2 - 33/4$ (e) $3(x - 2)^2 - 12$ (h) $3(x - 3/2)^2 - 19/4$

9. (c) $(x^2 + y)(x - y^2)$ (f) $(x + 7)(x - 4)$ (h) $5x(x - 1)(x + 1)$

10. (c) $(5x - 2)(x - 2)$ (e) $(2x + 1)(3x + 2)$ (f) $(2x + 1)(3x - 2)$

11. (a) $(x - 0.2)(x + 0.2)$ (e) $5(x - \sqrt{11})(x + \sqrt{11})$ (g) $(x - \sqrt[4]{2})(x + \sqrt[4]{2})(x^2 + \sqrt{2})$

12. (c) $(x - 1)(x^2 + x + 1)(x + 1)(x^2 - x + 1)$ (d) $(\sqrt[3]{x} + 1)(\sqrt[3]{x^2} - \sqrt[3]{x} + 1)$

13. (a) $(2x^2 + y)(y - 2)$ (c) $3(3y - 5x)(3y + 5x)$ (f) $(x/4 - y/7)(x/4 + y/7)$

(h) $(4x - 3)(x - 2)$ (i) $(3x + 1)(x - 3)$ (o) $(a + bc)(ab - c)$

14. (a) $2xy^{1/2}(2x^2 - y)$ (b) $a^x(a^4 - 1 + a)$ (h) $-a(x - y)(3 + b)$

(n) $(1 + x + y)(1 - x - y)$ (u) $(a - b)(a + b - b^2 - ab - a^2)$

15. (c) $\dfrac{1}{2a + b}$ (l) cannot be cancelled   (m) $-1/3$ (s) $-\dfrac{a^2 + 4a + 16}{a + 4}$

16. (c) $\dfrac{x - y}{x + y}$ (f) $\dfrac{x(x^2 + y^2)}{y(x + y)}$

17. (e) $\dfrac{1 + a^2}{a}$ (g) a^{x-y}

18. (c) -1 if $x > 5/3$ and 1 if $x < 5/3$

19. (a) $\dfrac{-x^2 + x - 2}{(x - 2)(x - 4)}$ (b) $\dfrac{-2x^3 + 5x^2 - 2x + 3}{x(x - 1)^2}$ (c) $\dfrac{x^2 - x + 4}{(x - 2)(x - 3)}$

20. (g) $\dfrac{b^2 + 6b + 12}{2(b - 2)(b + 4)}$ (l) $\dfrac{x^2 + 3x + 9}{x + 3}$ (m) $\dfrac{x^2(x - 1)}{2x + 1}$ (v) $\dfrac{x}{x - 3}$ (w) $\dfrac{x}{x - 2}$

21. (a) $6\left(\dfrac{1}{8}x^4 - x^2 - \dfrac{x}{12} - \dfrac{11}{6}\right)$ (f) $x^{-3/2}\left(-x^{9/2} + 3x^{7/2} - x^{5/2} - 12x^{3/2}\right)$

(i) $\dfrac{x^{-2/3}(x - 5)}{3} \cdot 5(x - 1)$ (l) $\sqrt{x}\left(x^{3/2} - 3 - \dfrac{5}{\sqrt{x}} + \dfrac{4}{x^{3/2}} - \dfrac{1}{x}\right)$

22. (a) $x^2 + 4x + 13 + \dfrac{57}{x - 4}$ (b) $x + 6 - \dfrac{8}{x + 1}$ (g) $x^2 - 7x + 49 - \dfrac{343}{x + 7}$

23. (c) Subtract and add 15; $3 + \dfrac{15}{2x - 5}$ (d) Add and subtract 2; $2 - \dfrac{2}{x^2 + 1}$

24. $(x+4)(x-3)(x+1)$

25. (a) $-6-2\sqrt{7}$ (d) $\dfrac{(4-\sqrt{x})(2-\sqrt{x})}{4-x}$ (g) $3(\sqrt{x}+\sqrt{x-1})$

Section 4. Equations and Inequalities

1. (a) $x=0$

2. (a) $x=-1$ (b) $x=80/39$ (c) $x=0.4/6.5=0.061538$ (d) $x=\sqrt{3}+2$

3. (a) $x=-47$ (b) $x=5/3$ (c) $x=1$

4. (a) $x=5/3$ (b) $x=-9/5$ (c) $x=1$

5. (b) $x=\pm\sqrt[6]{2}=\pm2^{1/6}$ (e) $x=(5\pm\sqrt{2})/2$

6. (a) No solutions   (b) $x=6\pm2\sqrt{3}$ (c) $x=-4,\ x=-6$ (d) $x=4/3,\ x=-1$

7. (a) No solutions   (b) $x=\dfrac{1\pm\sqrt{15}}{2}$ (c) $x=\dfrac{1\pm\sqrt{61}}{6}$

8. (a) $x=9$ (b) $x=-1$ (d) $x=5/2$ (e) $x=-3,\ x=2$

9. (a) $\left(x-(-1+\sqrt{5})/2\right)\left(x-(-1-\sqrt{5}/2)\right)$ (b) $(2x+3)(2x-5)$
(c) $2\left(x-(-1+\sqrt{7})/2\right)\left(x-(-1-\sqrt{7})/2\right)$

10. (a) $(2,\infty)$ (b) $[2,3]$ (c) $[5/3,2]$

11. (a) $(-\infty,-8]$ and $[8,\infty)$ (b) $(-8,8)$ (c) $[-2,2]$ (d) $(-\infty,2)$
(e) $(-\infty,-7)$ and $(3,\infty)$ (f) $(-\infty,5)$ and $[8,\infty)$ (g) $(-\infty,-1]$ and $[0,1]$ (h) $[-1,2]$

12. (c) $(-\infty,-11]$ and $[13,\infty)$

13. (a) $|x|\le8$ (b) $|x-7/2|<1/2$ (c) $|x|\ge1$ (d) $|x-2|\ge2$

14. (a) $x=-2$ and $x=5$ (b) $x=2$ and $x=14$

15. (a) $1/2<x<5/2$ (b) $x\le-8/3$ or $x\ge0$ (c) $-8/3<x<0$
(d) $10/3<x<20/3$ (e) $7/2<x<13/2$ (f) $-35<x<29$

16. (a) $(-\infty,-5)$ and $(4,\infty)$ (b) $[0,2]$ (c) $[-2,2]$

17. (a) $x=3,\ y=-7$ (b) $x=1,\ y=5$ and $x=-2,\ y=2$

Section 5. Elements of Analytic Geometry

1. (a) $\sqrt{85}$ (b) $(0,1)$

2. $y=-7x+10$

3. (a) Line through the origin of slope $-1/2$ (b) Line of slope $-3/2$ and y-intercept 2
(c) Vertical line through $(-2,0)$

4. (a) No; their slopes are $-1/2$ and -3.   (b) $y=x/2-5/2$
(c) The product of their slopes is $(3/2)(-2/3)=-1$.

5. (a) $y = -4$ (b) $x = 3$ (c) $y = x/3 - 5$ (d) $y = -3x + 5$

6. (a) Slope is -1, y-intercept is 0 (b) Vertical line, slope is not a real number; no y- intercept

(c) Slope is 0, y-intercept is -4 (d) Slope is $3/5$, y-intercept is $-1/5$

7. (c) A, C, D, B (f) $x = 0$ and $y = -11$

8. (b) Slope is zero, y-intercept is $y = 9/7$ (horizontal line)

(f) Slope is not defined, no y-intercept (vertical line)

(h) Slope is $15/4$, y-intercept is $y = -25/2$

10. (d) $x = -4$ (vertical line)   (h) $y = -x - 3$ (k) $y = -\frac{a}{b}x + \frac{ax_0 + by_0}{b}$

11. (b)

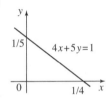

12. (a) Centre: $(5/2, 0)$, radius: $\sqrt{21}/2$ (b) $(1, -4)$, $\sqrt{21}$ (c) $(0, 0)$, $\sqrt{3}$

13. (a) Ellipse with semi-axes 3 and $\sqrt{3}$; x-intercepts are ± 3, y-intercepts are $\pm\sqrt{3}$

(b) Circle, centered at $(1, 3)$, radius $\sqrt{10}$

(c) Ellipse with semi-axes $\sqrt{2}$ and $2/\sqrt{3}$; x-intercepts are $\pm\sqrt{2}$, y-intercepts are $\pm 2/\sqrt{3}$

(d) Circle, centered at $(0, 1/2)$, radius $1/2$

14. (a) Parabola; x-intercepts: $x = -3 \pm \sqrt{6}$; y-intercept: $y = 3$; vertex at $(-3, -6)$; opens upward

(b) Parabola; x-intercept at $x = 2$; y-intercept at $y = 4$; vertex at $(2, 0)$; opens upward

(c) Parabola; no x-intercepts; y-intercept at $y = -1$; vertex at $(0, -1)$; opens downward

15. (a) Hyperbola, $a = 2/\sqrt{3}$, $b = \sqrt{8} = 2\sqrt{2}$; asymptotes are $y = \pm\sqrt{6}\,x$; y-intercepts are $\pm 2\sqrt{2}$; lies above and below its asymptotes; see below, left

(b) Hyperbola, $a = \sqrt{11/2}$, $b = \sqrt{33}$; asymptotes are $y = \pm\sqrt{6}\,x$; x-intercepts are $\pm\sqrt{11/2}$; lies to the left and to the right of its asymptotes; see below, right

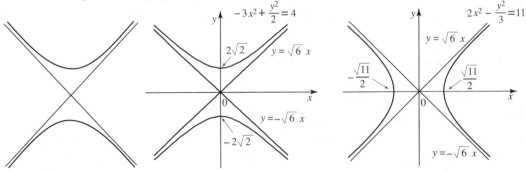

(c) Parabola, vertex is at the origin, opens towards the positive x-axis; see below, left

(d) Parabola, vertex is at the origin, opens towards the negative x-axis; see below, right

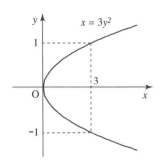 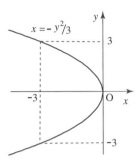

16. (e) Centre: $(2,6)$, radius: $\sqrt{44} = 2\sqrt{11}$

17. (b) Centre: $(-1/4, 0)$, semi-axes: $a = 3/4$ and $b = 3/\sqrt{8}$

18. (d)

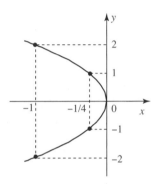

19. (b) Asymptotes: $y = \pm\frac{1}{\sqrt{5}}x$; no y-intercepts, x intercepts: $x = \pm\sqrt{2}$; the hyperbola lies in the regions to the left and to the right of its asymptotes.

(f) Asymptotes: $y = \pm\frac{7}{\sqrt{21}}x$; no x-intercepts, y intercepts: $y = \pm7$; the hyperbola lies in the regions above and below its asymptotes.

20. (e) Circle, centred at $(9/2, 0)$, of radius $\sqrt{93}/2$

(j) Ellipse, centred at $(-3, 0)$ with semi axes $a = 3$ and $b = 3/\sqrt{8}$

21. (c) $(1, 12)$ and $(-1, 12)$ lie on the curve, $(1, 0)$ does not lie on the curve

22. (f) Parallel lines, no points in common

(i) $x^2 - y^2 = 1$ is a hyperbola, $x - 2y = 0$ ia line; they intersect at $(2/\sqrt{3}, 1/\sqrt{3})$ and $(-2/\sqrt{3}, -1/\sqrt{3})$

(m) $4x^2 + 3y^2 = 1$ is an ellipse, $x + y = 1$ is a line; the two curves do not intersect.

23. (b) Parabola; opens upward, with its vertex at $(0, 1.4)$.

(e) Line of slope 2, going through the origin in the $z_1 z_2$-coordinate system.

(i) Ellipse centred at the origin; horizontal semi-axis: $\sqrt{5}$, vertical semi-axis: $\sqrt{5}/2$

(j) Ellipse centred at the origin; horizontal semi-axis: $\sqrt{5}/2$, vertical semi-axis: $\sqrt{5}$

Section 6. Functions

1. (c) All real numbers   (g) $D = \{x \mid x > 2\}$ (h) $D = \{x \mid x \neq 0, 1, -1\}$

(i) $D = \{x \mid x < 0 \text{ or } x \geq 1\} = (-\infty, 0) \cup [1, \infty)$

3. Note: the domain of f is $D = \{x \mid x \geq -1\}$. See the graph below.

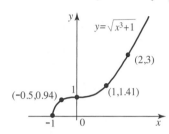

4. (a) $R = (0, \infty)$ (b) $R = (-\infty, 1] \cup (3, \infty)$

5. Range is indicated by the thicker line on the y-axis.

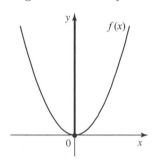 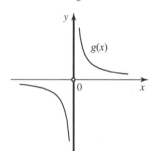 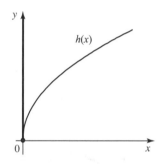

6. (d) $D = \mathbb{R}$, $R = [4, \infty)$ (f) $D = \mathbb{R}$, $R = \mathbb{R}$ (i) $D = \{x \mid x \neq 0\}$, $R = \{y \mid y > 0\}$
(j) $D = \mathbb{R}$, $R = \{y \mid y \geq 0\}$

7. (a) horizontal line, crosses y-axis at -4 (b) mirror image of $y = x^2$ across the x-axis
(c) $f(x) = 0$, if $x < 0$ and $f(x) = 2x$ if $x \geq 0$; see below (left).
(e) $y = 1$, if $x > 0$ and $y = -1$, if $x < 0$; see below (right).

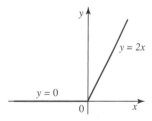 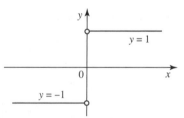

8. (a) $3x/2 + 4$ (b) $9x + 16$ (c) $(3x + 4)/2$

9. (a) $(x^2 + x + 1)^5$ (b) x^{25} (c) $x^{10} + x^5 + 1$

10. (a) $f^{-1}(x) = \frac{2}{x} + 4$ (b) $f^{-1}(x) = 2 - \left(\frac{x+1}{4}\right)^3$ (c) $f^{-1}(x) = \sqrt[3]{1 - x}$.

11. (b) $f(g(x)) = -5$; $g(f(x)) = 19$; $f(f(x)) = -5$
(e) $f(g(x)) = \frac{6}{|x+13|}$; $g(f(x)) = \left|\frac{6}{x} + 13\right|$; $f(f(x)) = x$
(h) $f(g(x)) = \sqrt{x^4 + 1}$; $g(f(x)) = x^2 + 1$; $f(f(x)) = \sqrt{x^2 + 2}$

13. (c), (j) does not exist   (h) $f^{-1}(x) = (x + 11)^4 + 4$ (m) $f^{-1}(x) = -\sqrt{x}$

14. They are inverse functions.

15. (a) Move the parabola $y = x^2$ to the left for 2 units and then 3 units up.

(b) Move the graph of $y = \sqrt{x}$ to the right for 4 units and then 2 units down.

(c) Move the graph of $y = 1/x^2$ to the right for 1 unit and then 2 units up.

16. (a) Compress the graph of $y = x^3$ by a factor of 2 and mirror across the x-axis.

(d) Move $y = \sqrt{x}$ for 4 units to the left, stretch by a factor of 3, and move one unit up.

(f) Move $y = \sqrt{x}$ for 4 units to the left, reflect across the x-axis, and move down by 3 units.

(j) Reflect $y = |x|$ across the x-axis and move one unit up.

(l) Move $y = |x|$ for 4 units to the right, expand vertically by a factor of 2 and move up by 3 units.

Section 7. Trigonometric Functions

1. (a) $5\pi/4$ radians   (b) 210 degrees   (b) $19\pi/45$ radians   (b) 211.99 degrees

2. $\sin\theta = 1/3$, $\cos\theta = \sqrt{8}/3$ and $\tan\theta = 1/\sqrt{8}$

3. (a) $\sin\frac{5\pi}{6} = 1/2$, $\cos\frac{5\pi}{6} = -\sqrt{3}/2$ and $\tan\frac{5\pi}{6} = -1/\sqrt{3}$

(b) $\sin\left(-\frac{\pi}{6}\right) = -1/2$, $\cos\left(-\frac{\pi}{6}\right) = \sqrt{3}/2$ and $\tan\left(-\frac{\pi}{6}\right) = -1/\sqrt{3}$

4. $\sin(-3\pi/2) = 1$, $\cos(-3\pi/2) = 0$; $\tan(-3\pi/2)$ and $\sec(-3\pi/2)$ are not defined

5. (a) To obtain $\cos 3x$, compress the graph of $\cos x$ along the x-axis by a factor of 3; to obtain $\cos 0.5x$, stretch the graph of $\cos x$ along the x-axis by a factor of 2.

(b) To obtain $-\cos x$, reflect the graph of $\cos x$ with respect to the x-axis; stretch $-\cos x$ vertically by a factor of 4 to obtain $-4\cos x$; to obtain $-\cos x - 4$, move the graph of $-\cos x$ down for 4 units.

6. Write $f(x) = 2\sin\left(3\left(x - \frac{\pi}{3}\right)\right)$. Start with the graph of $\sin x$, compress it horizontally by a factor of 3 to obtain $\sin(3x)$; then shift right for $\pi/3$ units and finally expand vertically by a factor of 2. The range is $[-2, 2]$.

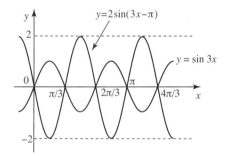

7. π/a

8. (a) Use the addition formula for $\sin x$.

(b) Write $\cot x = \cos x/\sin x$ and compute the common denominator.

(c) Combine the first and the third terms and then use the fact that $1 + \tan^2 x = \sec^2 x$.

9. $\sin 3x = 3\sin x - 4\sin^3 x$

10. Start with the addition and the subtraction formulas for $\sin x$ and multiply out the terms that you get. Then, using basic trigonometric identity rewrite the two cosine terms using sine function and simplify.

11. (a) $x = \pi + 2k\pi$ (b) $x = -\frac{\pi}{4} + k\pi$

12. (a) $x = \frac{5\pi}{6} + 2k\pi$ and $x = \frac{7\pi}{6} + 2k\pi$ (b) $x = \frac{\pi}{3} + k\pi$ (c) $x = \frac{\pi}{4} + 2k\pi$ and $x = \frac{3\pi}{4} + 2k\pi$

13. $x = k\pi$, $x = \frac{\pi}{3} + 2k\pi$ and $x = \frac{5\pi}{3} + 2k\pi$

14. $x = \frac{\pi}{6} + k\pi$ and $x = \frac{5\pi}{6} + k\pi$

15. (a) and (b) Expand by taking several values for k (for instance, take $k = -3, -2, -1, 0, 1, 2, 3$).

16. $\arcsin 1 = \pi/2$, $\arcsin(-1/2) = -\pi/6$, $\arcsin(1/\sqrt{2}) = \pi/4$, $\arcsin(-1/\sqrt{2}) = -\pi/4$

17. $\arctan(-1) = -\pi/4$, $\arctan(1/\sqrt{3}) = \pi/6$, $\arctan(\sqrt{3}) = \pi/3$, $\arctan(-1\sqrt{3}) = -\pi/6$

18. (c) -300° (e) 180° (f) $\pi^2/180 \approx 0.0548$ rad

19. (a) $\sin \alpha = \cos \beta = 21/29$, $\cos \alpha = \sin \beta = 20/29$

(b) $a = 12$, $b = 5$, $\sin \beta = 5/13$, $\tan \beta = 5/12$

(c) $\sin \alpha = 0.8 = 4/5$, $\cos \alpha = 0.6 = 3/5$, $\tan \alpha = 4/3$, $\csc \alpha = 5/4$, $\sec \alpha = 5/3$, and $\cot \alpha = 3/4$

20. (b) $\sin \theta = 3/\sqrt{10}$, $\cos \theta = 1/\sqrt{10}$, $\sec \theta = \sqrt{10}$, $\csc \theta = \sqrt{10}/3$, $\cot \theta = 1/\tan \theta = 1/3$

21. (e) $\frac{2k\pi}{3}$ (f) $\frac{(2k+1)\pi}{3}$

22. (a) third   (b) fourth   (c) third   (d) second

23. $\tan \theta$

24. (a) positive   (b) positive   (c) negative   (d) positive

25. (a) $\sin 1$ (b) $\cos 2^{\circ}$

26. (d) 5π (g) 2.5π

27. (a) Start with the graph of $\cos x$ and move it $\pi/4$ units to the left.

(c) Start with the graph of $\sin x$ and move it π units to the right.

(f) Start with the graph of $\tan x$ and move it 1 unit to the left.

(k) Compress $\cos x$ by a factor of 4 to obtain $\cos 4x$. Then shift it $\pi/4$ units to the left.

(m) Expand $\sin x$ horizontally by a factor of 2 to obtain $\sin(x/2)$. Then shift it $\frac{2\pi}{3}$ units to the right.

28. (a) Reflect $\sin x$ across the y-axis, to obtain $\sin(-x)$. Reflect $\sin x$ across the x-axis, to obtain $\sin x$; see below and top of next page.

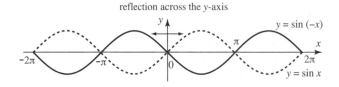

reflection across the y-axis

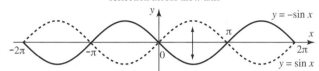

reflection across the x-axis

(e) Write $\sin(\pi/2 - x) = \sin(-x + \pi/2) = \sin(-(x - \pi/2))$. Reflect $\sin x$ across the y-axis to obtain $\sin(-x)$ and then move the graph $\pi/2$ units to the right. See below.

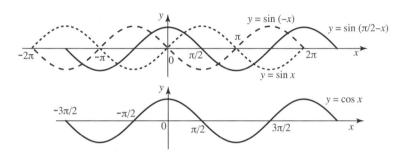

30. Write $y = \sin^2 x = \frac{1 - \cos 2x}{2} = \frac{1}{2}(-\cos 2x + 1)$. Compress $\cos x$ horizontally by a factor of 2 (to get $\cos 2x$), reflect across the x-axis (to get $-\cos 2x$), move it up by 1 unit (to get $-\cos 2x + 1$), and compress vertically by a factor of 2.

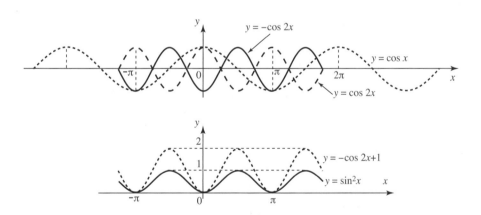

31. (a) $\tan^2 x$ (b) $\sec x$ (c) $2/\sin x$

32. (c) $x = k\pi/2$ (g) $x = -\frac{\pi}{6} + k\pi$ (h) $x = \frac{3\pi}{4} + k\pi$

(i) $x = \frac{\pi}{6} + 2k\pi$ and $x = \frac{11\pi}{6} + 2k\pi$ (l) $x = \arctan 12 + k\pi \approx 1.488 + k\pi$

(m) $x \approx 1.8234 + 2k\pi$ and $x \approx 4.4596 + 2k\pi$

33. (b) no solutions (c) $(2k + 1)\pi$

34. (e) Write $\cot x = \cos x / \sin x$ and then use the subtraction formulas for sin and cos.

35. (a) Cross-multiply. (b) Replace $\tan x$ by $\sin x / \cos x$ and $\cot x$ by $\cos x / \sin x$, and simplify.

36. (c) $\arcsin(-1) = -\pi/2$ (d) not defined (f) $\arctan(-1) = -\pi/4$

37. (b) $\arccos(-1) = \pi$ (c) not defined

Section 8. Exponential and Logarithmic Functions

1. (a) Move the graph of $y = 2^x$ up 4 units.

(b) Move the graph of $y = 2^x$ to the right 4 units. Or write $y = 2^{x-4} = 2^{-4}2^x$; so scale the graph of $y = 2^x$ vertically by a factor of $2^{-4} = 1/16$.

(c) Reflect the graph of $y = 2^x$ with respect to the x-axis.

(d) Reflect the graph of $y = 2^x$ with respect to both the x-axis and the y-axis (in either order). Or write $-2^{-x} = -(1/2)^x$; reflect the graph of $y = (1/2)^x$ with respect to the x-axis.

2. As x approaches $-\infty$, a^{-x} approaches ∞ faster as a increases. As x approaches ∞, a^{-x} approaches zero faster as a increases.

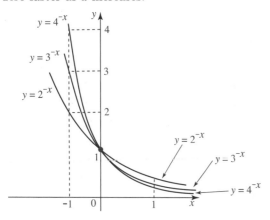

3. (a) 5^{-x+4} (b) 3^{6x-14} (c) 2^{-x+20}

4. (a) $x = \pm\sqrt{3}$ (b) $x = 1$ (c) $x = 0$ and $x = 2$

5. missing entries, from top to bottom: $10^1 = 10$, $\log_3(1/9) = -2$, $5^{-2} = 0.04$, $\log_{10} 0.001 = -3$, $\log_{10} 1 = 0$, $10^6 = 1,000,000$

6. Take $x = y = 1$; then $\log_a x + \log_a y = 0$, but $\log_a(x + y) = \log_a 2 \neq 0$. Take $x = 2$, $y = 1$; then $\log_{10}(x - y) = 0$, whereas $\log_{10} x - \log_{10} y = \log_{10} 2 \neq 0$.

7. (a) One answer is: since it is log of a sum, it cannot be simplified. However, the sum $y^3 + 8$ can be written as a product, using the sum of the cubes formula. In that case, the answer is $\log_{12}(y^3 + 8) = \log_{12}(y + 2) + \log_{12}(y^2 - 2y + 4)$.

(b) $2 + 4\log_{10} a - \log_{10} c - \log_{10}(a + b)$ (c) $-1/2$

8. $\log_4 x = 2\log_{16} x$, $\log_{0.5} x = -\log_2 x$; $\log_{11} 1.45 \approx 0.15495$, $\log_{0.4} 44 \approx -4.12990$

9. (a) $x = 16$ (b) $x = 243$

(c) $x = 2$ only ($x = 0$ and $x = -2$ are not solutions since they are not in the domain of $\log_2 x$)

(d) $x = 2$

10. (a) 20 (b) $\ln(48e^2)$ (c) $x = (\ln 4 + 2)/3$ (d) $x = -2$ and $x = 1$

11. (d) $\log_{10} 0.001 = x$ (e) $y = e^x$ (f) $\log_6 D = C$

12. (a) 10^{17} (b) 3^8 (c) 3^{12} (d) 6   (j) $\dfrac{e^{5x} - 3e}{e^{2x} + e^{-6x}}$

13. (e) 5   (f) 10^4 (g) -2 (h) -4 (i) -2 (o) $5/2$ (p) $1/32$

14. (a) 4   (b) 5   (c) 5   (d) 64   (m) -2 (n) 2   (o) $1/23$

15. (a) 14   (b) e (d) x^2 (g) $\ln 5 + x^2$ (h) x^4

16. (a) $\log_5 x = \log_{10} x / \log_{10} 5 \approx 1.43068 \log_{10} x$; $\log_5 x \approx 1.54369 \log_{12} x$; $\log_5 x \approx 0.62133 \ln x$;

(b) $\ln x \approx 2.30259 \log_{10} x$; $\ln x \approx 2.48491 \log_{12} x$

(Answers to parts of (a) and (b) might vary in the last two decimals, depending on which logarithm is used ($\ln$ or $\log_{10}$) and how the answers to intermediate calculations are rounded off.)

17. (b) Start with the graph of $y = e^x$, compress it horizontally by a factor of 5 (to obtain e^{5x}) and then reflect across the y-axis.

(c) Think of $g(x) = 1 - e^{-5x}$ as $g(x) = -e^{-5x} + 1$. Start with the finished graph in (b), reflect across the x-axis (to obtain $-e^{-5x}$) and then shift up by 1 unit.

(j) Start with the graph of $y = \ln x$, shift it right by 5 units (to obtain $\ln(x - 5)$), and then reflect across the x-axis.

(m) Start with the graph of $y = \log_{10} x$ and compress it horizontally by a factor of 2. Alternatively, write $y = \log_{10}(2x) = \log_{10} 2 + \log_{10} x$; so start with the graph of $y = \log_{10} x$ and shift it up by $\log_{10} 2 \approx 0.301$ units.

18. (b) Incorrect. Take $x = y = 1$; then $\ln(x + y) = \ln 2$, whereas $\ln x \cdot \ln y = \ln 1 \cdot \ln 1 = 0$.

(f) Correct (see the Laws of Exponents).

(h) Incorrect. Take $x = 2$; then $\ln(x/2) = \ln 1 = 0$, whereas $\ln \sqrt{x} = \ln \sqrt{2} = \frac{1}{2} \ln 2 \neq 0$.

19. (d) $-3 \log_{10} x + \frac{1}{2} \log_{10} y + 2 \log_{10} z$ (f) $-\frac{5}{3} \ln x - \ln(e^x + 1)$

20. (b) $\ln(x + y)$ (d) $\log_{10} x^5 y^6$

21. (a) -2 (b) $-1/2$ (c) -2 (j) $-8/3$ (k) $\ln 2$

(l) $x = \frac{\pi}{3} + 2k\pi$ and $x = \frac{5\pi}{3} + 2k\pi$ (p) 10098   (q) e^e

22. $\log_4 7 = \ln 7 / \ln 4 \approx 1.94591 / 1.38630 \approx 1.40368$

Section 9. Mathematical Language; Mathematical Thinking and Logic

1. (a) If a number is even, then its square is even.

(b) If a function is increasing, then it has an inverse function.

(c) If x is a real number, then $|x| \geq 0$.

(d) If $a = b$, then the equation $x^2/a^2 + y^2/b^2 = 1$ represents a circle.

2. (a) A="x is positive", B="e^x is positive"; "if A, then B" is true (proof: look at the graph); "if B, then A" = "if e^x is positive, then x is positive" is false (counterexample: e^{-2} is positive, but its exponent is not).

(b) A="$a = b$"; B="$a^2 = b^2$"; "if A, then B" is true; "if B, then A" = "if $a^2 = b^2$, then $a = b$" is false (counterexample: $5^2 = (-5)^2$, but 5 is not equal to -5).

(c) A="$m_1 m_2 = -1$"; B="the lines $y = m_1 x$ and $y = m_2 x$ are perpendicular"; "if A, then B" is true; "if B, then A" = "if the lines $y = m_1 x$ and $y = m_2 x$ are perpendicular, then $m_1 m_2 = -1$" is true.

3. (a) If $\csc x$ is not defined, then $\sin x = 0$.

(b) If $f(x_1) = f(x_2)$, then $x_1 = x_2$.

(c) If a curve does not have the same slope at all points, then it is not a line.

4. (a) False; conterexample: $p = 7$ is prime, but $p + 2 = 9$ is not prime.

(b) True; $p = 11$ is prime, and so is $p + 2 = 13$.

(c) True; see the definition of the square root.

(d) False; the discriminant is $D = -19$, so there are no real number solutions.

5. (d) If a number is even, then its square is divisible by 4.

(g) If lines are parallel, then their slopes are equal.

6. (e) Converse: If $f(x)$ is an inverse function of $g(x)$, then $f(g(x)) = x$. Contrapositive: If $f(x)$ is not an inverse function of $g(x)$, then $f(g(x)) \neq x$.

(i) Converse: If the lines $y = m_1 x + b_1$ and $y = m_2 x + b_2$ are not parallel, then $m_1 \neq m_2$. Contrapositive: If the lines $y = m_1 x + b_1$ and $y = m_2 x + b_2$ are parallel, then $m_1 = m_2$.

7. (d) A="$x = 7$" and B="$x^2 = 49$". The given implication implication is true. Converse: "If $x^2 = 49$ then $x = 7$." Converse is not true: if $x^2 = 49$, Then x could be 7, or it could be -7.

(e) A="$f(g(x)) = g(f(x))$" and B="$f(x)$ and $g(x)$ are inverse of each other". The given implication is not true. Converse: "If $f(x)$ and $g(x)$ are inverse of each other then $f(g(x)) = g(f(x))$." This statement is true, as it is part of the property of being inverse.

8. (a) We would need to check that every single country in South America is not landlocked.

(b) We would need to identify one country which is landlocked. [By the way, this statement is true: for instance, Bolivia is landlocked.]

(g) We would have to check that every single dog in Ontario barks.

(h) We would need to find one dog in Ontario which does not bark.

9. (a) True. All we need is one example: if $a = 0$ and $b = 1$, then $\sqrt{a+b} = \sqrt{1} = 1$ and $\sqrt{a} + \sqrt{b} = \sqrt{0} + \sqrt{1} = 1$.

(b) False; we need one counterexample. For instance, if $a = 4$ and $b = 1$, then $\sqrt{a+b} = \sqrt{4+1} = \sqrt{5}$ and $\sqrt{a} + \sqrt{b} = \sqrt{4} + \sqrt{1} = 2 + 1 = 3$. Since $\sqrt{5} \neq 3$, we are done.

(f) False. The range of $y = b\sin x$ as $[-b, b]$. There is no b for which $[-b, b] = [0, 2]$. This is true, since b would have to satisfy $-b = 0$ and $b = 2$ at the same time.

(g) True. The range of $y = c + \sin x$ as $[c-1, c+1]$. We see that if we take $c = 1$, then $[c-1, c+1] = [1-1, 1+1] = [0, 2]$.

Index

absolute value, 8.
  algebraic properties, 10.
  definition in words, 8.
  distance on a number line, 9.
  graph of absolute value of a function, 112.
  graph, 101.
  of a number, 8.
  simplifying, 8.
  solutions of $|A| \leq a$, $|A| \geq a$, etc., 65.
  solutions of $|A| = a$, 65.
  solving equations, 65.
  solving inequalities a, 65.
  solving inequalities by graphing, 69.
algebraic function, 103.
algebraic operations with fractions, 4.
angle, 115.
  positive and negative, 115.
annular region (between two circles), 45.
  area, 45.
arcsin (inverse sine function), 132.
  cancellation formulas, 134.
  definition, 133.
  domain and range, 133.
  graph, 134.
  how to calculate, 133.
arctan (inverse tangent function), 134.
  cancellation formulas, 136.
  definition, 134.
  domain and range, 135.
  graph, 135.
  how to calculate, 135.
assumption (in a theorem), 161.
asymptotes of a hyperbola, 86.
axiom (mathematical statement), 162.
a^x (general exponential function)
  exponentiation and logarithm are inverses, 147.
  for negative a, 141.
  graph, properties, 141.

basic trigonometric identity, 117, 122.
binomial, 23.

cancelling fractions, 4, 31.
Cartesian coordinate system, 75.
  x-axis and y-axis, 75.
  x-coordinate and y-coordinate, 75.
  origin, 75.
  quadrants, 75.
circle, 45, 82.
annular region (between two circles), 45.
diameter, circumference, area, 45.

equation in Cartesian coordinates, 82.
sector of a circle, 45.
closed interval, 6.
common denominator, 33.
completing the square, 26.
composition of functions, 103.
conclusion (in a theorem), 161.
cone, 47.
  frustum, surface area, 49.
  frustum, volume, 48.
  slant height, 47.
  surface area, volume, 47.
constant function, 99.
contrapositive statement, 165.
convention, 160.
converse statement, 165.
conversion between degrees and radians, 115.
corollary (mathematical statement), 162.
cos (cosine function)
  addition and subtraction formulas, 125.
  basic trigonometric identity, 117, 122.
  complementary angle formula, 124.
  definition for acute angles, 116.
  definition for general angles, 117.
  double angle formulas, 125.
  graph, 121.
  is even, 125.
  is periodic, 121.
  main period, 122.
  period of $cos(ax)$, 122.
  range, 122.
  reflection formulas, 125.
  solutions of $cos x = 0$, 121.
  table of values, 120.
  unit circle definition, 118.
  values for special angles, 118.
cot (cotangent function)
  definition for acute angles, 116.
  definition for general angles, 117.
  definition, 127.
  domain, 127.
  graph, 127.
  range, 127.
  table of values, 120.
  values for special angles, 118.
counterexample, 168.
csc (cosecant function)
  definition for acute angles, 116.
  definition for general angles, 117.
  definition, 126.
  domain, 127.
  graph, 126.
  range, 126.

table of values, 120.
   values for special angles, 118.
cube (solid), 46.
   surface area, volume, 46.
cube of sum and difference, 25.
cube root function, 101.
   graph, 101.
cylinder, 46.
   cylindrical shell, volume, 46.
   surface area, volume, 46-47.
cylindrical shell, 46.
   volume, 46.

definition (mathematical statement), 160.
   convention, 160.
   how to use it, 160.
degrees, 115.
   conversion into radians, 115.
difference of cubes, 29.
difference of squares, 24.
difference of squares, 29.
discriminant, 57.
distance between numbers on a number line,
   9.
distance between two points, 75.
division by zero, 3.
domain of a function, 93.
   given domain, 93.
   natural domain, 93.
   what is not allowed, 93.
double fraction
   simplifying, 5, 16.

ellipse, 45, 82.
area, 45.
centre and semi-axes, 82.
   equation in Cartesian coordinates, 82.
ellipsoid, 46.
   surface area, volume, 46.
equations
   linear, 53.
   quadratic, 55.
   quadratic formula, 57.
   solution, 53.
   solving $x^2 = a$, 55.
   solving product equals zero, 55.
   solving quotient equals zero, 56.
   solving systems of equations, 70.
equivalence (it if-and-only-if), 56, 167.
even function, 125.
EWE (each-with-each multiplication), 24.
existential quantifier (*there exists*), 167.
   how to prove, how to disprove, 168.
explicit equation of a line, 78.

exponential equations, 144.
   practice in solving, 144.
exponential function, 141.
   a^x, graph, properties, 141.
   e^x, graph, properties, 145.
   exponentiation and logarithm are in-
     verses, 147.
   solving equations, 152.
exponents, 11.
   exponent of zero, 11.
   integer exponents, 11.
   laws of exponents, 12.
   radicals, 12, 13.
   rational exponents, 12, 13.
   real number exponents, 17.
e^x (natural exponential function)
   graph of e^{ax}, 145.
   graph, properties, 145.

factoring polynomials, 27.
   difference of cubes, 29.
   difference of squares, 29.
   factoring $a^n - b^n$ and $a^n + b^n$, 31.
   factoring by grouping, 27.
   factoring out a common expression, 27.
   factoring quadratic polynomials, 27.
   quadratic, when solutions are known, 59.
   sum of cubes, 29.
   using long division, 37.
for all statement *see*: universal quantifier.
formulas that do not work, 18.
fractions, 33.
fractions
   algebraic operations, 4.
   cancelling fractions, 4, 31.
   common denominator, 33.
   division, 5, 16.
   long division, 35.
   multiplication, 5.
   rationalizing denominator, 38.
   solving equations with fractions, 54.
frustum of a cone, 48.
function, 93.
   absolute value, 101.
   algebraic, 103.
   composition, 103.
   constant function, 99.
   cube root $y = root3 of x$, 101.
   cubic parabola $y = x^3$, 100.
   defined piecewise, 101.
   definition, 93.
   domain, 93.
   even, 125.
   graph is a curve, 96.

graph, 95.
hyperbola $y = 1/x$, 100.
inverse, 104.
linear (line), 99.
odd, 125.
parabola $y = x^2$, 100.
polynomial, 102.
range, 95.
rational, 102.
square root $y = sqrtx$, 100.
transcendental, 103.
vertical line test, 96.

given domain, 93.
graph of a function, 95.
   absolute value of a function, 112.
   defined piecewise, 101.
   reflection: horizontal and vertical, 112.
   scaling: stretching and compression, 111.
   shift: left, right, up, down, 109.
graphs of quadratic expressions, 87.

horizontal line test, 105.
hyperbola, 85.
   asymptotes, 86.
   equation in Cartesian coordinates, 85.
   graph of $y = 1/x$, 100.
   with x-intercepts, 85.
   with y-intercepts, 86.
hypotenuse, 43.

if-and-only-if statement, *see*: equivalence.
if-then statement, *see*: implication.
implication (*if-then* statement), 163.
   contrapositive statement, 165.
   converse statement, 165.
   diagram, 163.
   necessary condition, 164.
   sufficient condition, 164.
inequalities
   basic rules, 60, 61.
   solution of an inequality, 60.
   solutions of $|A|leqa$, $|A|geqa$, etc., 65.
   solutions of x^2leqa, x^2geqa, etc., 65.
   solving $a^x < 0$, 145.
   solving by factoring, 61.
   solving by graphing, 68.
   solving linear inequalities, 60.
   solving pair of inequalities, 60.
   solving x^2leqa, 64.
infinite interval, 6.
integer exponents, 11.
integers, 3.

non-negative integers, 3.
interval, 6.
   closed, 6.
   infinite, involving ∞, 6.
   open, 6.
   representation using inequalities, 6.
   set notation, 6.
inverse function, 104.
   graph, 107.
   horizontal line test, 105.
   how to find inverse function, 107.
   how to recognize inverse functions, 105.
inverse trigonometric functions, 132.
irrational numbers, 3.

laws of exponents, 12, 143.
laws of logarithms, 148, 150.
laws of radicals, 14.
lemma (mathematical statement), 162.
line
   equation containing intercepts, 80.
   equation, graph, 76, 99.
   explicit equation, 78.
   horizontal, 76.
   linear equation, 78.
   parallel and perpendicular lines, 79.
   point-slope equation, 77.
   slope-intercept equation, 78.
   slope, 76.
   vertical, 76.
linear equation, 78.
ln (natural logarithm function), 150.
   cancellation formulas, 150.
   conversion into another base, 150.
   domain and range, 150.
   graph, 150.
   laws of logarithms, 150.
   solving equations, 152.
log_a (logarithmic function), 147.
   conversion from one base to another, 149.
   conversion into base e, 150.
   definition, 147.
   domain and range, 147.
   exponentiation and logarithm are inverses, 147.
   graph, 147.
   laws of logarithms, 148.
   simplifying expressions, 148.
   solving equations, 152.
logarithm, 146.
   definition, 146.
   domain, 146.
   exponentiation and logarithm are inverses, 147.

long division, 35.

mathematical statement, 159.
midpoint of a line segment, 80.
midpoint
  between points on a number line, 7.
  of a line segment, 80.
monomial, 23.

natural domain, 93.
natural numbers, 3.
necessary condition, 164.
number line, 6.

odd function, 125.
open interval, 6.

parabola, 83.
  $x = ay^2$, 85.
  $y = ax^2$, 83.
  $y = x^2$, graph, 100.
  $y = x^3$, graph, 100.
  equation in Cartesian coordinates, 83.
  intercepts, 84.
  vertex, 83.
parallelepiped, 46.
  surface area, volume, 46.
period of a function, 121.
piecewise defined function, 101.
point-slope equation of a line, 77.
polynomial, 23, 102.
  addition, subtraction, 23.
  coefficients, 23.
  degree, 23.
  domain, 103.
  equal polynomials, 23.
  free coefficient, 23.
  linear, 23.
  long division, 35.
  multiplication, EWE, 24.
  quadratic, 23.
  see also: factoring polynomials.
products
  cube of sum and difference, 25.
  difference of squares, 24.
  square of the difference, 24.
  square of the sum, 24.
proposition (mathematical statement), 162.
pyramid, 47.
  volume, 47.
Pythagorean Theorem, 43.

quadrant (in a coordinate system), 75.

quadratic equation, 57.
quadratic formula, 57.
quadratic function, see: quadratic polynomial.
quadratic inequalities
  solving by graphing, 68.
quadratic polynomial
  factoring when solutions are known, 59.
  factoring, 27.
  graphs, 87.

radians, 115.
  conversion into degrees, 115.
radicals, 12.
  laws of radicals, 14.
  simplifying expressions, 15.
range of a function, 93, 95.
  finding range algebraically, 98.
  finding range from graphs, 97.
rational exponents, 12, 13.
rational function, 102.
  domain, 103.
rational numbers, 3.
  algebraic operations, 4.
rationalizing denominator, 38.
real numbers, 3.
  decimal representation, 3.
  ordering, 6.
rectangle, 44.
  perimeter, area, diagonal, 44.
  sum of angles, 45.
rules for inequalities, 61.

sec (secant function)
  definition for acute angles, 116.
  definition for general angles, 117.
  definition, 126.
  graph, 126.
  period, 126.
  relationship with tan, 126.
  table of values, 120.
  values for special angles, 118.
sector of a circle, 45.
  arclength, area, 45.
similar triangles, 44.
sin (sine function)
  addition and subtraction formulas, 125.
  basic trigonometric identity, 117.
  basic trigonometric identity, 122.
  complementary angle formula, 124.
  definition for acute angles, 116.
  definition for general angles, 117.
  double angle formulas, 125.
  graph, 121.

is odd, 125.
is periodic, 121.
main period, 121.
period of $sin(ax)$, 122.
range, 122.
reflection formulas, 125.
solutions of $sinx = 0$, 121.
table of values, 120.
unit circle definition, 118.
values for special angles, 118.
slope-intercept equation of a line, 78.
slope, 76.
    of a horizontal line, 76.
    of a vertical line, 76.
    parallel and perpendicular lines, 79.
    positive and negative slopes, 77.
solving linear equations, 53.
solving quadratic equations, 55.
    discriminant, 57.
    quadratic formula, 57.
    strategies, 55.
solving
    $x^2 = a$, 55.
    $a^x = 0$, $a^x < 0$, 145.
    by completing the square, 57.
    by factoring, 56.
    equations with fractions, 54.
    inequalities a, 60.
    inequalities by factoring, 61.
    inequalities by graphing, 68.
    inequalities with absolute value, 65.
    linear equations, 53.
    logarithmic equations, 152.
    product equals zero, 55.
    quadratic equations a, 55.
    quadratic equations, strategies, 55.
    quadratic formula, 57.
    quotient equals zero, 56.
    systems of equations, 70.
    trigonometric equations, 129.
    $x^2 \leq a$, 64.
sphere, 46.
    surface area, volume, 46.
square, 44.
square
    perimeter, area, diagonal, 44.
    sum of angles, 45.
square of the difference, 24.
square of the sum, 24.
square root function
    graph, 100.
sufficient condition, 164.
sum of angles in a polygon, 45.
sum of cubes, 29.

systems of equations, 70.

tan (tangent function)
    definition for acute angles, 116.
    definition for general angles, 117.
    definition, 125.
    graph, 125.
    period, 125.
    relationship with sec, 126.
    solutions of $tanx = 0$, 126.
    table of values, 120.
    values for special angles, 118.
theorem (mathematical statement), 161.
    assumption and conclusion, 161.
    how to use it, 161.
there exists statement, *see*: existential quantifier.
transcendental function, 103.
trapezoid, 45.
    perimeter, area, 45.
    sum of angles, 45.
triangle, 43.
    equilateral, 43.
    inscribed into a circle, 46.
    perimeter, area, 43.
    Pythagorean Theorem, 43.
    right, 43.
    scalene, 43.
    similar triangles, 44.
    similar triangles, 44.
    sum of angles, 43.
    sum of angles, 45.
trigonometric equations, 129.
    practice in solving, 129.
    simplifying answers, 131.
trigonometric formulas
    what to remember, 124.
trigonometric identities, 127.
    practice in proving, 127.
    what to remember, 124.
trinomial, 23.

universal quantifier (*for all, every*), 167.
    how to prove, how to disprove, 168.

vertical line test, 96.

zero
    division by zero, 3.